INDEX NUMBERS
Theory and Applications

By

WALTER R. CROWE

B.Com., A.C.I.S., A.Comm.A.

Head of Department of Business Studies
Mid-Herts College of Further Education

MACDONALD & EVANS LTD

8 John Street, London W.C.1

1965

First published February 1965

©

MACDONALD & EVANS LTD

1965

*Printed in Great Britain by Richard Clay (The Chaucer Press), Ltd.,
Bungay, Suffolk*

PREFACE

THIS book is intended to assist students in first-year university courses, in technical colleges, those studying at home, and others interested in statistics by explaining the basic theories on which index numbers are calculated and by giving a comprehensive treatment of the applications of indexes published or available in Great Britain plus a selection of important American ones.

It may be asked why a whole volume should be devoted to this topic. There are two main reasons. First, I believe that no book on it by an English writer has appeared for many years, and since the variety of index numbers is increasing rapidly it is time a "guide book" was available. Second, my treatment is wide rather than restricted, and I have included other relevant topics in my explanations.

This book is written for the non-mathematical student. The writer has had considerable experience in teaching students of commercial statistics and knows that the usual level of maths is far lower than many textbooks assume! It is hoped that it will be used in addition to the standard college textbook. A large number of questions on theory and application are to be found, intended for both class and homework.

Statistics cannot be learned in isolation, since it is an aid to the interpretation of business matters and the reaching of decisions by management. For this reason, the student should refer to the references quoted, especially periodicals. Regular reading of these latter will bring familiarity with the sources of statistics.

In Part I the theory of the subject is explained and there is a short history of index numbers. Part II consists of brief summaries of all indexes published in England and a selection of other significant ones. The degree of detail varies according to how much information was supplied to me. I make no claim to originality, since I have merely adapted the information, but I bear full responsibility for any errors or misinterpretations that have occurred.

Any book dealing with published statistics must inevitably contain out-of-date material. I have indicated the indexes that are likely to be altered in the near future, but the reader should always bear the point in mind. Wherever possible I have left blank spaces in the tables of index numbers in Part II, so that the reader may insert the latest figures as they become available.

A list of the examining bodies (both professional and university) who set papers requiring a knowledge of index numbers, and for whose examinations this book is suitable, will be found on page 330.

W. R. C.

ACKNOWLEDGMENTS

I have drawn heavily on the knowledge and experience of Government departments, private organisations, and individuals. In every case their help has been willingly given and my thanks are now duly recorded.

The Secretary of the Actuarial Tuition Service
The Agricultural Marketing Service of the United States Department of Agriculture
The Banker's Magazine
The Bank of England
The Board of Trade—the Solicitor, several departments, the library, Mr Jessop, and Miss West have all assisted
University of Cambridge Department of Applied Economics
The Central Statistical Office
The Chamber of Shipping of the United Kingdom
The Commonwealth Economic Committee
Comtelburo Ltd
Co-operative Permanent Building Society Ltd
The Economist Statistics Department and the Industries Department of *The Economist* Intelligence Unit
Electronics Weekly
Eurosyndicat Investment Research Bureau, Brussels
Federal Reserve Bank of New York
Federal Reserve System Board of Governors, Washington
The Financial Times
Professor A. Goudeket
Mr H. Hake of *The Investor's Chronicle*
Hatfield College of Technology library
Holland & Hannen and Cubitts Ltd
Mr G. P. Hyett of Associated Newspapers Ltd
The Iron and Steel Trades Confederation
The Journal of Accountancy, New York
Miss Klein of Birkbeck College, University of London
Lloyds Bank Review
The library of the London School of Economics, University of London
Management Selection Ltd
The Manager
Manchester Central Library

Manchester College of Commerce library
University of Manchester Department of Economics
Mid-Herts College of Further Education library
The Midland Bank Review
Miss A. McCr'rick of the Ministry of Labour
Ministry of Agriculture Fisheries and Food
Ministry of Works
Moodies Services Ltd
Mrs Y. Doré and Mr C. J. Austin-Billinghurst of the National
    Cash Register Financial Computing Centre
The National Federation of Building Trades Operatives
The National Institute of Industrial Psychology
The New York Times
Northern Ireland Ministry of Commerce
The library of the Royal Statistical Society
Mr George Schwartz of the *Sunday Times*
Standard & Poor's Corporation, New York
The Statist
Steel, Cleveland, U.S.A.
The Times
Trades Union Congress Research and Economics Department
United States Department of Commerce, Bureau of International
    Commerce
United States Department of Labor, Bureau of Labor Statistics
The library of the United States Information Service, London
United States Securities and Exchange Commission, Division of
    Trading and Exchange
The Wall Street Journal
Wholesale Textile Association

In addition I have been able to include in each chapter a selection of specimen examination questions obtained from a variety of examining bodies. I wish to acknowledge the courtesy these examiners have extended to me in permitting the use of their copyright material.

Association of Certified and Corporate Accountants
Building Societies Institute
College of Marketing (I.M.S.M.)
Institute of Cost and Works Accountants
Institute of Municipal Treasurers and Accountants
Institute of Personnel Management
Institute of Statisticians
Institute of Transport
London Chamber of Commerce
Queen's University of Belfast

Royal Society of Arts
University of Birmingham
University of Bristol
University of Exeter
University of Liverpool
University of London
University of Manchester (Manchester University Press)

ABBREVIATIONS

A.C.C.A.	Association of Certified and Corporate Accountants
B.S.I.	Building Societies Institute
I.C.W.A.	Institute of Cost and Works Accountants
I.M.S.M.	Institute of Marketing and Sales Management
I.M.T.A.	Institute of Municipal Treasurers and Accountants
I.O.S.	Institute of Statisticians
I.O.T.	Institute of Transport
I.P.M.	Institute of Personnel Management
R.S.A.	Royal Society of Arts

SOME COMMON SYMBOLS

THE statistician uses symbols—some of them from the Greek alphabet—not to confuse the reader but to avoid long verbal explanations which can be given simply in algebraic notation. If some of them are unfamiliar the following list should help. My own abbreviations are also included here.

Σ (Sigma, the Greek capital S). An instruction to add all items together.

x denotes the data we are interested in studying; the dependent variable.

x_1, x_2, x_3, etc. The subscripts denote individual items of data and are not instructions to alter the value of the items (not to be confused with x^2, x^3, x^4, etc.).

x_n The last item in a series, irrespective of the number of them in the series.

n The number of items in a series.

$\bar{x}$ x-bar. Arithmetic average.

$A.M., G.M.$ Averages or means, arithmetic and geometric.

$M.$ or $M.D.$ Median.

$H.M.$ Harmonic mean.

f The frequency of occurrence of the dependent variable we are studying.

$Cum.$ Cumulate, that is, add the next number to the total of all previous numbers and so on.

$S.D.$ or σ (small Greek s, or sigma). Standard deviation.

d The deviation of each item x from the group average.

S^2 Sample variance: the square of the standard deviation (important in the analysis of variation).

$C.V.$ Coefficient of variation. The standard deviation as a percentage of the appropriate average.

P or p Prices.

p_0 Price in the base year.

p_1 Price in the current year (or P_n).

q Quantity.

q_0 Quantity in the base year.

q_1 Quantity in the current year (or q_n).

p_0', p_0'', p_0''', p_0^n The superscripts represent individual items of data.

I The index (plural: indexes, index numbers, or indices).

w   The weights.
v   Index of value.
$\sigma_{\bar{x}}$ Standard error of the mean (sampling).
X, Y   The two variables being studied for correlation.
r   The coefficient of correlation.

CONTENTS

xiii

Part I
THE THEORY OF INDEX NUMBERS

CHAPTER 1

WHAT ARE WE TALKING ABOUT?

INTRODUCTION: A TALE OF NEGLECT

INDEX numbers are probably the least studied subject in statistics, and whole areas of the topic are often neglected. The usual treatment includes:

1. Assembling the parts, that is, considering which items to include—the base year, weighting, and the method of construction. Except for the latter they are mostly matters of fact.

2. Developing the method of construction, by enumeration of the many methods that can be used.

3. Comparing and appraising these methods.

4. Explaining other and more specialised aspects of construction, such as whether to use fixed or chain base, moving weights and a system of link relatives (after You Poh Seng).

Of these four groups the first two have been fairly well treated in various publications. The more analytical sections 3 and 4 have been relatively neglected. This volume attempts to remedy the defect somewhat by providing an overall view of the subject.

In the remainder of this chapter an attempt will be made to answer the question "What is an index number?" but explanation and justification may not be the same thing. The rest of the first part of the book will argue the usefulness of index numbers, and it is hoped that by the end of it the reader will be in a position to judge whether or not the labour involved is justified. Suffice it to say at present that a businessman needs two sets of facts to make intelligent decisions:

1. Those covering his own operations.

2. Those telling him what is happening in his industry and in the economy as a whole.

With the help of indexes of wages, prices, and production the manager will have a measuring rod available, irrespective of how significant is the proportion his activities bear to the whole industry.

SOME DEFINITIONS OF INDEX NUMBERS

Professor Sir Arthur Bowley wrote:

"When measurable phenomena (such as prices or wages) are influenced (1) by causes *special* to particular instances, (2) by *general* causes presumably acting on all the phenomena, it is important to disentangle the general causes from the special. Thus the price of wheat is influenced by the weather, acreage under the crop, and the harvests in all the wheat-growing countries; the price of coal by the fluctuations in demand."

General causes that affect the prices of both wheat and coal *and* all other commodities include

". . . the relation of the amount of money and its substitutes to the work that has to be done by them . . ."

So to find out the effect of the general causes it is necessary to get rid of the special ones first.

"This is done by averaging together the price changes shown for a number of different commodities."

Take as many commodities as possible with definite price quotations, adjusting carefully for changes in quality. Then take an average of a period of years as a base.

It is not a simple definition, and further explanation is needed. If we wish to study data about a group of materials to analyse the trend of price changes, we must remember that all the materials (*e.g.* oil, coal, gas, if we are studying fuels) will be acted upon by certain influences—shortages of material or labour, market demand, state controls, and so on—but in addition there will be particular influences affecting individual items: thus the price of oil is affected by the variety of end uses like heating and transport. An index number shows the general composite changes in price of the whole group after individual tendencies have been eliminated.

Marris (whose book *Economic Arithmetic* deserves the attention of every economics student) calls index numbers "devices for mitigating deceptions caused by changes in the value of money" and describes the two major kinds, price and volume indexes. An index in the common sense of the word is an "indicator" and no more than that. "Indexes," "index numbers," or "indices" are forms of the plural, but they all mean the same thing.

An index number "represents the general level of magnitude

of the *changes* between two or more situations of a number of variables taken as a whole" (Karmel). In this definition, the word "variable" refers to any measurable quantity which can vary from one individual to another—in other words, the subject matter we wish to study is composed of variables, such as the prices of the ingredients of "Splash" (*see* Example 1).

CONSTRUCTION OF AN INDEX

1. A simple example

Although later chapters will deal in detail with the construction of index numbers, it will serve as an introduction to the terms to be used if we consider here an imaginary product and attempt to construct a simple price index.

Index numbers are ratios based on the percentage system and therefore are comparisons between two variables or one variable at different times. The idea of using percentages enables awkward decimals to be avoided. Thus if one commodity cost £1 in January 1963 and 15s. in January 1964 the ratio would be

$$\frac{15}{20} \text{ or } 0.75$$

(three-quarters). If instead of this we turn the ratio into a percentage:

$$\frac{15}{20} \times \frac{100}{1},$$

we say that the index is now 75, based on January 1963, which is 100. Not all index numbers use 100 as their starting-point—some use 10, others 1000, but 100 is the base for the large majority of those published. This is a "derived" number and is a unit which can be added to other percentage units. One of the main advantages of using index numbers can now be stated. If we wish to study changes in the prices, expressed in different real units, of several commodities we cannot calculate an average of them all until they are reduced to common terms.

EXAMPLE 1

A manufacturer is costing his best known product, "Splash," the household cleanser. His factory is automated; much of his production cost is raw materials, and he therefore wishes to keep regular records of the prices of these raw materials. At the date of first production, January 1955, his material costs were:

	£	s.
Chlorine (per gallon)	1	10
Abrasive (per ton)	8	0
Perfume (per flagon)		15
Dampness inhibitor (per drum)	20	0

It is meaningless to tot them up and call the cost £30 5s., since you cannot add gallons, tons, flagons, and drums together to obtain an average cost. So he decides to construct an index number using 1st January 1955 as the starting date and, at intervals, he can compare current prices with the original "base" prices to show how the cost of the mixture is changing. Each one is converted into a percentage, and therefore on 1st January 1955 each component becomes 100 (per cent). When all components are added together an average can be taken:

$$\frac{100 + 100 + 100 + 100}{4}\% = 100.$$

This final number is the "index number." Imagine a jump of several years, to 1964. Of the raw materials chlorine is now £2 5s. a gallon, the abrasive is up to £10 per ton, perfume prices having fallen to 12s. a flagon, and the drying agent is unchanged in price at £20 a drum. For each item we calculate the ratio

$$\frac{\text{Current price}}{\text{Base price}} \times 100,$$

which gives a figure called a "price relative" (see Chapter 4).

A table can be constructed and an index number obtained:

"Splash" household cleanser

Items	Price in January 1955	As a price relative	Price in January 1963	As a price relative
Chlorine (gallon)	30s.	100	45s.	150
Abrasive (ton)	£8	100	£10	125
Perfume (flagon)	15s.	100	12s.	80
Inhibitor (drum)	£20	100	£20	100
Total		400		455
Index number		100		113·75

Thus 113·75 is the index number of "Splash" costs, based on 1st January 1955 = 100; in other words, costs rose as a whole by 13¾%. Each price relative has some influence on the final average.

A word of warning must be given to scientific readers. "Splash" is, of course, an imaginary product, the writer has no knowledge of how to construct a household cleanser and recommends that students do not attempt to make the example more realistic in their homes or colleges.

By now students will be wondering why we proceed at length with these calculations when the original data must obviously be available before any arithmetic can proceed. The answer involves understanding a major use of index numbers, which is to show *relative* changes in values as distinct from *absolute* changes. The manufacturer of "Splash" knows that his abrasive costs £2 more than in 1955, his chlorine only 15s. more. But these changes cannot be compared because of their absolute nature. We need to show him the relative changes, which are: abrasive 25% rise, chlorine 50% rise.

"Uniform changes in groups of variables practically never occur in practice" (Tuttle). This is sufficient reason for the calculation of price relatives, which enable both the general situation and individual details to be observed concurrently.

2. Weighting

A further point may be briefly mentioned. The tables of data above ignore the fact that the product is mixed in different proportions—we do not use one gallon, one ton, one flagon, and one drum to make one mix of "Splash." In practice, allowance is made in the calculation for the different quantities used, and this "weighting" process is a very necessary part of calculating any index number. The matter is fully explained in Chapter 6.

3. Sampling

Our "cleanser" is a mixture of only four ingredients. Imagine the problems involved in calculating an index of prices of consumer goods in Great Britain (a well-known index compiled by the Ministry of Labour). Thousands of items of food, clothing, hardwear, travel goods, etc., are bought by 50 million persons, prices of many of them varying from place to place throughout the country and all of them changing upwards or downwards at different times. There is but one practical solution, which is to select (*a*) representative goods, and (*b*) representative consumers, and assume that the items and consumers omitted behave in a similar manner to their chosen representatives. This is the basis on which a parliamentary democracy is operated, whereby the Member of Parliament and his electors remain in harmony, since he is merely one of them.

Of course, the reader may deduce from my example that, just as on occasion a Member's personal opinions may lead him to deviate from the "line" of his electors, so an item in the index may get out of line and a similar solution be necessary, *i.e.* to replace the errant representative. The process of choosing a few is known as "sampling" and is used in constructing all published index numbers.

Reference to the second part of the book, which describes published index numbers, will show the methods used by compilers of indexes to select samples. Provided that the sample is not too small, results should be reliable. It has been said (by F. C. Mills) that:

> "It is the business of the maker of price index numbers to bring order out of a multiplicity of price movements by defining broad movements that are the net resultant of the diverse forces impinging on prices."

THE USERS OF INDEX NUMBERS

Index numbers are one of the "tools of management." Which people use this tool and how does it help them?

1. Businessmen

Managers of a business will in most cases control it in the face of competition from other companies in that particular industry. A consideration of one company's position as to sales, wages, profits, prices of raw materials, and other items in comparison with that of other companies is necessary if its competitive position is to be maintained or improved. The information will not usually, however, be available for each competitor, and so the next best alternative must be used, *i.e.* the data for the whole industry.

EXAMPLE 2

The Footwear Sales Manager of a department store in England is aware (from reading the *Board of Trade Journal*) that the index numbers for sales in the whole "field" were:

1960	100
1961	105
1962	109
1963	122

This indicates a 22% increase above the base year of 1960. If the store is to maintain its competitive position the sales in its own store must be at least 22% above the 1960 average. In the same journal monthly figures are available for more detailed comparisons.

Another common use of index numbers will be to aid estimates of future trading prospects. In this context the "future" may signify anything from a week hence (on the stock exchange) to some years away (in shipbuilding).

Thirdly, businessmen need price data if their products require large quantities of raw materials which are subject to considerable fluctuations, such as imported food materials. Since raw materials are measured in different units (tons, bales, pounds), the best way of showing price changes is by using index numbers.

It is doubtful whether management would make decisions solely on consideration of index numbers, but they are most valuable as an additional tool in the executive's work box.

2. Trade-union leaders

The leaders of trade unions will need to be as well informed as the employers if they are to negotiate on an equal footing. Index numbers of wages, profits, and prices are studied by trade unionists for this purpose.

Bargaining between union representatives and employers is frequently conducted in an atmosphere reminiscent of a court of law, especially as regards the necessity for the opposing parties to prove their points by evidence. Index numbers provide such evidence, especially as the compilers of such indexes as the Retail Price Index are above suspicion of bias. Escalator clauses or sliding scales of wages based on index numbers are found in many contracts of employment.

In Great Britain the Ministry of Labour has the duty of collecting information about employment, wages, hours of work, and other working conditions, and many series are expressed as index numbers. Workers' representatives often rely on such publications as the *Ministry of Labour Gazette* to provide national information on all these conditions.

3. Farmers

Farm support programmes in the U.S.A. are based on changes in agricultural indexes. The Ministry of Agriculture in Britain compiles large quantities of statistics; indexes of agricultural prices for materials that farmers buy, and indexes of farmers' output are available to them. These will provide, in an up-to-date manner, trends useful for comparisons.

4. Economists

Those who study professionally the workings of the economy use indexes as a method of observing price changes and their influence on the economy. Data concerning the behaviour of "economic man" can be adjusted by index numbers to remove the influence of price from their calculations.

Index numbers grew into their present form because of the desire of economists to measure changes in the purchasing power of money, and they are still primarily used for this purpose. Price changes can thus be compared with (for example) changes in gold reserves, bank deposits, or physical output of goods and wages. The reasons for such comparisons are many, and include the need for controlling or preventing untoward changes in the economy.

5. Accountants

The accountant is chiefly concerned with recording and interpreting the performance of variables concerning his business; but indexes may be useful in some circumstances, as when he attempts to judge probable price changes when fixing his estimates of depreciation for fixed assets, since replacements will have to be made at some future date.

EXAMPLE 3

As a rather advanced illustration of this, reference should be made to an article by Professor A. Goudeket called "An Application of Replacement Value Theory." The aim of the theory is to prove that the net income (or loss) and the capital of an enterprise can only be calculated properly by this method and to demonstrate that it has practical applications. The following notes are a summary of the article, which is well worth reading in full.

The writer describes the accounting organisation of Philips of Eindhoven (with which he is associated). The system is decentralised, each section preparing its own balance sheet and income statement each month on uniform principles. All section managers receive details of income and capital employed in total and in detail, using replacement-value principles. Philips do not recognise income for a period as being a true figure unless the purchasing power of the capital at the end is equal to that at the beginning of the period. This means that capital equipment price levels must be carefully watched, and therefore Philips follow the trends (see Chapter 9) for each separate item, e.g. buildings, machinery, or houses, using index numbers on which to base revaluation. For example, the costs-of-building indexes are used to revalue factory buildings; machine tools are revalued on market prices. A special accounting department is responsible for following price movements.

All goods bought, all semi-finished and finished goods are valued at standard prices, from which the basis for establishing replacement values comes. When fluctuations in prices of materials take place these standard prices are adjusted by means of index numbers which are calculated by the Estimating Department from data issued by the Purchasing Department. The Estimating Department keeps rough price lists of major articles purchased, together with the indexes and adjustments, and a detailed price list whose index numbers are determined by the values of the articles appearing in the rough price list.

For labour and overheads, indexes are calculated on the trend of prices. For finished and semi-finished goods, the company has considerable data on which it constructs an index number for an article which is taken to represent a whole group of similar articles.

Profits are not finally calculated until the company is satisfied that the purchasing power of shareholder investment has been maintained. Fixed assets and stocks are revalued as mentioned above, but that part of the shareholders' investment which is in the form of other assets will be affected by a change in the value of money. Philips calculate, on the basis of a cost of living index, how many currency units represent the same purchasing power as that part of the capital which Philips have invested in monetary assets at the beginning of the trading period. For an interesting detailed account of revaluation, see Batty, *Management Accountancy* (Macdonald and Evans, 1963).

6. The public

The British "public" is that large section of people which is the target of a tremendous quantity of statistical information, including a variety of index numbers; the "man in the street" may with their aid judge the state of the economy and gauge the "cost of living." I do not suggest that he will interpret the index numbers himself, but there are professionals who will do it for him. Each month a comment on the Cost of Living Index appears in most newspapers, and the two million people whose wages are linked to it are among those who should be interested. Many papers feature a share price index so that investors can discover day by day how equity trends are progressing or otherwise. The Industrial Production Index is also of interest to serious-minded people, who realise that it is a guide (however approximate) to national prosperity.

7. Sociologists

Sociologists use a wide variety of index numbers, especially when measuring standards of living between different income classes and over diverse areas. The various United Nations agencies compile or assemble vast quantities of statistics on human problems, and many of them are index numbers such as cost of living indexes. United Nations statistics have by now reached such a bulk that it has been necessary to omit them entirely from consideration here.

8. Historians

Historians use index numbers as a means of tracing movements in the economy over past years. Prices have been put into index terms as far back as the Middle Ages. R. G. Lipsey, taking 1451–75 as equal to 100, found that the price index of consumables in 1960 was about 4500, an increase of 45 times in 500 years. However, reliable records for index-number purposes have not been kept in sufficient detail for long historical trends to be discernible as a rule.

9. Psychologists

Psychologists use a form of index number. It is really outside the scope of this book, but since I.Q. or Intelligence Quotient is often badly understood a consideration of it may not be out of place. Although index numbers are more often used to measure changes in variables over time, others are calculated as a means of comparing two sets of variables at the *same* time. The index known as the intelligence quotient is of this latter type.

Although psychologists offer a number of different definitions for "intelligence," such as the ability to learn, to adapt to new situations, to perceive relationships, and to educe correlates, they all agree that the term embraces a number of distinct factors which contribute to an individual's capacity to act intelligently. This capacity, although not comparable to physical attributes, varies from one individual to another in much the same way as height or weight. When planning the manufacture of clothes, for example, it is useful to know how many people there are of any particular size. Similarly, when planning an educational programme it is useful to know not only how many people there are at any one level of intellectual development but also which people they are, so that all may receive the most suitable education.

Two important points have been confirmed by investigation. First, the capacity to solve certain types of problem grows with age (subject to important reservations).

Second, this growth does not always keep pace with increases in age. It was found that the relationship between these two variables—(a) the capacity of solving problems graded in terms of age and (b) the ages at which the average child would be expected to solve these problems—was best expressed as a ratio, where the numerator, variable (a), became known as "mental age" and the denominator, variable (b), the "chronological age." This ratio, multiplied by 100 to get rid of the decimal point, has become known as the Intelligence Quotient,

i.e.
$$\frac{\text{Mental age}}{\text{Chronological age}} \times 100 = \text{I.Q.}$$

It is important to remember that both "mental age" and "chronological age" do not have their literal meaning here, but represent test scores expressed in terms of years and months.

The use of tests was found to be so helpful to educationalists that it was extended to adults, particularly in selection, such as recruitment for the armed forces or for jobs in civilian life. Unlike selection for general education, selection for training or for jobs requires a knowledge not only of the general mental capacity of a person but also of certain specific abilities, aptitudes, or skills. In such cases therefore the traditional tests of intelligence are being increasingly supplemented and sometimes replaced by tests of specific abilities, aptitudes, or skills. The scores of these tests are no longer expressed in terms of age but rather in terms of the standards attained by people who are proficient in the job under consideration; they are not calculated as an index in the sense of a comparison between two sets of variables at the same time, and cannot therefore be included in the present discussion.

LIMITATIONS IN USING INDEX NUMBERS

Freund and Williams give a plain warning to the statistician:

"The increasingly significant role that index numbers have been assuming in business planning and in the formulation of executive decisions not only puts a tremendous burden on the statisticians who are responsible for their construction, but it also presents to the businessman who uses them the responsibility of using them intelligently, in full awareness of what through their strength they show and through their inherent weaknesses and limitations they fail to show."

A similar pertinent warning is:

"It ought to be conceded that index numbers are essentially arbitrary. Being at best re-arrangements of data wrenched out of their original market and technological contexts, they strictly have no economic meaning. Changes in tastes, technology, population composition, etc., over time increase their arbitrariness. But, of course, there is no bar to the use of index numbers 'as if' they did have some unequivocal meaning, provided that the users remember that they themselves made up the game and do not threaten to 'kill the umpire' when the figures contradict expectations" (Siegel).

SUMMARY

Index numbers can be useful or misleading. The quality of the results derived from using them will depend not only on the accuracy of the statistics themselves but also on the validity

of interpretations placed upon them. It is important to remember these points.

1. Consistency is important, especially for historical comparison.

2. Within their limits they should be reliable and accurate.

3. The end should justify the means. If a skilled mathematician must be employed to interpret the indexes, they
should be scrapped and more accurate methods used in the
first place.

QUESTIONS AND EXERCISES

1. The expenditure of a certain business on materials can be grouped
under three main headings in the ratio 6 : 5 : 3. If the average prices
in these groups rise by 42%, 35%, and 28% respectively, by what percentage is expenditure on materials increased if the same quantities of
the items are purchased as before?

2. Obtain and look through a copy of each of the following:

    (a) *The Monthly Digest of Statistics* (H.M.S.O.)
    (b) *The Board of Trade Journal* (weekly)
    (c) *The Ministry of Labour Gazette* (monthly)

Observe the kind of subject matter dealt with by them.

3. An ice-cream manufacturer uses milk, sugar, vanilla, and edible
oils to make his product. On 1st July 1963 the costs to him of these
items were:

Milk	24*d*. per gallon	Vanilla	18*s*. per jar
Sugar	£4 per bag	Oils	25*s*. per drum

On 1st February 1964 the prices were:

Milk	30*d*.	Vanilla	18*s*.
Sugar	£3	Oils	30*s*.

Construct a table to show price relatives for each item in February 1964,
based on 1st July 1963 = 100, and construct an index number for all
items.

4. In the last few years there has been a considerable increase in the
prices of your company's products, due largely to the higher costs of
raw materials.

You want to find out to what extent a similar situation is facing other
companies in the same and other industries. Where can you find
information on national levels of prices? What limitations are inherent
in such comparisons?   (*I.C.W.A. 1958*)

5. Write a short report in good business style on the purpose and use
of index numbers. Illustrate your answer if possible with a particular
example with which you are familiar.   (*R.S.A. 1957*)

6. Revise your knowledge of logarithms now. What are the logs of

  (a) 32·74   (d) 0·0000124
  (b) 3·274   (e) 124,100
  (c) 0·3274   (f) 1,978?

Calculate, using logs:

$$(a)\ \frac{41 \cdot 09 \times 7 \cdot 63}{14 \cdot 02} \qquad (b)\ 9781 \times 2074 \qquad (c)\ 47^3.$$

7. Prepare a list of textbooks, sources of published statistics, journals, and papers that you would recommend for a statistical service to one of the following departments of a large industrial undertaking: (a) Commercial Department; (b) Research Department. Each recommendation should be accompanied by a brief note of the significant features that warrant its inclusion. (This could begin early in your course and be added to during the year.)   (I.O.S. 1962)

CHAPTER 2

BUILDING AN INDEX NUMBER

REQUIREMENTS FOR THE COMPONENTS OF AN INDEX NUMBER

Before an index number can be presented in a completed state many practical and theoretical problems must be solved. An index number is an average of various components which should satisfy certain conditions before being included.

1. They should be relevant

The list of items composing an index is sometimes called the "regimen." In general, an index is created for a certain primary purpose; the regimen should be chosen so as to reflect this and, if possible without compromise, to enable it to serve subsidiary purposes as well.

In the early years of this century the British "Cost of Living Index" consisted of elements of consumer goods which were important to the working classes, since it was that section of the population the index was designed for. Today its successor, the "Index of Retail Prices," attempts to follow the cost of living of a much wider group of consumers and the regimen is relevant to that wider purpose.

2. They should be representative

Imagine that we wish to construct a measure of changes in the prices of textile raw materials imported into the United Kingdom. We could list all grades of cotton, wool, jute, hemp, silk, and other materials and have a fully comprehensive regimen. In statistics the complete group is called the "population" (or "universe"), and if our regimen were, simply, the whole population our index would of necessity be fully reliable, provided our arithmetic were correct. To obtain the full list of textile prices at frequent intervals would involve an amount of work that would give even a computer some tense milliseconds and the expense would be prohibitive. We must resort to "sampling," which means the selection of representative items. The mathematical basis of sampling is common knowledge to the statistician, and it enables him to select an appropriate method and size of sample. An important consideration is practicability—for provided the purpose of the index is achieved, the size of the sample is immaterial.

At this stage the student would be well advised to read Chapter 11 on sampling, where the fundamental ideas are described.

Sampling for index numbers differs from market research sampling in that random methods are usually *not* used. Some form of stratified sampling is employed, the size of the sample varying greatly. In one wholesale price index thirty-one commodities are selected; in the U.S. Bureau of Labor's Wholesale Price Index 2000 commodities are incorporated. Again, the famous *Financial Times* Index of Share Prices has thirty items. The equivalent published by the *Daily Mail* incorporates 640 items. No judgment of the efficiency of the above indexes should be read into this, since all are discussed in detail later. Briefly, the more items that are included the more expensive the index becomes and the less "sensitive" as a measure of change. Sometimes a sensitive index is needed which will respond to slight changes rapidly.

3. They should be reliable

The reliability of the index will be greatly affected by the accuracy of the quotations given for each constituent item. Data that come from external sources (as much usually does) must be carefully selected to ensure that homogeneous units are used. The grades, qualities, and units should be well understood. This is not difficult in the case of raw materials entering commerce, since they are usually highly graded for sales purposes—cotton, wool, raw metals, raw foodstuffs, for example. However, the nearer we approach retail markets, the more difficult it is to grade and classify. Thus a reliable grading of cotton sheets is difficult, cotton sheeting is less difficult, while grey cloth is comparatively easy to grade (Holmes). This is sufficient reason for the prevalence of wholesale index numbers. The government is often the main source of reliable information, possibly because it can afford to collect it, and may have a statutory duty to disseminate it.

4. They should be comparable

There is a danger that items which were once well classified will change in quality. Paints today may be the same colours as those manufactured years ago, but the quality is very different. Again, many commodities that were not in existence when the original index was compiled may now be of considerable importance—man-made fibres, plastic materials, television, to name only three. Thirdly, modern industry no longer uses certain materials in the same quantities as it used to. Solid woods have given place to plastics and veneers, production of candles has decreased, railway engines are diesel- instead of steam-powered. A compromise must often be reached between an index whose components are fixed and one which keeps up to date, and the settlement requires some ingenuity—as you will discover when you study published index numbers. It is essential that those who are given the task of compiling a new index number should have full instructions as to its purpose and facilities to follow the major principles of construction.

OBTAINING THE DATA

Having considered the principles of selecting the information, thought must be given to obtaining the data. This was briefly considered under heading 3, but a few further points need to be made. A private business cannot force its competitors to provide it with statistics, but for the benefit of the whole industry (in negotiations with trade unions, foreign governments, and so on) full statements of the industry's position may be needed. For this reason, trade associations, such as the British Iron and Steel Federation, collect statistics from member companies. The more efficient the trade association, the better the statistical knowledge.

The Government usually has statutory power to demand regular data, although care is always taken to conceal the identity of any business when the figures are published. Much information is submitted voluntarily to government departments, notably the Ministry of Labour and the Board of Trade.

Companies can compile index numbers from their own data, especially if they have an efficient research department or if the trade journals for that particular industry are useful sources of statistics. Since most such statistics are for internal use only one cannot estimate the extent to which this is done nor how much use is made of indexes.

CHANGES OVER TIME

When choosing data it is best to concentrate on standard qualities which are easy to describe. When items become outmoded a switch can be made to whatever replaces them, *e.g.* nylon replaces silk for garments in a consumers' index. The problems of collection are mainly practical and are limited by the expense, and the availability of data.

In a series of data each price relative starts at the base date with a value of 100%. As time (years rather than months) goes by, and especially in times of rapid change such as war and its aftermath, the old series becomes ever less representative of the situation it was designed for. In the index as first conceived and introduced, the items were selected in certain relative proportions to correspond to their relative importance. For example, if in a wholesale price index cotton is regarded as being five times more important than jute, that will be allowed for. Later the relationship may change. Cotton may be only three times more important, but the old proportions are still the ones shown. Originally the items could be said to fit neatly together, but in time gaps appear and the structure begins to "leak" (metaphorically speaking). The measure of the compactness or leaking is known as "dispersion." Reference should be made to Chapter 3 for a fuller treatment of this term.

The degree of dispersion found in a frequency distribution of price relatives may therefore be said to increase with the passage of time. A high degree of dispersion shows that the "average" no longer has much relevance, and in this circumstance weighting must of necessity be used, this being fully discussed in Chapters 4 and 6.

A reasonable conclusion is that the accuracy of index numbers is greater for short-run price indexes than for those covering a greater span of time. A practical answer is to restrict comparisons to periods of comparative stability if high accuracy is required.

CHANGES OVER SPACE

The difficulties of comparisons over time have been indicated. Even more difficult is the comparison of prices to measure the cost of living in different places. A common exercise of economists is to compare purchasing powers in different lands at the same time. The cost of living is a function of the amount spent, that is (Price of goods × Quantity consumed by the average person). This notion of a fixed "basket" of goods offends basic economic theories of demand and utility. For one thing, if prices change the "demand theory" as explained in textbooks will suggest that the quantities demanded will alter, especially if the price change is of the kind to alter price relationships. A price increase of all vegetable products will probably reduce the demand for them as a whole, although the proportionate

B

demand for each may well remain the same. But if the price of one vegetable rises while that of others remains stationary the relative proportions will alter.

This will affect the index, which is usually not capable of handling such changes, unless an attempt is made to alter the weights; but then the calculations become involved. Internationally, the consumers do not have the same goods in their basket. To compare English, Indian, and Russian living costs in such terms may be misleading. A middle way would be to select what *is* a typical basket in each country and merely compare the results.

EXAMPLE 4

The following short table indicates the relative importance (weight) in the Cost of Living Indexes in the United Kingdom and the U.S.A.

	U.K. Index of Retail Prices, % of total	U.S.A. Consumer Price Index, % of total
	Importance	*Importance*
Transport vehicles:	6·8	11·3
(*a*) Purchase of motor vehicles	1·4	4·9
(*b*) Public transport	3·5	1·3

This indicates the conditions in the two countries quite well. Transport is of less importance in the average United Kingdom family budget than in the equivalent American one (7% to 11%), but, of that, public transport (trains, buses, etc.) is almost three times as significant a charge on British as on American pockets.

QUESTIONS AND EXERCISES

1. If the wages of a group of workers are increased by 40% and the cost of living rises by 25%, how much greater is their purchasing power (real income) than before?

2. Define the term "index number."

The 1948 wages of six grades of male clerks A, B, C, D, E, and F were:

38*s*.9*d*.   85*s*. 4*d*.   116*s*. 7*d*.   129*s*. 10*d*.   151*s*. 8*d*.   196*s*. 5*d*.

Their wages in 1958 were:

62*s*. 8*d*.   123*s*. 6*d*.   132*s*. 1*d*.   146*s*. 6*d*.   165*s*. 10*d*.   201*s*. 7*d*.

The corresponding wages for females were:

1948: 31*s*. 10*d*.   45*s*. 9*d*.   67*s*. 2*d*.   80*s*. 5*d*.   98*s*. 7*d*.   126*s*. 10*d*.
1958: 49*s*. 9*d*.   72*s*. 11*d*.   88*s*. 5*d*.   99*s*. 5*d*.   118*s*. 5*d*.   145*s*. 6*d*.

Express the 1958 wages in each case as a percentage of the corresponding 1948 wage. Hence calculate for 1958 an index of wages for both male and female clerks. (*R.S.A. 1959*)

3. "By their nature, index numbers can seldom be used for more than very rough comparison over long intervals" (R. G. D. Allen in *International Trade Statistics*). Comment on this statement, illustrating your answer by reference to any index number known to you.

(*I.O.S. 1959*)

4. It is desired to study changes in the amount of employment and earnings in the radio industry in the last twelve months. Outline a plan for this research, paying particular attention to the precise nature of the data you would seek and the methods you would adopt to obtain it. Discuss briefly any difficulties of definition that are likely to arise.

(*I.P.M. 1956*)

5. The articles of household use owned by wage-earning families differ today in kind and in materials used in their manufacture from those found in a similar home in, say, 1938. List as many items as you can under two headings:

(*a*) Items which are common now but were unknown then, and
(*b*) Items now made of different materials to those used in 1938.

6. How could we compare standards of living statistically for similar families in: (*a*) China, (*b*) Canada, and (*c*) England?

CHAPTER 3

CALCULATION OF INDEX NUMBERS: CHOICE OF A SUITABLE AVERAGE

AN index number is the result of averaging a series of data, expressed in percentage form, and it therefore provides the interested person with *one* figure which can be taken to represent the whole. There are more ways than one of averaging a series, and in this chapter we consider the kind of average to use.

THE FIVE MAJOR AVERAGES

The economic statistician recognises five major averages, two of which are thought to be the more suitable for index number calculation. In what follows, the subject of weighting the series is mainly ignored, since it is important enough to merit a separate chapter. I shall use the words "mean" and "average" as interchangeable terms.

1. The arithmetic mean (A.M.)

This measure is the one most commonly taught in schools. Sum a series of variables (*i.e.* the data we wish to average) and divide the result by the number of items in the group:

$$\bar{x} = \frac{\Sigma x}{n}$$

where x signifies the individual items of data;

Σ represents the instruction to add up and find the total, *i.e.* "the sum of";

n represents the number of items in the series;

$\bar{x}$ or A.M. (the answer) the arithmetic mean (x-bar).

EXAMPLE 5

A group of students achieve the following G.C.E. results at ordinary level: Albert 5 passes, Basil 4, Charles 6, David 3, and Edward 7. To obtain the arithmetic average, apply the formula; thus: $x = 25/5 = 5$ passes.

In this example the answer is a whole number, but the arithmetic mean often produces an answer with decimals, in which case the experience and common sense of the investigator will advise him whether to show the answer in whole numbers or include the decimals. Suppose Charles had five passes. Σx would then have been 24 and the average 24/5 or 4·80, but we must obviously give the answer as five passes. A second snag is that the answer may not correspond with the score of any one member of the group. As it happens, Albert did obtain five passes, but it frequently occurs that no member of the group coincides exactly with the average $\bar{x}$.

EXAMPLE 6

Another group of students taking G.C.E. at ordinary level achieved these results: Frank passed in two subjects, George in six, Hugh in two, Ivor in four, while James only succeeded in gaining one pass. Thus a total of fifteen passes was shared among five boys. The average number of passes will be 15/5 = 3, but no boy actually had three. This does not usually affect the value of the average as a measure of "typicality," since if we *must* have coincidence between boy and average we can use another measure—the median (*q.v.*).

The arithmetic mean is usually simple to calculate. It is useful to business people who wish to obtain a bird's eye view of a series, and it is well understood by the majority of people. But in addition to the disadvantages observed above, of decimals and non-coincidence, another weakness is distortion. Since the arithmetic mean uses all the data of the group and since in social sciences "abnormal" items are often found, the value will be displaced by the force of that item.

EXAMPLE 7

In the head office of a company the earnings of five people are:

Position	Weekly wage, £
Typist	8
Typist	7
Book-keeper	10
Clerk	10
Director/Office Manager	100

$$\Sigma x = £135$$

$$\text{and } \bar{x} = £\frac{135}{5} = £27$$

This result cannot be regarded as "representative." It would be a temptation to exclude the Director from the calculation, but if that were done the result would be as distorted as before. Fortunately in a small series such as the last example large items are easily noticed, whereas in a large group the tendency (as can be seen in the section on sampling) is for abnormalities to cancel out to a great extent.

2. The geometric mean (G.M.)

This has been widely advocated for use by index number theorists, but in fact it is not by any means exclusively used. The calculation involves taking the nth root of the product of n numbers:

$$\sqrt[n]{x_1 \times x_2 \times x_3 \ldots x_n}.$$

The little number or letter below the x is a subscript and *not* an instruction to alter the number. p^2 means "square p," *i.e.* p multiplied by p, but in the above x_2 means the second item in a group of x's, and x_n is the last of the group which, since there may be any number of x's, we cannot provide with a numerical subscript.

EXAMPLE 8

The G.M. for the information in Example 5 is:

$$\sqrt[5]{5 \times 4 \times 6 \times 3 \times 7} = \sqrt[5]{2520} = 4 \cdot 7896 \text{ or } 5 \text{ passes.}$$

Notice that the G.M. is smaller than the A.M. of the same data. This method "damps down" large abnormalities, which is a major reason for its recommended use, but it also gives more effect to *smaller* abnormalities, and this could be equally misleading. Perhaps the A.M. will appeal to the go-ahead salesman, whose one good week will be regarded as his average; while the cautious businessman will favour the G.M., since business is always bad, but could get worse! If the data are large the G.M. should be calculated in its entirety by logs.

EXAMPLE 9

The profits of a firm's three branches were £367, £1024, and £1648. What is the geometric mean?

Number	Log
367	2·5647
1024	3·0103
1648	3·2169
	8·7919

$$\sqrt[3]{} = 2 \cdot 9306; \text{ anti-log} = 852 \cdot 3$$

Therefore the average profit G.M. = £852.

The above examples show that the calculation of the geometric mean is more tedious than that of the A.M. The possibility of an arithmetical error is therefore increased.

3. The mode

The "mode" is the average which measures the value of the most important item in any group.

EXAMPLE 10

In an office we may find a wage distribution such that ten people earn £8, thirty-five earn £10, eight earn £12, and four earn £14 or more. Of the 57 people, the largest group is those who earn £10, and since this is the commonest it is the modal wage. It can usually best be shown by a frequency curve (*see* Fig. 1).

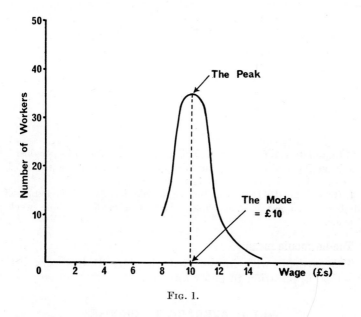

FIG. 1.

The mode is simple but is not often used because of two major drawbacks:

1. If the items are few in number the mode may not stand out.

2. Some distributions of data give several peaks, and to choose one would be to ignore the claims of others.

4. The median

If a distribution is arrayed or "sorted out" so that the x's are in order of size the "median" is the value which divides the group into two parts, so that there are as many to the upper side as to the lower side. This is the positional value. Like the mode, it is not as a rule thrown off-centre by abnormal items at the ends.

EXAMPLE 11

A report to the personnel officer of an engineering works, concerning absence through influenza and similar complaints, shows that 20 workers had no weeks' absence, 55 had one, 42 had two, 20 had three, 6 had four, and 2 had five or more weeks away. Calculate the median number of weeks' absence.

1. Assemble into order of size (f is the symbol for "frequency of occurrence"):

No. of weeks' absence (x)	No. of workers (f)	Cumulative f
0	20	20
1	55	75
2	42	117
3	20	137
4	6	143
5+	2	145

2. Cumulate the frequencies. This gives the total of 145 persons.

3. Find the middle person in this germ-laden line-up (number 72); there are 71 to his "right" and 71 to his "left."

4. Read from the table which class he falls into, which is 1 (persons number 21–75 are in this class). Thus the median is one week's absence.

5. The harmonic mean

This is dealt with in the next chapter. It has very little practical application to index numbers.

WHICH AVERAGE TO CHOOSE?

The mode has the merit of simplicity, but may be indefinite. The median suffers from the same disadvantage. Moreover, neither of them allows for the size of the items at each end of a distribution, although these may be significant. In effect, neither of the two is used in the calculation of index numbers, nor is the harmonic mean. The geometric mean has been criticised as difficult to calculate. Thus, the arithmetic mean remains—and indeed it is the one commonly used.

The arithmetic mean is suitable so long as the series of data is not widely dispersed and a measure of dispersion should accompany the index, although this is rarely done. The terms used in the following example are explained subsequently.

EXAMPLE 12

In the Toolup Machine Tool Company Ltd. Rejects—Files and Rasps Division for the week ending 10th June for Department A were as follows:

Operator	No. of rejects (x)	Deviation from A.M. (d)	Square of deviation (d^2)
A	7	−2	4
B	11	+2	4
C	8	−1	1
D	10	+1	1
E	9	0	0
F	10	+1	1
G	8	−1	1
	$\Sigma x = 63$		Sum of squares 12

$$\text{A.M.} = \frac{63}{7} = 9 \text{ rejects}$$

$$\text{Variance } (S^2) = \frac{12}{7} = 1\tfrac{5}{7}$$

$$\text{Standard Deviation (S.D.)} = \sqrt{\frac{12}{7}} = 1\cdot31 \text{ rejects}$$

$$\text{The coefficient of variation (C.V.)} = \frac{1\cdot31 \times 100}{9} \simeq 15\%.$$

In the same company the corresponding rejects for Department B were:

Operator	No. of rejects (x)	Deviation from A.M. (d)	Square of deviation (d^2)
Z	0	−9	81
Y	2	−7	49
X	25	+16	256
W	8	−1	1
V	4	−5	25
U	18	+9	81
T	6	−3	9
	$\Sigma x = 63$		502

$$\text{A.M.} = \frac{63}{7} = 9 \text{ rejects}$$

$$S^2 = \frac{502}{7} = 71\tfrac{5}{7}$$

$$\text{S.D.} = \sqrt{\frac{502}{7}} = 8\cdot51 \text{ rejects}$$

$$\text{C.V.} = \frac{8\cdot51 \times 100}{9} \simeq 95\%.$$

Comments on the results. In common with earlier examples, the calculations have been made in real units rather than in the form of index numbers because the principles introduced will, it is hoped, be more easily understood.

In Departments A and B the average number of rejects per operator were identical at nine each. This in itself is correct but incomplete, since no idea of dispersion is provided. The standard deviation shows, in Department A, 1·31 rejects or 15% of mean; in Department B, 8·51 rejects or 95% of mean, showing that the average of A is more representative of the whole group than is the average of B.

DISPERSION

With ungrouped data

Dispersion measurement occurs frequently in much statistical analysis and can be a valuable addition to any report which incorporates measures of average. In its simplest form dispersion concerns the breadth or narrowness of a distribution around an average; it aims at providing a comparison between one series and another, to show which average is the truest representative of its group.

Most frequency distributions can be profitably analysed by calculating:

(*a*) the "central value" or average;

(*b*) the degree of dispersion around the central value—the present subject of study—and

(*c*) the degree of symmetry or skewness (not dealt with in this book in any detail).

EXAMPLE 13

The examination marks of two groups of students are compared. Those in Group A obtained 7, 6, 8, 8, and 6 respectively. Group B obtained 3, 10, 5, 10, and 7 marks respectively. Both groups have an average of 7 marks, but the "dispersion" is greater in Group B: it is obvious that in Group A the marks cluster more closely round the average than they do in the second group.

Standard deviation

The next aim is to attach a measurement to dispersion, and perhaps the most useful method is that of the "standard deviation," although others may be met in practice—the range, quartile deviation, and mean deviation.

Standard deviation is defined as "the square root of the

average of the squared deviations measured from the mean" or, "root mean—square deviation."

Given a series of data which is ungrouped, the formula is

$$\text{Standard deviation (S.D. or } \sigma) = \sqrt[2]{\frac{\Sigma fd^2}{\Sigma f}}.$$

σ (little sigma) is the common symbol for standard deviation; d represents the deviation of each unit of data (in the x column) from its average, showing the signs $+$ or $-$.

EXAMPLE 14. *Bonus earnings of two groups of girls in a laundry*

TABLE 1

Bagwash Department			Pressing and Cleaning Department		
Bonus in s. (x)	Number of girls (f)	fx	Bonus in s. (x)	Number of girls (f)	fx
5	4	20	5	—	—
10	5	50	10	2	20
15	15	225	15	30	450
20	20	400	20	24	480
25	10	250	25	4	100
30	6	180	30	—	—
	60	1125		60	1050

The average bonus $= \dfrac{1125}{60}s.$

$= 18 \cdot 8s. \simeq 19s.$

The average bonus $= \dfrac{1050}{60}s.$

$= 17 \cdot 5s.$

The full calculation of the dispersion by the most common method is now given. The first stage is to calculate the average—usually the arithmetic mean—and this occupies the first three columns:

TABLE 2 — *Bagwash Department*

Bonus in s. (x)	Number of girls (f)	fx	Deviation from the average (19s.) (d)	d^2	fd^2
5	4	20	−14	196	784
10	5	20	−9	81	405
15	15	225	−4	16	240
20	20	400	+1	1	20
25	10	250	+6	36	360
30	6	180	+15	225	1350
	60	1125			3159

The fourth column (d) is calculated by $(x - \bar{x})$ for each item, *e.g.* 5s. bonus is (5–19s.) below the average $= -14s$. Next, square this column to obtain d^2, since this is required by the formula (Σfd^2). Note that fd^2 is built up as $d \times d \times f$ and *not* as $fd \times fd$. Multiply by f, applying the formula.

Then
$$\sigma = \sqrt[2]{\frac{3159}{60}} \simeq 7s.$$

The standard deviation is a measure of absolute variability, *i.e.* the greater the variability of the distribution the larger will be the value of σ.

Coefficient of variation

As a better means of assessing the size of the dispersion it is commonly calculated as a percentage and called the coefficient of variation (C.V.). This may be given as:

$$\frac{\text{The measure of dispersion}}{\text{The average}} \times 100 = \text{C.V.}$$

In Table 2, the C.V. would be:

$$\frac{7}{19} \times 100\% = 37\%.$$

The C.V. is a relative measure and is a valuable additional calculation.

EXAMPLE 15

A men's physical education class reported a mean height of 69 in., with σ of 4 in., and a mean weight of 160 lb with σ of 20 lb. Is the class more variable in height or in weight?

$$\text{Height: C.V.} = \frac{4 \times 100}{69} = \frac{400}{69} = 5\cdot8\%$$

$$\text{Weight: C.V.} = \frac{20 \times 100}{160} = \frac{200}{16} = 12\cdot5\%.$$

Therefore the class is more variable in weight.

If we now return to our figures shown in Example 14 it is possible to calculate the S.D. and C.V. of the bonuses of the Pressing and Cleaning departments and compare the results in a small table:

TABLE 3 *Bonuses*

	Bagwash	Pressing
Average earnings	19s.	18s.
S.D.	17s.	?
C.V.	37%	?

You should find that the percentage dispersion in the bonuses of the Pressing Department is much less than in the Bagwash Department, indicating possibly a more homogeneous group. The dispersion therefore is most useful where two or more series are to be compared. To state that the C.V. of any group is (say) 45% is meaningless without some comparison.

With grouped data

Where the variable x covers many items it is convenient for most commercial purposes to combine several units into "groups." In the laundry, if bonuses could be earned from 1s. to 30s. the table would be thirty lines long and for several units there might be no girls represented. To group too narrowly renders averages meaningless; to group widely means more work. The laundry example has really been grouped in five-shilling units, viz.:

$$x$$

0–5s.
6–10s.
11–15s.
16–20s., etc.

Care must be taken, when using continuous variables, that the division between one group and another is unambiguous. It would be misleading to write, for example, "0–5s." then "5–10s.," since it would not be clear which group anyone who earned exactly 5s. should fall into.

When averaging grouped data two alternate methods may be applied: mid-points or assumed averages. All textbooks deal with the mid-point method. They can easily be referred to, so I shall explain the use of the "method of assumed averages." The two formulae concerned are:

$$\bar{x} \text{ (usually A.M.)} = x_0 + c \times \frac{\Sigma fd}{\Sigma f}$$

and

$$\sigma = c \times \sqrt[2]{\frac{\Sigma fd^2}{\Sigma f} - \left(\frac{\Sigma fd}{\Sigma f}\right)^2}$$

where c is the "class interval," *i.e.* the number of items in each group or class;

x_0 is the assumed average;

d here is the deviation *in groups* from the group in which x_0 is situated.

EXAMPLE 16

Ages of lunatics and idiots chargeable to the parishes of England and Wales in August 1844 (*vide* G. Porter, *Progress of the Nation*, 2nd edition, 1851).

1	2	3	4	5
Ages of lunatics (x)	Number of lunatics (f)	Deviation in groups from assumed mean x_0 (d)	fd	fd^2
Under 10 years	70	−3	−210	630
10 to under 20	980	−2	−1,960	3,920
20 to under 30	3,350	−1	−3,350	3,350
x_0} 30 to under 40	3,780	0	−5,520	—
40 to under 50	3,640	+1	+3,640	3,640
50 to under 60	2,720	+2	+5,440	10,880
60 to under 70	1,730	+3	+5,190	15,570
70 and over	730	+4	+2,920	11,680
	17,000		+17,190	49,670
	Σf		$\Sigma fd = +11,670$	Σfd^2

Step 1.—By inspection of the frequencies, choose a group in which you consider the average may be found. If you choose a group which later proves to have been wrong the calculation will still give the right answer, although the arithmetic may be rather more complicated. If we used mid-points the multiplications would give large numbers, *e.g.* 30–40. Mid-point is 35, f is 3780, therefore $fx = 132,300$, etc.

In this example the greatest number is much less difficult than this.

Step 2.—Measure the deviations from this x_0, calling lesser groups minus and larger groups plus (column 3).

Step 3.—Calculate fd and sum, and thus calculate the arithmetic mean by the formula first given:

$$\bar{x} = 35 + 10 \times \frac{+11,670}{17,000} = 35 + \frac{116,700}{17,000} \simeq 42 \text{ years.}$$

The mid-point of the group (x_0) is 35 and the class interval is 10, since each group contains 10 years.

Step 4.—The calculation to obtain σ will involve column 5. By formula,

$$\sigma = 10 \times \sqrt{\frac{49,670}{17,000} - \left(\frac{11,670}{17,000}\right)^2}$$

$$= 10 \times \sqrt{2\cdot922 - 0\cdot4714} = 15\cdot66 \text{ years.}$$

The coefficient of variation is

$$\frac{15\cdot66}{42} \times 100 = 37\cdot3\%$$

Warning! It is possible that Σfd (column 4) may be negative, in which case the product of $\Sigma fd/\Sigma f$ will be negative too. This will be so if we have over-estimated the average when choosing our assumed group.

To obtain the maximum benefit from the above data and calculation, a comparable series should be obtained, possibly the national age distribution in that year.

Dispersion and index numbers

Over the passage of time any series with fixed weights tends to show increasing dispersion, *i.e.* the weights become less applicable to current conditions than at earlier dates. As an illustration, consider the former Index of Retail Prices. I use this example since the Index is well known, although the amount of dispersion variation may not be great. The Index was in existence from January 1956 to 1962.

EXAMPLE 17

Ministry of Labour: Index of Retail Prices
(17th January 1956 = 100)

(a) *Mid-1957*

	Base year weights (%)	Mid-1957 price relatives (x)	fx (approx.)	Deviation from the average of d (106)	fd	fd²
Food	350	105	36,750	−1	−350	350
Drink	71	104	7,380	−2	−142	284
Tobacco	80	106	8,480	0	—	—
Housing	87	110	9,570	+4	+348	1,392
Fuel	55	108	5,940	+2	+110	220
Household goods	66	101	6,670	−5	−330	1,650
Clothing	106	102	10,810	−4	−424	1,696
Transport	68	110	7,480	+4	+272	1,088
Miscellaneous goods	59	108	6,870	+2	+118	236
Services	58	109	6,320	+3	+174	522
	1,000 Σf		106,270 Σfx			7,438 Σfd^2

$$\text{The weighted average} = \frac{106,270}{1000} = 106\cdot3$$

$$\text{S.D.} = \sqrt{\frac{7438}{1000}} = 2\cdot7$$

$$\text{C.V.} = \frac{2\cdot7}{106\cdot3} \times 100 = 2\cdot5\%$$

(b) *October 1961*

q_0	October 1961 (x)	fx	d (116)	fd	fd^2
350	108	37,800	−8	−2,800	22,400
71	108	7,670	−8	−568	4,544
80	124	9,920	6	480	2,880
87	140	12,180	24	2,088	8,352
55	123	6,770	7	385	2,695
66	101	6,670	−15	−990	14,850
106	106	11,240	−10	−1,060	10,600
68	126	8,570	10	680	6,800
59	127	7,490	11	649	7,139
58	129	7,480	13	754	9,802
1,000		115,790			90,062

$$\text{The weighted average} = \frac{115,790}{1000} = 115\cdot8$$

$$\text{S.D.} = \sqrt{\frac{90,062}{1000}} = 9\cdot5$$

$$\text{C.V.} = \frac{9\cdot5}{115\cdot8} \times 100 = 8\cdot2\%$$

If the weights given in 1957 were still fully applicable we should expect the dispersion to stay the same even though the index, of course, would change. The C.V. has increased from 2·5 to 8·2%, which is significant although not considerable.

Every average should be accompanied by a measure of dispersion in order that management or other users may be given the fullest information necessary to reach intelligent decisions.

The standard deviation measure should normally be used, for reasons which can be summarised thus: (*a*) every value of the distribution is included; (*b*) it is the product of correct mathematical processes and is available for further calculations; and (c) it is the best measure for important sampling theory.

QUESTIONS AND EXERCISES

1. Plot the distributions shown in Example 12 on one graph and thus show the contrasting dispersions.

2. It has been suggested that the G.M. is to be preferred to the A.M. in the construction of an index of prices. What special property does the G.M. possess to account for this preference? Illustrate your answer with an example.   (*I.P.M. 1956*)

3. The following table shows the recorded rainfall for a particular area over the past years.

Rainfall in inches	No. of years in which this rainfall was recorded
27	1
28	2
29	3
30	4
31	3
32	1
33	1
34	1

Calculate the average annual rainfall, the variance, and standard deviation of the rainfall.   (*I.C.W.A. 1960*)

4. Find the simple average price of the following piece goods and the weighted average price, using the quantities as weights:

Piece goods	Price per yard (pence)	Quantity (10 million yd)
Unbleached	2·79	236
Bleached	3·17	205
Printed flags	3·09	5
Other sorts	3·27	118
Dyed in piece	4·54	115
Dyed yarn	3·98	29

Account for the difference between the two results.
                                          (*I.M.S.M. 1960*)

5. Explain the importance of exact definitions in statistical work. Illustrate your answer with examples from statistics of trade, prices, and earnings.   (*I.M.S.M. 1957*)

6. Line a group of students up in front of the class and select the one of median height.

7. A frequency distribution of shoes sold by sizes for adults shows two separate modes. Can you explain why? What other similar examples can you suggest?

8. Define *in your own words* the arithmetic mean, the median, and the mode; discuss briefly the merits and demerits of each.

9. (*a*) Calculate the arithmetic mean and standard deviation of the following:

Age structure of the population of England and Wales in 1951

Age group	Number of persons (00,000's)
0–10	77
11–20	63
21–30	69
31–40	71
41–50	73
51–60	58
61–70	44
71 and over	33
Total	488

(*b*) Then compare your results with the following:

Percentage distribution of population of England and Wales in 1841

Age group	%
0–10	25·0
11–20	20·8
21–30	18·0
31–40	13·0
41–50	9·5
51–60	6·5
61–70	4·4
71 and over	2·8
Total	100·0

(*I.M.S.M. 1958 for* (a) *and G. Porter* Progress of the
Nation, *1851, for* (b))

10. Refer to Example 17 in the text. From the *Ministry of Labour Gazette* obtain the Retail Price Index figures for the latest month and compare the standard deviation and coefficient of variation with those in Example 17.

11. Find the A.M. and standard deviation of the distribution below, where x = score in an aptitude test and f = number of candidates.

x	20–	28–	36–	44–	52–	60–	76–92
f	27	81	178	297	213	180	24

(*I.P.M. 1957*)

12. Find the A.M. and S.D. of each of the sample distributions tabulated below.

Weight of schoolchildren aged 11 years

Weight (lb)	No. of children living in homes with:	
	Less than two persons per room	Two or more persons per room
40–	6	15
50–	163	241
60–	590	708
70–	640	539
80–	220	152
90–	64	21
100–	23	9
120–140	4	3

Can you draw any conclusions?   (*I.P.M. 1960*)

13. Find two measures of dispersion for the following data, and discuss their respective advantages:

Age distribution of responses to an interview survey

Age (yrs)	20–29	30–39	40–49	50–59	60–69	70–79	80 and over
Frequency	141	223	249	233	152	94	17

(*University of Liverpool 1961*)

14. From the following table, calculate the mean number of readers of subscribers' copies of *The Economist* and the standard deviation of their distribution.

Number of readers	Percentage of copies
1	31
2	21
3	15
4	8
5	5
6	6
7 or more	14
	100

(*University of Exeter 1961*)

15. Calculate the arithmetic mean and standard deviation of each of these distributions. What do these measures tell you about the average size of vehicle and about the variation within each distribution?

Road vehicles from 1–6 tons' unladen weight: number with "A" and "B" licences

Unladen weight (tons)		Number of vehicles	
Over	Not over	"A" licences	"B" licences
1	2	2,607	7,893
2	3	24,936	42,494
3	4	16,747	16,339
4	5	7,849	4,072
5	6	2,933	794

(I.O.T. 1962)

16. A biscuit manufacturer produces half-pound packets of line "X." A random sample of packets was weighed and the following figures recorded:

Net weight (oz)	Number of packets
Less than 7·4	0
7·4 and less than 7·6	1
7·6 and less than 7·8	8
7·8 and less than 8·0	24
8·0 and less than 8·2	31
8·2 and less than 8·4	20
8·4 and less than 8·6	4
8·6 and more	2

(a) Calculate the mean and standard deviation of the weight per packet.
(b) With what degree of certainty can the manufacturer state "Minimum net weight $7\frac{1}{2}$ oz"? *(I.C.W.A. 1961)*

17. Index numbers of the value of retail sales (1957 = 100):

	Grocers	Butchers	Green-grocers	Bakers	Dairy-men
1958	103	102	104	105	102
1962	118	110	112	130	123

From this abbreviated table calculate the index number for each year, and compare measures of dispersion.

18. A sample 100 brackets were measured to the nearest tenth of an inch, the recorded lengths being as follows:

Length (in.)	Number of brackets
5·0 and under 5·1	2
5·1 and under 5·2	5
5·2 and under 5·3	8
5·3 and under 5·4	23
5·4 and under 5·5	25
5·5 and under 5·6	20
5·6 and under 5·7	10
5·7 and under 5·8	7
Total	100

Calculate: (a) the arithmetic mean, and (b) the standard deviation of the lengths.   (*London Chamber of Commerce 1961*)

CHAPTER 4

CALCULATION OF INDEX NUMBERS, USING RELATIVES

THE previous chapter was concerned with the commonest measures of average, enabling us to begin the construction of indexes. For this purpose the following discussion refers to price indexes unless otherwise stated. There are two main ways of calculating indexes:

1. By means of price relatives.
2. By means of aggregates (*see* next chapter).

THE PRICE RELATIVE

An index can be produced which is an average of a series of numbers which themselves are percentages, or price relatives. If we record prices of a variety of commodities in real terms at a given date and at a later date record the prices of similar items, the change in price can be simply expressed as a percentage of the new compared with the old for each commodity. This provides us with price relatives, and if weights are available the next stage will be to multiply the relatives by the weights. Finally, we add together the weighted relatives and calculate an average.

Let us first look at an unweighted index, which actually involves treating each commodity in a series as though its importance were equal to that of each other item in the series.

EXAMPLE 18. *Unweighted index of the cost of living (beverages)*

Using 1st December 1960 as the commencing date and giving all components at that date the same number, viz. 100, to represent the stated quantity:

Item	Unit of Measurement	Price at 1st Dec. 1960 (base)	Price relative 1st Dec. 1960	Price at 1st Dec. 1962 (current date)	Price relative
Instant coffee	2-oz tin	4s.	100	2s.	50
Coffee essence	4-oz jar	3s.	100	3s.	100
Cocoa	16-oz tin	4s. 6d.	100	2s. 3d.	50
Tea	per lb	8s.	100	12s.	150
Sum of items	—	—	400	—	350
Index, by A.M.			100		87·50

The price relatives are, of course, 100 each at the base date. The method of calculation of the price relative is:

$$\frac{2s.}{4s.} \times \frac{100}{1} = 50.$$

The index number is the simple arithmetic mean of the price relatives: $350/4 = 87 \cdot 5$.

Two items in the series will be seen to have fallen in price, one has increased and the price of one is stationary. The total effect is a fall in the cost of living of $12\frac{1}{2}\%$ in the two years.

WEIGHTING

It has been assumed that the consumption of each commodity has been equal (in Example 18 we said our consumer uses one tin, bottle, or pound of each beverage in each period). This is probably unrealistic, and most indexes take account of the proportions of each item actually used. This method of weighting shows the *relative* importance of each in the series. Students of gracious living will know that a certain cocktail is made up with the following ingredients: oranges, gin, French vermouth, Italian vermouth, ice, and bitters. However, not equal quantities of each are incorporated. One mixture which might be acceptable would consist of

Item	Quantity
Orange	juice of a quarter
Gin	$\frac{1}{2}$ of dry gin
Vermouth	$\frac{1}{4}$ French
,,	$\frac{1}{4}$ Italian
Bitters	a dash

and the result would be a Bronx.

1. Using the arithmetic mean

Weights are assigned to each item and multiplied with the corresponding unit of the series; a "weighted average" is obtained by using the formula:

$$\text{Weighted A.M.} = \frac{\Sigma xf}{\Sigma f}$$

where Σ (sigma) simply indicates that individual items are added, and f represents the weights assigned to the various items.

EXAMPLE 19

In an office we may find the following wage distribution and its unweighted A.M.:

Wages per week (x)	Frequency of occurrence (weight f)	Product (xf)
£8	30	240
£12	15	180
£100	1	100
	$\Sigma f = 46$	$\Sigma xf = 520$

If we are informed that three wages are paid in the office, viz. £8, £12, £100, an average would be £120/3 = £40. This takes no heed of the relative importance of each wage. We then discover that the numbers of persons earning these wages are (in order) 30, 15, and 1. Obviously these are suitable for weights, since they measure the importance ideally. The man earning £100 is probably very important, but since he is the only one, it would be unfair to bias the average as though he represented $33\frac{1}{3}\%$ of the workers.

Applying the formula:

$$\text{Weighted A.M.} = \frac{\Sigma xf}{\Sigma f} = \frac{£520}{46} = £11 \cdot 3 \text{ or £11 } 6s. \text{ } 0d.$$

This differs considerably from the unweighted mean of £40, the latter giving equal prominence to the large wage of the director and to the lower typists' wages.

2. Using other averages

Note that the A.M. has been used so far. To calculate the median of the above example we should cumulate the frequency column and find the middle item, reading the answer in the corresponding x group, viz.:

x	f	Cum. f
£8	30	30
£12	15	45
£100	1	46
	46	

46/2 = 23—the 23rd person is earning the median wage, which is £8 (person number 23 comes in the first 30 of the distribution).

The modal wage is that which is represented most often. Thirty people earn £8, more than earn any other wage. Thus £8 is the modal figure.

The average wage by the geometric mean is rather more complicated to compute. This is dealt with fully later, but the G.M. wage would be

$$£\sqrt[46]{8^{30} \times 12^{15} \times 100^1} \backsimeq £9 \cdot 647 \backsimeq £9 \; 13s. \; 0d.$$

which, you will notice, is lower than the A.M. wage.

EXAMPLE 20. *Weighted index of the cost of living (beverages)*

Item	Unit	Price at 1st Dec. 1960 (base date) (x)	Quantity sold (f)	Price at 1st Dec. 1962 (current date) (x)	Price relative	Weighted price relative
Instant coffee	2-oz tin	4s.	20	2s.	50	1,000
Coffee essence	4-oz jar	3s.	5	3s.	100	500
Cocoa	16-oz tin	4s. 6d.	15	2s. 3d.	50	750
Tea	per lb	8s.	60	12s.	150	9,000
			100			11,250

Thus the weighted A.M. is 11,250/100 = 112·5, which is the index number required. The unweighted index was 87·50, but the difference is caused by acknowledging that tea (which has risen in price) more than offsets in importance those other drinks whose prices have fallen.

Weights are numbers assigned on a basis of importance. In a price index the measure of importance will most likely be the total spent by all consumers on each commodity, so the weights in Example 20 may derive from trade statistics of total sales in £ million. Tea sales outweigh sales of all other beverages and are assigned 60% of the weights. Those who understand the elementary laws of economics may criticise this method of weighting, since we are using the same weights (*i.e.* the same total sales in £ million), even though prices have altered in the second period, and this is unlikely unless the demand elasticity is unity. It is more likely that the relative quantities demanded would be altered.

Price relatives are often useful quantities to be used by themselves. In journals such as those published by government departments price relatives are frequently given instead of the actual data.

PRICE RELATIVE FORMULAE

At this stage the student should attempt the first three questions at the end of this chapter. Then, assuming the exercises to have been carefully worked, it will be possible to tackle the formulae connected with the various measures of average.

1. Using the arithmetic mean

Weights should always be used in practice where possible, since a truer average is obtained. It is unlikely that a given series will comprise items of equal importance, and to ignore the differences would be to distort the average.

Unless there are good reasons to the contrary, the A.M. should be used in preference to other measures. It is relatively simple to calculate and is well understood (and often perhaps misunderstood) by laymen. Sub-groups can be averaged, to be added to other groups, and this is not possible with the mode or median.

Exponents of the geometric mean claim that an important disadvantage of the arithmetic mean is its tendency to over-emphasise increases and undervalue decreases:

EXAMPLE 21

Alpha rises in price from £1 to £2. Increase 100%.
Beta falls from £2 to £1. Decrease 50%.

	Old price (£)	Average new price (£)	Price relative
Alpha	1	2	200
Beta	2	1	50

Index = 250/2 = 125, denoting a 25% increase in prices, although the expenditure in both periods was the same, £3.

The geometric average does not mislead in this way:

$$\sqrt{200 \times 50} = \sqrt{10,000} = 100.$$

However, this assumes unit weights, *i.e.* that each item is bought in equal quantities. It is not possible to say what the effect will be in a weighted average without knowledge of the weights.

In spite of this, the A.M. *is* the mean used most often in published statistics.

(a) *The unweighted A.M.*

This is more correctly called the unit-weighted A.M. (*i.e.* implicit weights). Given n commodities with base year prices of $p_0' p_0'' \ldots p_0{}^n$, and current prices of $p_1' p_1'' \ldots p_1{}^n$ the index number will be

$$\frac{\sum \left(\frac{p_1}{p_0}\right)}{n} \times \frac{100}{1} \quad \ldots \quad \ldots \quad (1)$$

where the subscript 0 refers to the base year and subscript 1 refers to the current year. The superscripts are not in this case indexes, but represent the individual commodities.

EXAMPLE 22

The following shows the calculation of a price index for cheese using the unit-weighted A.M.:

	Price at base date (p_0)	Price at current date (p_1)	Price relatives $\left(\frac{p_1}{p_0} \times \frac{100}{1}\right)$
Cheddar (lb)	p_0' 3s. 6d.	p_1' 3s. 6d.	100
Cheshire (lb)	p_0'' 3s.	p_1'' 2s. 8d.	89
Stilton (lb)	p_0''' 4s.	p_1''' 5s.	125
		$\sum \left(\frac{p_1}{p_0}\right) \times \frac{100}{1} = 314$	

$$\frac{\sum \left(\frac{p_1}{p_0}\right) \times 100}{n} = \frac{314}{3} = 104 \cdot 6.$$

The use of symbols such as p and p_0 is intended to simplify explanations which would otherwise be wordy.

(b) *The weighted A.M.*

A price index is constructed with the purpose of measuring changes in a variety of prices over time. The most suitable weights to use in most circumstances are the physical quantities of each item, which have the symbol q (or sometimes w).

From an earlier explanation, you may remember that the quantities demanded of any commodity will vary over periods of time. For example, the sales of 45 r.p.m. gramophone records have expanded greatly in recent years and to compile a weighted average of the sales we should have to consider the problem of whether

(i) to use the quantities sold in year 0 as the weights, or
(ii) to alter the weights from time to time, *i.e.* to use current weights.

Both calculations are shown below.

(i) *Base year weights.*—Ignoring the "× 100" instruction, the formula is as follows:

$$\frac{\sum\left(\dfrac{q_0 p_1}{p_0}\right)}{\Sigma q_0} \quad \cdot \quad \cdot \quad \cdot \quad \cdot \quad \cdot \quad (2)$$

This corresponds to the Laspeyres formula, which will be explained in detail in the discussion of aggregates in the next chapter. Base weighting preserves continuity, but we lose "up-to-dateness" in the course of time.

EXAMPLE 23

The table below shows the average takings by British Railways per journey on passenger services (adapted freely from Ministry of Transport data). Calculations are made using base year weights (1938 average = 100).

Class of ticket	(1) 1938 weights No. of passenger journeys, *i.e.* quantity (q_0) millions	(2) 1938 takings per journey (p_0) pence	(3) 1959 takings per journey (p_1) pence	(4) 1959 price relative $\left(\dfrac{p_1}{p_0}\right)$ (× 100)	(5) 1959 weighted price relatives on base quantity $\dfrac{q_0 p_1}{p_0} \times 100$
Ordinary full fare	23	12	60	500	11,500
Excursions, etc.	25	6	30	500	12,500
Early morning	20	4	15	375	7,500
Season tickets	32	5	14	280	8,960
	100			1655	40,460
	Σq_0				$\sum\left(\dfrac{q_0 p_1}{p_0}\right) \times 100$

Applying Formula 2 we obtain:

$$I_{59} = \frac{40,460}{100} = 404\cdot6.$$

I_{59} represents the index number for the year 1959.

Note that we have arranged for the sum of the weights to equal 100. It is advantageous if a convenient round number can be used for the weights, since the arithmetic is simplified.

The increase shown by the index is large and might suggest that British Railways were a highly prosperous organisation. The bulk of the increase, however, is a feature of the general rise in prices which has occurred in the 21 years covered.

(ii) *Current year weights.*—The formula for this is

$$I_n = \frac{\sum\dfrac{q_1 p_1}{p_0}}{\Sigma q_1} \quad \cdot \quad \cdot \quad \cdot \quad \cdot \quad (3)$$

where q_1 represents current year weights which we may consider adopting. This corresponds to the Paasche formula to be used in a later chapter.

EXAMPLE 24

The table below shows the average takings by British Railways per journey on passenger services. Calculations are made using current year weights (1938 = 100).

Class of ticket	(1) 1938 takings per journey (p_0) pence	(2) 1959 takings per journey (p_1) pence	(3) 1959 weights No. of passenger journeys originating, *i.e.* quantity (q_1) millions	(4) 1959 price relative $\left(\frac{p_1}{p_0}\right) \times 100$	(5) 1959 weighted price relatives on current quantities $\frac{q_1 p_1}{p_0} \times 100$
Ordinary full fare	12	60	25	500	12,500
Excursions, etc.	6	30	26	500	13,000
Early morning	4	15	9	375	3,375
Season tickets	5	14	27	280	7,560
			87	1655	36,435
			Σq_1		$\sum\left(\frac{q_1 p_1}{p_0}\right) \times 100$

Applying Formula 3 we obtain:

$$I_{59} = \frac{36,435}{87} = 418 \cdot 8.$$

This compares with 404·6 obtained by base-year weighting, the difference being accounted for by the change in the pattern of passenger journeys since 1938:

(Millions)	Ordinary	Excursions	Early morning	Seasons	Total
Passenger journeys 1938	23	25	20	32	100
Passenger journeys 1959	25	26	9	27	87

These figures reveal that the first two classifications have attracted more passengers while the latter two have carried diminishing numbers of passengers. Since the first two also show larger fare increases, they outweigh the drop in carrying power of the second pair.

In the fourth column of each table the price relatives are shown unweighted. This may be useful in some calculations, but it is obvious that weights give a more realistic picture. The index without using weights would be:

$$I_{59} = \frac{1655}{4} = 413 \cdot 8.$$

For the sake of completeness other averages are now considered.

2. Using the geometric mean

Many experts deny that the G.M. has inherent superiority over the A.M., but the purpose of the index will be the determining factor as to which is adopted.

If we are comparing the amount of money required at two different times or in two different places to purchase the same quantity of commodities (or amounts of satisfaction) the weighted A.M. is used.

When the primary object is the study of price relatives and the behaviour of the average thus derived, the G.M. may prove useful. We have noticed that the G.M.'s advantage lies in its "moderation" in giving equal importance to equal rates of change. It is, however, tedious to calculate, and has the disadvantage of being unfamiliar to many business people.

(a) *The unweighted G.M.*

The formula, using logarithms, is:

$$p_{01} = \frac{\sum \log \frac{p_1}{p_0}}{n} \quad . \quad . \quad . \quad . \quad (4)$$

where p_{01} is a price index in Year 1 on the base of Year p_0.

In the calculation of the A.M. we have seen that the price relatives must be calculated separately before averaging. This is not necessary with the geometric mean calculation, since

$$p_{01} = n\sqrt{\frac{p_1' p_1'' \ldots p_1^n}{p_0' p_0'' \ldots p_0^n}} \quad . \quad . \quad . \quad (5)$$

which is better calculated by logs as in Formula (4).

An alternative method of expressing Formula (5) is

$$p_{01} = n\sqrt{\Pi\left(\frac{p_1}{p_0}\right)} . \quad . \quad . \quad . \quad (6)$$

where Π (large Pi) means "the product of."

EXAMPLE 25

Calculate an index number for the following data, using the unweighted G.M.

Product	Price in base period January 1957 (p_0)	Price in current period, July 1961 (p_1)
A	15s.	17s. 6d.
B	3s.	6s.
C	4s.	2s.

The calculation by Formula (4) is:

$\log p_1$	$\log p_0$
1·2430	1·1761
0·7782	0·4771
0·3010	0·6021
2·3222	2·2553

$\frac{1}{3} \log (p_1 - p_0) = \log 0·0669/3 = \log 0·0223.$

The anti-log table supplies a figure of 1·053, and when this is multiplied by 100 we obtain the answer:

$$p_{01} = 105·3.$$

(b) The weighted G.M.

Weighting is used with the geometric mean for the same reasons as mentioned in connection with the arithmetic mean. The following formula shows clearly the composition of the index (using w as the symbol for the weights):

$$p_{01} = (\Sigma w)\sqrt{\left(\frac{p_1'}{p_0'}\right)^{w'} \times \left(\frac{p_1''}{p_0''}\right)^{w''} \dots \left(\frac{p_1''}{p_0^n}\right)^{w^n}} \qquad (7)$$

which is perhaps very alarming! Whereas the weighted A.M. involves the products of price $\times$ weight, the G.M. method involves the prices being raised to the power of the weights.

EXAMPLE 26

The table shows a statement of boiler-fuel prices. It is required to calculate an index number by the weighted geometric mean, using January 1958 = 100.

	Price in January 1958 (p_0)	Quantity used in base period in tons (q_0)	Price in current month, July 1961 (p_1)
Coke, grade A	£5 ton	300	£6 ton
Coke, grade B	£3 ton	400	£4 ton
		700	

$$p_{01} = 700\sqrt{\left(\frac{6}{5}\right)^{300} \times \left(\frac{4}{3}\right)^{400}} \quad \text{where } \Sigma w \text{ is 700.}$$

Calculation by logs gives:

No.	log
$1·2^{300}$	$0·0792 \times 300 = 23·76$
$1·333^{400}$	$0·1250 \times 400 = 50·00$
Their product	73·76

$$\text{Taking the root } \frac{73 \cdot 76}{700} = 0 \cdot 10537$$

$$\text{Anti-log} \qquad\qquad = 1 \cdot 275$$

therefore the weighted geometric mean is 127·5.

The full formula, using logs, is

$$\log p = \frac{1}{\Sigma w} \sum \left(w \log \frac{p_1}{p_0} \right) \qquad . \quad . \quad . \quad (8)$$

The above data become

$$\log p = \frac{1}{700} \, (300 \times 0 \cdot 0792 + 400 \times 0 \cdot 1250)$$

and the remainder is as above.

3. Using the mode and median

These measures are seldom used in index-number calcula-tions. The mode, or item of most frequent occurrence, is often badly defined. The median might find a use if there is doubt about the representative nature of some of the data. Extreme items do not affect the size of the average; and the average is simple to compute.

Many indexes are (it will be discovered) composed of averages of sub-groups which themselves are averaged. This cannot be done using mode or median, since they are positional averages.

4. Using the harmonic mean

The main exponent of this is Ferger. The harmonic mean of a series of numbers is the reciprocal of the arithmetic mean of the reciprocals of the individual numbers.

The harmonic mean is useful if you want to use the reci-procal of a price index as an index of the purchasing power of money. The idea of the harmonic mean is conveyed best in the motion of speed—the reciprocal of speed of a car is the time taken to travel a fixed distance.

EXAMPLE 27

A car travels a given distance at 30, 50, 20, 30 m.p.h. There were four runs involved, which are symbolised by N; therefore the H.M. =

$$\frac{N}{\sum\left(\dfrac{1}{x}\right)} = \frac{4}{\dfrac{1}{30} + \dfrac{1}{50} + \dfrac{1}{20} + \dfrac{1}{30}} = \frac{4}{\left(\dfrac{41}{300}\right)} = \frac{4 \times 300}{41} \simeq 30 \text{ m.p.h.}$$

The purchasing power of money is the reciprocal of the level of prices, since the higher the prices, the smaller is the pur-chasing power. In this way is the harmonic mean helpful.

(a) *The unweighted H.M.*

The following formula gives an unweighted index:

$$\text{H.M.} = \frac{N}{\sum\left(\dfrac{p_0}{p_1}\right)} \quad \ldots \quad (9)$$

EXAMPLE 28. *Quantities of goods which can be purchased for £1.*

	Quantity in 1938 (q_0)	Quantity in 1960 (q_1)	$\dfrac{p_0}{p_1}$ or $\dfrac{q_1}{q_0}$
Bacon	10 lb	3 lb	0·3
Eggs	20 doz	4 doz	0·2
Tea	6 lb	3 lb	0·5
Sugar	140 lb	30 lb	0·2
Bread	40 loaves	20 loaves	0·5
Milk	80 pints	30 pints	0·4

$$\text{H.M.} = \frac{6}{2\cdot1} \times 100 = \frac{600}{2\cdot1} = 286.$$

The cost of living has increased by the reciprocal of the amount of food which can be purchased for £1, *i.e.* by about three times.

(b) *The weighted H.M.*

The above calculation is unweighted. If the student wishes, he can apply the formula

$$p_{01} = \frac{\Sigma p_1 q_1}{\sum \dfrac{p_0}{p_1} \times p_1 q_1}$$

to obtain the weighted price index.

QUESTIONS AND EXERCISES

1. Calculate, using logs, a simple (*i.e.* no explicit weights) geometric average index number of the data below:

Commodity	How quoted	Average price in base year	Average price in current year
A	*d*. lb	16·1	14·2
B	£ ton	9·2	8·7
C	*s*. oz	15·1	12·5
D	*d*. yard	5·6	4·8
E	*s*. gal.	11·7	13·4
F	% on a base figure	100	117

C

2. Describe the difficulties involved in the construction of price-index numbers and state how some of them may be overcome.

Calculate a *quantity* index number for 1958, using a simple G.M. of quantity relatives:

Consumption of edible oils and fats in the U.K.

Oils and fats	lb per head of population per annum	
	Pre-war	1958
Butter	24·7	20·2
Margarine	8·7	13·4
Lard	9·3	10·8
Other oils and fats	7·3	8·9

(Source: *Board of Trade Journal 1959*)
(*R.S.A. 1960*)

3. The B.A.A. record to 31st July 1959 (*Investors' Chronicle*):

	Trading profit (£000's)	Net profit (£000's)
1954	3,983	1,064
1955	3,804	1,229
1956	2,403	602
1957	3,117	997
1958	3,265	962

Calculate an index number of trading profit and of net profit, taking 1954 = 100 in each case. (*R.S.A. 1960*)

4. Calculate the weighted geometric price index for 1957 (1951 = 100) for the following group of selected textile items:

Wholesale prices of selected textiles

	Weights	Price 1951	Price 1957
Cotton: American yarns per lb	10	74·75	51·88
Wool yarn, worsted: *s.*/lb	8	24·53	17·73
Rayon fabric: *d.*/yd	4	24·24	18·75
Linen yarn: *s.*/bundle	4	31·76	24·66
18-oz tarpaulin cloth: *d.*/yd	2	81·66	47·24

(*I.M.T.A. 1959*)

5. *Index of Retail Prices—12th November 1956*

Group	Index figure 17th January 1956 = 100	Weight
1. Food	104·8	350
2. Alcohol	105·7	71
3. Tobacco	107·8	80
4. Housing	115·9	87
5. Fuel and light	115·3	55
6. Durable household goods	101·3	66
7. Clothing and footwear	103·0	106
8. Transport and vehicles	112·7	68
9. Miscellaneous goods	111·1	59
10. Services	114·0	58
All items	107·7	1,000

Explain briefly:

(a) The meaning of "index figure."

(b) What is understood by 17th January 1956 = 100?

(c) What is the purpose of the "weights"?

(d) What is meant by "services" and "all items"?

(e) What general conclusions are to be drawn from the index figure relating to "services" compared with the figures of other groups?

(*I.M.S.M. 1958*)

6. The table below relates to the weekly pay (before tax and other deductions) of the manual wage-earners on a company's payroll:

	Numbers (1950)	Total pay (£)	Numbers (1960)	Total pay (£)
Men aged 21 and over	350	2,500	300	4,200
Women aged 18 and over	400	1,600	1,200	8,000
Youths and boys	150	450	100	560
Girls	100	250	400	1,540
	1,000	£4,800	2,000	£14,300

You are required to construct an index of weekly earnings based on 1950, showing the rise of earnings for all employees as one figure.

(*I.C.W.A. 1961*)

7. Write notes on the following statistical terms:

(*a*) weighted average; (*b*) the moving average; (*c*) the geometric average.

8. Explain what is meant by a weighted average. Indicate the significance of such averages in the construction of index numbers.

(*London Chamber of Commerce 1947*)

9. Calculate the index in Example 25 by using the A.M. and check that the answer is larger than the G.M.

10.   *Index of Industrial Production* (Average 1954 = 100)

Industry	Weight	Percentage increase in production, 1960
1. Food	53	+13
2. Drink and tobacco	28	+26
3. Textiles	77	−5
4. Clothing and footwear	33	+20
5. Bricks and cement, etc.	19	+8
6. China and earthenware	4	+3
7. Glass	7	+35
8. Timber, furniture, etc.	22	+3
9. Paper, printing, and publishing	53	+33
10. Other manufacturing industries	22	+34
	318	

(*a*) Calculate the index for the above groups combined for 1960.

(*b*) Explain what the "weights" in the above table represent and how they are derived.   (*Queen's University of Belfast 1962*)

11. From the distribution below estimate the arithmetic mean and the median. Explain which you think is the most satisfactory. Would any other measure of average be as adequate?

Salaries reported by Fellows of the Royal Statistical Society, 1957

Salary earned (£)	Under 750	750–	950–	1150–	1450–	2000–
No. of statisticians (%)	7	12	14	18	24	25

(*University of Liverpool 1959*)

Hint: Look up method of calculating an average of a grouped series.

12. A motor car, starting from rest, travels the first one-twentieth of a mile at 12 m.p.h., and the next three twentieths of a mile at 16, 24, and 48 m.p.h. respectively. Explain why the average speed over the first fifth of a mile is not 25 m.p.h. and calculate the correct answer.

(*I.O.T. 1962*)

13.   *Index of Retail Prices, 17th January 1956 = 100*

	Housing (a)	Fuel and light (b)	Durable household goods (c)	All items (d)
Weight	87	55	66	1000
March 1957	105·4	106·3	101·9	104·1
March 1958	118·2	115·6	101·5	108·4
March 1959	126·2	117·0	100·1	110·3

Calculate a price index for the three items (a), (b), and (c) combined for March 1957, 1958, and 1959. Then compare graphically the price movements of each series, the combined series, and the "all items" index (col. (d)).   (*University of Exeter 1961*)

CHAPTER 5

CALCULATION OF INDEX NUMBERS, USING AGGREGATES

IN the previous chapter we dealt with price relatives. The second method of calculating index numbers concerns aggregates or "baskets of goods." This measures (if a price index) a given selection of commodities whose average value in a given year is compared with the average value at the base year.

Although the formulae may seem more alarming than those previously given, aggregates are actually more straightforward than price relatives, since they call for less calculation. There are many formulae designed for index-number calculation, but only the more commonly used and a few less common but interesting ones are given here.

PRICE INDEXES

1. The Laspeyres formula

A price-index number can be obtained by calculating:

$$\frac{\text{Base year quantities at current prices}}{\text{Base year quantities at base year prices}}$$

where
$$L = \frac{p_1'q_0' + p_1''q_0'' + \ldots + p_1^n q_0^n}{p_0'q_0' + p_0''q_0'' + \ldots + p_0^n q_0^n}$$

which gives the formula:

$$L = \frac{\Sigma p_1 q_0}{\Sigma p_0 q_0} \quad \ldots \quad (10)$$

The superscripts p', p'', etc., refer to the prices of the individual components of the "basket," q_0', q_0'', etc., are the actual quantities bought or sold in the base year 0.

It can be seen that this index has fixed base weights (q_0) and is equivalent to a weighted arithmetic mean of price relatives. The weights used should be actual quantities bought or sold, and these are kept constant until such time as the whole index needs revising.

EXAMPLE 29. *Laspeyres Index Number of prices of raw materials*

Crops 1937 and 1960 (quantities are in millions of metric tons).
All nearest futures prices, in U.S. currency per bushel.
(Average 1937 = 100)

Items	Quantities produced in base year (q_0)	Base prices (p_0)	Current (August 1960) prices (p_1)	Value of output at base prices (p_0q_0)	at current prices (p_1q_0)
Wheat	125	100 ¢	190 ¢	$125·00	$237·50
Rye	23	70	105	16·10	24·15
Maize	125	60	115	75·00	143·75
Oats	50	54	80	27·00	40·00
Barley	40	65	100	26·00	40·00
				269·10	485·40
				Σp_0q_0	Σp_1q_0

$$L = \frac{\$485·40}{269·10} \times \frac{100}{1} = 180·4.$$

The Value columns will actually be in millions of dollars, but for simplicity the millions have been omitted. The Value columns are the products of price and quantity produced, and in the Laspeyres formula both use the same quantity, that produced in the base year.

The Laspeyres formula found a large measure of support in the U.S.A. after its recommendation by Wesley Clair Mitchell in 1915 (see *Bureau of Labor Statistical Bulletin*, p. 284, 1921). The advantages and disadvantages of base-weighted indexes will be explained in a later section.

2. The Paasche formula

This consists of:

$$\frac{\text{Current year quantities at current prices}}{\text{Current year quantities at base prices}}$$

i.e.
$$p = \frac{p_1'q_1' + p_1''q_1'' + \ldots + p_1^n q_1^n}{p_0'q_1' + p_0''q_1'' + \ldots + p_0^n q_1^n}$$

where q_1', q_1'', q_1''' are the quantities actually bought or sold in the current year (or month, etc.).

Therefore
$$p = \frac{\Sigma p_1q_1}{\Sigma p_0q_1} \qquad \ldots \quad \ldots \quad (11)$$

Paasche thus provides us with an index equivalent to the arithmetic mean of price relatives with weights $p_0'q_1'$, the values of current sales at base year prices.

EXAMPLE 30. *Paasche Index Number of prices of raw materials*

Crops 1937 and 1960 (quantities are in millions of metric tons).
Prices are nearest futures, quoted per bushel in U.S. currency.

Items	Price in 1937 (p_0)	Price in 1960 (p_1)	Quantity produced in current year (q_1)	Output values At 1937 prices (p_0q_1)	At 1960 prices (p_1q_1)
Wheat	100 ¢	190 ¢	165	$165	$313·50
Rye	70	105	20	14	21·10
Maize	60	115	160	96	184
Oats	54	80	52	28·08	41·60
Barley	65	100	75	48·75	75
				$351·83	$635·20

$$\text{Paasche Index} = \frac{635·20}{351·83} \times 100 = 180·5.$$

The Laspeyres Index gave us a result of 180·4, which is very close, mainly because in this case the pattern of the weights (*i.e.* the proportions of outputs) has altered very little. Often this may not be true, especially in indexes based on raw material output.

QUANTITY INDEXES

If we wish to construct a quantity index instead of a price index the various formulae can be adapted for the purpose by dividing the value index by the price index.

Using Paasche, the quantity index becomes (using the relationship $q = v/p$):

$$q = \frac{v}{p} = \frac{\Sigma p_1 q_1}{\Sigma p_0 q_0} \div \frac{\Sigma p_1 q_0}{\Sigma p_0 q_0} \text{ which gives } \frac{\Sigma p_1 q_1}{\Sigma p_1 q_0}$$

or, writing quantities first:

$$P(q) = \frac{\Sigma q_1 p_1}{\Sigma q_0 p_1} \quad . \quad . \quad . \quad . \quad (12)$$

Using Laspeyres:

$$q = \frac{v}{p} = \frac{\Sigma p_1 q_1}{\Sigma p_0 q_0} \div \frac{\Sigma p_1 q_1}{\Sigma p_0 q_1} \text{ which gives } \frac{\Sigma p_0 q_1}{\Sigma p_0 q_0}$$

or, writing quantities first:

$$L(q) = \frac{\Sigma q_1 p_0}{\Sigma q_0 p_0} \quad . \quad . \quad . \quad (13)$$

V, or *value*, represents an index of value. The product of price by quantity sold in any period is the value (or revenue) obtained for that period, and the index consists of:

$$\frac{\text{Total sales in the current year}}{\text{Value of sales in the base year}}$$

so that:

$$v = \frac{\Sigma p_1 q_1}{\Sigma p_0 q_0} \quad \ldots \ldots \quad (14)$$

and this is converted into an index of volume, or quantity, by correcting it for price changes, that is, by dividing it by the price index (as in Formulae (12) and (13) above).

Of course, a simple (or unit-weighted) quantity index can always be constructed using the formula:

$$q = \frac{\Sigma q_1}{\Sigma q_0} \quad \ldots \ldots \quad (15)$$

but this would only be of use where the prices were steady, or where we should wish to study changes in quantities irrespective of price. This is hardly logical; therefore the weighted formulae should always be used. The aggregate index of quantity is the counterpart of the corresponding price index in terms of physical volume involved; that is, it measures the changing value of a varying aggregate of goods at fixed prices. The price index supplies the answer to the question, "If we buy the same assortment of goods each year, but at different prices, how much shall we spend each year?" The physical volume index answers the question, "If we buy a quantity of specified goods each year, but at the *same* price, how much shall we spend each year?"

This is something of an anomaly, in that a price index in which prices are weighted by base-year quantities corresponds to a quantity index in which quantities are weighted by current prices, and vice versa! It is explained by R. G. D. Allen in this way:

"The price and volume index numbers of the Laspeyres and Paasche formulae are quite simply related.

If $V_{01} = \dfrac{\Sigma p_1 q_1}{\Sigma p_0 q_0}$ is taken to denote change in *value*, then

$$\underset{\text{(Laspeyres)}}{p_{01}} \times \underset{\text{(Paasche)}}{q_{01}'} = \underset{\text{(Paasche)}}{p_{01}'} \times \underset{\text{(Laspeyres)}}{q_{01}} = V_{01}$$

Therefore, in explaining the change in value we can associate the Laspeyres price formula with the Paasche volume formula or conversely. Notice also that q_{01} must exceed q_{01}' if p_{01} exceeds p_0' and conversely."

The symbol V means the value at the current date compared with that at the base date.

1. A simple aggregative index

EXAMPLE 31

Production of beverage materials (in millions of metric tons)

	Production in 1937 (q_0)	Production in 1949 (q_1)	Production in 1956 (q_2)
Tea	0·4	0·5	0·7
Coffee	2·4	2·2	2·6
Cocoa	0·7	0·7	0·8
Aggregate	3·5	3·4	4·1
Index on 1937 base	100	97·1	117·1

2. A weighted aggregative index (using base prices as weights)

EXAMPLE 32

	Price in 1937 (p_0)	Value of the amount produced in each year at fixed 1937 prices (£ million)		
		1937 ($q_0 p_0$)	1949 ($q_1 p_0$)	1956 ($q_2 p_0$)
Tea	15s. 2d. per lb	55·7	69·7	97·5
Coffee	11 U.S. ¢. per lb.	145·2	133·1	157·3
Cocoa	11 U.S. ¢. per lb	42·9	42·4	48·4
Aggregates		243·3	245·2	303·2
Index on 1937 base with base weights		100	100	124·6

Thus the quantity index has increased by 24·6% in 1956 over the 1937 base, measured at constant 1937 prices. Note that the U.S. currency has been converted in each case at the rate of $4 = £1 which was current before the devaluation of autumn 1949. The formula used above is:

$$q = \frac{\Sigma q_n p_0}{\Sigma q_0 p_0}$$

where q_n refers to the current year quantities (Formula 13).

3. A weighted aggregative index (using current prices)

EXAMPLE 33

A further method is to weight the quantities by current prices (only 1937 and 1956 are shown here), using the formula derived from Paasche, namely:

$$q = \frac{\Sigma q_1 p_1}{\Sigma q_0 p_1} \text{ (Formula 12).}$$

	Price in 1956 per unit (p_1)	Value of amount produced in current year at 1956 prices (£ million)	
		1937 ($p_0 q_1$)	1956 ($q_1 p_1$)
Tea	50d. lb	183·3	320·8
Coffee	42 U.S. g. lb	792	858
Cocoa	35 U.S. g. lb	231	264
Aggregates		1,206·3	1,442·8
Index on 1937 base with current weights		100	119·7

The results can be summarised (using 1937 and 1956 only):

	1937	1956
Unweighted	100	117·1
Base weights	100	124·6
Current weights	100	119·7

Similar arguments in favour of base weighting and current weighting apply as with price indexes. Notice that in Example 33 the U.S. conversion rate was $2·80 = £1. The current weighted index is less than the base weighted one, but nothing should be deduced from this, since the change in exchange rates has complicated matters. The student should now recalculate Example 33, using a $4 = £1 rate.

OPINIONS: LASPEYRES OR PAASCHE?

There has been much discussion by experts (and others) on the merits of the various aggregate systems. There are, however, certain general points on which agreement may be found.

The Laspeyres calculation is simpler, since the denominator needs calculating only once. But a rise in prices tends to be overstated, since it does not take into account falls in demand or changes in output. Paasche, on the other hand, tends to understate the rise in prices because it uses current weights. In practice, neither all prices nor all quantities move in the same ratio and the relationship between the two systems depends on the correlation between the price and quantity movements, which is normally negative (as one increases, the other decreases). Therefore those goods which have risen in price more than others at a time when prices in general are rising —or the reverse—will tend to have current quantities relatively *smaller* than the corresponding base quantities, and they will thus have less weight in the Paasche index. This analysis follows the normal laws of supply and demand, which always tend to operate.

The Laspeyres Index is probably the more commonly used, since it is administratively convenient to use fixed weights. But it is realised that the passage of time renders the weights out of date. To take a putative example, in 1938 the number of television sets in Birmingham was nil. In 1954 there were more television sets than bathtubs.

The Paasche Index uses the preferable current weights, although if up-to-date information is difficult to obtain promptly the Laspeyres Formula has a great advantage. For example, the prices of metals are immediately available through the various exchanges but the quantities used by industry would take far longer than a day to discover; indeed, for materials which were imported, several weeks could elapse and by that time the weights would, of course, no longer be current. Readers requiring a more detailed analysis of the relationships between Laspeyres and Paasche could usefully refer to Marris, *Economic Arithmetic* and Mudgett, *Index Numbers.*

COMPROMISE FORMULAE

The search for the perfect index number has been going on for a century or more. In the process several useful compromises have been discovered, each with claims on the attention of those responsible for statistical work.

1. The Marshall–Edgeworth formula

Suggestions have been made for using the average of every q_0 and q_1 as weighting in a price index (see Edgeworth). This would give, as a compromise between base and current weights,

$$p_{01} = \frac{\Sigma p_1(q_0 + q_1)}{\Sigma p_0(q_0 + q_1)} \quad . \quad . \quad . \quad (16)$$

which is known as the Marshall–Edgeworth formula. Adapted for a volume index:

$$q_{01} = \frac{\Sigma q_1(p_0 + p_1)}{\Sigma q_0(p_0 + p_1)} \quad . \quad . \quad . \quad (17)$$

The following data will be used for examples in this section.

Basic fuel price index

	Producer's price		Quantity in hundred millions	
	1957	1961	1957	1961
Coal (tons)	£10	£8	5	3
Crude oil (barrels)	4	6	5	6

Exercises

(a) Calculate a weighted aggregative index for basic fuels, using 1957 weights, by Laspeyres.

(b) Calculate a similar index, using 1961 quantities as weights, by Paasche. The aggregative index unweighted would, you may notice, be 100, *i.e.* £14/14 × 100.

EXAMPLE 34

Using Formula (16), the Marshall–Edgeworth price index would be derived as follows:

	Producer's price				Quantities (hundred millions)	
	1957	1961			1957	1961
	p_0	p_1	$p_0(q_0 + q_1)$	$p_1(q_0 + q_1)$	q_0	q_1
Coal (tons)	£10	£8	80	64	5	3
Crude oil (barrels)	4	6	44	66	5	6
Aggregates	14	14	124	130		

$$\text{Index } p_{01} \quad \frac{130}{124} \times 100 = 104{\cdot}8.$$

There is a smaller rise than Paasche in this instance because full weight is given to the tendency for the two fuels to cancel out their changes, as one has fallen in price and quantity while the other has increased by a roughly similar amount. If we were interested primarily in the output a quantity index could be calculated.

Exercises

(*a*) Calculate a quantity index weighted with base prices using Laspeyres.

(*b*) Calculate a quantity index weighted with current prices using Paasche.

The answers should be interesting, since they indicate how the current year quantities show a fall in spite of one price increase.

EXAMPLE 35

The quantity index by Formula (17) would be:

| | Price | | Quantity | | | |
| | 1957 | 1961 | 1957 | 1961 | | |
	p_0	p_1	q_0	q_1	$q_0(p_0 + p_1)$	$q_1(p_0 + p_1)$
Coal	£10	£8	5	3	90	54
Oil	4	6	5	6	50	60
Aggregates			10	9	140	114

$$\text{Index } q = 114/140 \times 100 = 81\cdot4$$

The result in this case is half-way between Paasche and Laspeyres.

In all the three quantity indexes the fall in mined coal more than offsets the rise in oil production and the price changes do not reverse the position.

The Marshall–Edgeworth formula is used sometimes, but not so often as Paasche or Laspeyres, perhaps because the compromise is not entirely satisfactory in that historical analysis over a long period cannot be applied, nor is it up-to-date.

2. Fisher's formula

Whereas Formulae (16) and (17) are compromises between Paasche and Laspeyres, Fisher proposed what was termed the "Fisher Ideal Index Number," the formula for which is:

$$p_{01} = \sqrt{\frac{\Sigma p_1 q_0}{\Sigma p_0 q_0} \times \frac{\Sigma p_1 q_1}{\Sigma p_0 q_1}} \qquad . \quad . \quad . \quad (18)$$

or in other terms $I = \sqrt{L \times P}$, which is the geometric average of the Paasche and Laspeyres formulae. Fisher's book on the subject should be read if possible. Many articles have been written discussing it.

Using the fuel data, the index of prices would be:

$$p_{01} = \sqrt{\frac{70}{70} \times \frac{60}{54}} = 105\cdot4$$

which, when compared with the three indexes previously compiled, gives the following price indexes:

Laspeyres	100·0
Paasche	111·1
Marshall–Edgeworth	104·8
Fisher Ideal	105·4

showing Fisher midway between Laspeyres and Paasche. I should warn the reader that no firm conclusions should be drawn from the results of this exercise, since it is hardly "ideal" in having but two variables.

A previous "mixture" was proposed by Drobisch in 1871, and by Sidgwick in 1883:

$$I = \frac{L + P}{2} \text{ or } \tfrac{1}{2}\left[\frac{\Sigma p_1 q_0}{\Sigma p_0 q_0} + \frac{\Sigma p_1 q_1}{\Sigma p_0 q_1}\right]$$

Fisher gives many pages of formulae and suggestions, but most compilers of published index numbers rely on the ones mentioned above, or adaptations for their own purposes.

PRICE RELATIVES OR AGGREGATES?

Providing the formula chosen is used regularly, either aggregates or price relatives gives fair results as a rule. The weighted aggregate method is simpler to calculate, in spite of its apparently difficult formulae, and should normally be used but the price relative method is especially useful: (a) where we wish to discover the effect on the index of a change in one constituent; (b) where the whole index is divided into groups for each of which a sub-index has been calculated—for examples of this *see* Part II.

QUESTIONS AND EXERCISES

1. What purpose is served by the calculation of a price index number? Explain what difficulties would be encountered in the calculation of an index number for the prices of manufactured goods.   (*I.O.T.*)

2. Suggest a method of constructing an index number to measure the wholesale prices of components bought by a firm engaged in assembly work. What considerations would guide you in deciding the base periods and prices?   (*I.C.W.A.*)

3. Summarise the general information to be found in the *Board of Trade Journal*.   (*London Chamber of Commerce 1960*)

4. (*a*) Show that the Laspeyres index numbers of prices may be interpreted as the rates of two expenditures or as a weighted average of price relatives.

(*b*) Examine the effects that faulty estimates of the distribution of expenditure in the base year would have on the Laspeyres Price Index.

(*c*) The following index numbers were calculated for electrical machinery:

	Price (1958 average = 100)	
	1959 (average)	1960
Appliances (without motor)	101·2	104·1
Appliances (with motor)	100·2	94·3

The sales of these appliances were thought to be approximately (£ millions):

	1958	1960
Appliances (without motor)	69	73
Appliances (with motor)	42	65

Find base-weighted and currently weighted price index numbers and comment on your results.   (*University of Birmingham 1962*)

5.   *United Kingdom imports of board from Finland*

Type	1956 Quantity (000 cwt)	1956 Value (£000)	1957 Quantity (000 cwt)	1957 Value (£000)	1958 Quantity (000 cwt)	1958 Value (£000)
Machine glazed	90	296	143	549	184	654
Folding box-board	71	262	5	20	9	30
Kraft board	184	567	225	649	235	648
Woodpulp board	94	254	81	227	83	228
Other board	39	108	104	264	101	258

Construct a quantity index to show the amount of board entering the United Kingdom from Finland. What sort of index have you constructed? How satisfactory is your index as a measure of the changes occurring?   (*University of Exeter 1962*)

CHAPTER 6

WEIGHTING THE ITEMS

IN commercial index-number construction we recognise that all components may not be of equal importance, and "weighting" is therefore introduced. By way of revision consider this example. The items A, B, and C below have been allotted weights which measure their relative importance. These weights are respectively 8, 3, 2. In other words, A is four times as "significant" as C.

Items	Base prices (p)	Base weights (w)	Current prices	Price relatives	Weighted price relatives
A	£1 per cwt	8	£1 5s. 0d.	125	1000
B	5s. per gal	3	5s. 0d.	100	300
C	6d. per lb	2	3d.	50	100
		13			1400

Index number = 107·8

Notice that without actual weights the index number would be 97·7, since A, B, and C would each exert the same influence on the average. With specific weights, A outweighs C, even though the rise of the former is a lesser percentage than the fall of the latter.

The simple average of price relatives is frequently called "unweighted," but in fact each item *is* weighted implicitly by the number:

$$\frac{100}{\text{Price in base year,}} \quad i.e. \quad \frac{100}{p_0}, \frac{100}{p_0''}, \text{ etc.}$$

An alteration of the base year to a year with a different set of prices is therefore simply equal to the introduction of a fresh set of weights. In the above example A is weighted by

$$\frac{100}{£1}, \quad i.e. \quad \frac{£1\ 5s.\ 0d. \times 100}{£1} = 125, \text{ etc.}$$

Prices are often weighted with quantities which may not be known accurately. This will have little effect on the accuracy of the index number. The aim should be, if possible, to use exact weights for the few important items, but to avoid expense and time in calculating weights to more than an approximate degree of accuracy for the numerous less important items. So long as the person responsible for the calculations has experience in handling this kind of data, the approximate weights he chooses are better than none at all.

An immediate problem arises regarding weights. Let us suppose that we can discover the relative importance of our items at the base date. Are we to assume these proportions will be maintained at all later dates? Should we, rather, change the proportions from time to time if and when necessary? An index of retail prices comprises selected commodities, weighted according to their importance on the base date. Over the years, consumer tastes change, and the weights (which in a retail index would be measured by goods *bought*, not by the goods produced) will be less applicable in later years. The difficulty of weighting is aggravated because there are two points of view as to the purpose of weights, which are:

1. The aim of the index is to measure the changing cost of a *constant* aggregate of goods—which ignores the taste problem.

2. The index should measure the changing cost of obtaining a constant amount of *satisfaction*. This is more to the liking of the economist, but satisfaction (or utility) is essentially a subjective, unmeasurable concept and is, moreover, an individual matter. Index numbers of retail prices are more easily compiled with reference to actual amounts consumed, rather than to the maintenance of satisfactions. Notwithstanding this, from time to time the weights will be brought up to date.

METHODS OF WEIGHTING

The weights adopted will depend on whether aggregates or price relatives are being used. A general set of rules is that:

1. The prices used in *price aggregates* should be weighted by quantities.

2. *Price relatives* and quantity relatives should be weighted by values.

3. Quantity aggregates should use prices as weights.

Since most indexes are weighted, a decision must be reached on this problem, and authorities suggest the use in a price index of one of the following methods of weighting.

1. Base year quantities

EXAMPLE 36. *Fruits sold wholesale in England and Wales*

(July 1947 = 100)

	Prices (pence)		Quantities (000 boxes)	
	July 1947	July 1961	July 1947	July 1961
Apples	6	18	70	400
Pears	8	20	84	560
Grapes	30	30	15	25
Peaches	10	25	10	70

Using the Laspeyres Formula, $L = \dfrac{\Sigma p_1 q_0}{\Sigma p_0 q_0} \times 100$

$$= \frac{(18 \times 70) + (20 \times 84) + (30 \times 15) + (25 \times 10)}{(6 \times 70) + (8 \times 84) + (30 \times 15) + (10 \times 10)} \times 100 = 221 \cdot 7.$$

This is the commonest method and it will usually be regarded as most satisfactory for an index produced regularly (say monthly), since the fixed weights ensure continuity for purposes of comparison. After a period of years it will be necessary to revise the pattern of weights, in which case the "old" series may be linked with the new one. Reference should be made to the Laspeyres method of calculation.

As a broad example of how weights have been adapted to changes in taste, consider the Cost of Living Index and the Index of Retail Prices:

Cost of Living Index (1914 = 100)	Weights	Adapted Index of Retail Prices (16th January 1962 = 100)		1963 Weights
1. Food	600	1. Food, alcohol, and tobacco		459
2. Rent and rates	160	2. Housing		104
3. Clothing	120	3. Clothing and footwear		98
4. Fuel and light	80	4. Fuel and light		63
5. Miscellaneous	40	5. Durable household goods	64	
		Transport and vehicles	93	
		Miscellaneous goods	63	
		Services	56	
				276
	1000			1000

Notice that definitions have been changed, so that strict comparisons are not possible. But between 1914 and 1963, the statisticians have evidently taken note of radical changes in expenditure. The weights for fuel and light, food and housing are all much reduced but "luxuries" are seven times greater.

2. Given period quantities

EXAMPLE 37

By the Paasche formula, using the same data as in Example 36,

$$P = \frac{\Sigma p_1 q_1}{\Sigma p_0 q_1} \times 100$$

$$= \frac{(18 \times 400) + (20 \times 560) + (30 \times 25) + (25 \times 70)}{(6 \times 400) + (8 \times 560) + (30 \times 25) + (10 \times 70)} \times 100 = 250{\cdot}9.$$

There is no downward bias here, *since all items save one have increased in price.*

"Up to date" weights are seldom used because the calculations are laborious and difficulties may arise in obtaining the necessary quantity data, especially as statistics of some commodities will only be published yearly. The Paasche formula uses current weights, and this tends to result in a downward bias of the index, since for those items whose price has fallen demand is likely to increase, giving a higher weighting than formerly. In other words, in indexes measuring price changes in consumables, the elasticity of demand for such items is not likely to be great, but it will be positive enough to affect the quantity demanded at any (new) given price.

3. An average of base and current quantities

As a compromise this method has the advantage of avoiding bias, but the main drawback is the lack of continuity caused by the frequent shift of weights. The method links with the Marshall–Edgeworth formula:

$$p_{01} = \frac{\Sigma p_1 (q_0 + q_1)}{\Sigma p_0 (q_0 + q_1)}$$

EXAMPLE 38

Using the data of Example 36:

$$\text{M.E.} = \frac{24{,}540}{9{,}972} = 246{\cdot}1$$

4. A run of several years

The U.S. Government recommended to its departments the use of 1957–9 average quantities as weights, recently brought up to date. New weights can be spliced on to the old to give reasonable continuity. Thus, taking 1962 as the current year, and the weight dates as the average of 1957–9:

$$p_{62} = \frac{\Sigma p_{62}\, q_{57-59}}{\Sigma p_{57}\, q_{57-59}}$$

For examples *see* the American indexes in Part II.

5. All years between the base and current ones

An average will be taken of quantities of all the years covered by the index. This has great advantages for people using data for historical purposes, but the commercial user of data cannot run to the considerable amount of labour necessary, since every year (or whatever period) new averages must be computed.

6. The highest common factor

The method proposed by J. M. Keynes, who recommended that the largest quantity of each commodity which appears in *every period* during the life of an index should be used as the weight for that item, *i.e.* the quantity weight for each commodity is the *smallest* quantity which appears in *any* period during the life of the index.

The application may be either to base and current year quantities only or to all years under consideration. In the latter case the whole group of years would be considered, and the smallest amount marketed in any of the years would be taken as the weight for each commodity. Thus weights would not as a rule be for the same year in any index.

Since current weights entail revision each year, this method suffers from the same failing as the preceding one, although it is a reasonable system for a historical survey.

7. Fisher's Ideal formula

By this method, the weights for the base and (usually) the current year are combined by means of a geometric average.

EXAMPLE 39

$$I = \sqrt{L \times P} = \sqrt{221 \cdot 7 \times 250 \cdot 9}$$
$$= 235 \cdot 8.$$

The Ideal formula finds few adherents, since it necessitates frequent revision, thus causing non-comparability over a period of time.

8. Sub-division of the items

All the methods given above attach weights to every item. An alternative method often used (*e.g.* for the Board of Trade wholesale price indexes) is to subdivide each item and include more or fewer sub-items according to the relative importance of each group. Let us construct an outline index of share prices.

EXAMPLE 40

We wish to weight in descending order of importance: engineering, food and tobacco, banks, British Funds, and oil. This may be done (hypothetically) by selecting the shares of the following companies:

Engineering: (i) B.S.A., (ii) Vickers, (iii) John Thompson, (iv) Metal Box, and (v) Tube Investments (a total of 5, *i.e.* weight 5).

Food and Tobacco: (i) Tate & Lyle, (ii) Imperial Tobacco, (iii) Unigate, and (iv) Bovril (total 4).

Banks: (i) Barclays, (ii) Martins, and (iii) Bowmakers (total 3).

British Funds: (i) Consols 2½% and (ii) British Transport 4% 1972–7 (total 2).

Oil: (i) British Petroleum (total 1).

If the index is compiled in this way, it should be plain that the Engineering group has five times the weight of the Oil group; a general rise in (say) engineering share prices will have greater effect on the index than a rise of the one oil share price.

SUMMARY

Whether one uses price relatives or aggregates, weighting should be adopted, and the foregoing pages give a choice of method. For a criticism of weighting, reference should be made to the best essay on the topic, by H. B. Arthur. He divides his criticism into two parts, theoretical and practical. From the theoretical standpoint he prefers the term "multiplier" to "weighted aggregate" or "quantity weights," since he suggests these weights are not commensurable in the way they are in a weighted price relative index. His arguments are rather complicated and mainly concerned with terminology. From the practical viewpoint he complains of the misuse of the mathematical accuracy of the calculations of quantity weights. In an index with "constant" weights we keep the weights at a constant figure even though prices alter—but surely this alteration of prices will alter the weights (since the laws of the market will certainly affect demand)? He concludes with a strong case for the use of a weighted average of relatives, although stating that aggregates are still useful if presented with care.

QUESTIONS AND EXERCISES

1. From the following information compute the "all items" index numbers of retail prices, using as weights: (a) those given, and (b) 1955 personal expenditure of all consumers at current market prices (£ million). Compare and comment on your results.

Group	Weights	Group Index October 1956	Personal expenditure 1955
Food	350	101·8	£4,135
Drink and tobacco	151	104·7	1,740
Clothing	106	101	1,270
Housing	87	104·5	1,065
Fuel and light	55	102·4	520
Household goods	66	101·3	900
Other goods and services	185	104	3,150
All items	1,000		£12,780 millions

(*I.O.T. 1957*)

2. From the following data relating to the Index of Industrial Production, calculate for each of the years 1955–8: (a) a combined Textile and Footwear Index, and (b) an index for the residual industries.

(Average 1954 = 100)

Group	Weights	1955	1956	1957	1958
Textiles	77	98	96	97	87
Clothing and footwear	33	104	106	105	101
All industries	1000	105	106	107	106

(*I.M.S.M. 1960*)

3. "Weighting is only one of many problems in constructing index numbers." Discuss with special reference to index numbers with which you are familiar. (*Queen's University of Belfast 1962*)

CHAPTER 7

THE BASE

THE matter of the starting date for our index is important, since the inevitable progress of time affects things considerably.

WHICH DATE?

The aim is to choose as a starting-point a date or length of time which is "normal" in the sense that the data chosen are not subject at that time to any irregular or abnormal influences. With raw materials, especially, a "normal" year rarely occurs, so that the experience of the compiler of the index will greatly influence its efficiency.

Every index must have this starting-point, which has been called "a statistical hitching-post," from which changes can be measured. The base may be one day (as with the Index of Retail Prices); the average of a year (the method commonly used by British Government indexes) or the average of a series of years (as with the *Statist* index with its 1867–77 base).

The U.S. Bureau of the Budget, for example, recommends the adoption of the years 1957–9 as base and this is being adopted by U.S. Government statisticians. It is the opinion of many authorities that a ten-to-twenty-year span is most suitable for one base date, and after that the index becomes progressively more "old fashioned." The statisticians must also decide whether to revise the index completely at long intervals or whether to bring it up to date more frequently. The alternatives will now be studied.

1. The fixed base system

A date is chosen and all changes are measured from it. The advantages are mainly that as the index ages historical comparisons extending back over its whole life are possible; that people using the index become familiar with it and so gain confidence in it; and that the calculation at regular intervals is a routine matter.

The major disadvantage has been noted above—that as the patterns of trade, imports, or consumer taste change, so the index becomes more and more outdated. In time the weights or

74

the date must be altered if the index is to be at all realistic and not merely a matter of habit.

These changes in consumer preference, conditions of trade, and so on can be incorporated into it by altering the base date or using a "chain base" with "linking."

2. Changing the base date

All important fixed-base indexes are brought up to date in various ways, one of which is to alter the base date. This, of course, is done at lengthy intervals, and the method is quite straightforward, enabling the old series to be linked with the new.

EXAMPLE 41

The following is a simple example of a base-date change. In successive years the indexes were:

$$
\begin{array}{ll}
1955 & 100 \\
1956 & 150 \\
1957 & 175 \\
1958 & 220
\end{array} \right\} \quad (1955 = 100)
$$

It is desired to change the base to 1957 = 100, and since at that date the relation between 1957 and 1955 is 175 : 100 we divide by 175 and multiply by 100, giving:

$$
\left. \begin{array}{l}
1955 = \dfrac{100}{175} \times 100 = \ \ 55 \cdot 6 \\[2mm]
1956 = \dfrac{100}{175} \times 150 = \ \ 85 \cdot 7 \\[2mm]
1957 = \dfrac{100}{175} \times 175 = 100 \cdot 0 \\[2mm]
1958 = \dfrac{100}{175} \times 220 = 125 \cdot 7
\end{array} \right\} \quad \text{New series } (1957 = 100)
$$

If, as may sometimes happen, we wish to link back a current figure with the old series we can do so, for a time at least, by reversing the above procedure. If we have to convert 1958 (based on 1957 = 100) back to a base of 1955 we multiply by 175/100:

i.e.
$$
\frac{125 \cdot 7 \times 175}{100} \backsimeq 220.
$$

Care must be taken here, since the method is not applicable to calculations such as the Laspeyres aggregate formula or the arithmetic mean of price relatives method. A full discussion of the mathematics of this is beyond the scope of this book (but see You Poh Seng).

3. The chain base system

Instead of using a fixed base, this system involves the calculation of the index for one period based on changes in the date since the previous period.

The system is of special importance where comparisons over short periods are more important than long-range trends.

EXAMPLE 42

The following is a simple example of "chaining."

A price index in the commencing year (1956)   = 100.
The index in 1957 based on the previous year (1956) = 125.
The index in 1958 based on the previous year (1957) = 110.
The index in 1959 based on the previous year (1958) = 120.

By the process of "chaining" or relating to the first period, we can obtain the index based on the year 1956 = 100 as follows:

$$\text{Price index for 1958 (1956 = 100)} = \frac{125 \times 110}{100} = 137\cdot5$$

$$\text{1959 (1956 = 100)} = \frac{137\cdot5 \times 120}{100} = 165\cdot0.$$

The series with 1956 = 100 then is 100, 125, 137·5, 165, after each year has been "linked" with its previous year and chained back to the original year.

Of course, any defect or bias in any year is perpetuated in following years. This would not be the case with the fixed-base method.

Using symbols, with a simple A.M.:

Stage 1

$$p_{01} = \frac{1}{n} \sum \left(\frac{p_1}{p_0} \right)$$

$$p_{12} = \frac{1}{n} \sum \left(\frac{p_2}{p_1} \right)$$

$$p_{23} = \frac{1}{n} \sum \left(\frac{p_3}{p_2} \right), \text{ etc.}$$

Stage 2 (chaining)

$$p_{01}' = p_{01}$$
$$p_{02}' = p_{01} \times p_{12}$$
$$p_{03}' = p_{01} \times p_{12} \times p_{23}, \text{ etc.}$$

In practice, since weighting is almost always used, chain index numbers are formed from weighted averages of link-relatives, namely

$$\frac{\text{Values of magnitudes for a given period}}{\text{Corresponding values in the previous period}}.$$

To summarise, the advantages may be that:

1. The yearly changes are damped down compared with changes from a fixed base. Whether this is an advantage is hotly disputed. Many economists feel that the main purpose of an index is precisely to *allow* such changes to show up plainly.

2. New items can be introduced as the years go by without the need for a completely new and revised base. Similarly, if a commodity is obsolete, it can be dropped quite simply.

The disadvantages are claimed to be that:

1. Long-range comparisons are made difficult—although as we have seen this can be overcome by linking.

2. Bias may be found if a faulty weight was introduced at some stage. It has been said that "a chain base index is as strong as its weakest link"—and bias may have a cumulative effect in later years.

SPLICING

With manufactured goods especially, and often with materials, price changes are not the only ones which take place. Qualities change too, in fact they may well account for apparent changes in price (or lack of them). For example, television sets sell today at prices not very different from those of ten years ago, but the quality of the sets is much higher. The same applies to other consumer goods, such as vehicles, plastics, and man-made fibres.

To adjust the series it may be necessary to eliminate price changes caused by alterations in quality by adjusting the old weights. The best explanation of the technique is found in Karmel and an adapted version of his method is given here.

Let q be the old weight and R the revised weight to be used in a period when a quality change has caused a price change. The formula is

$$R = q\frac{P \times A}{P \times B}$$

where A is the old variety and B the new one.

EXAMPLE 43

An index number of textile fibres gives 1953 as the base period, 1959 as the period when quality changes took place and 1960 as the next following period:

Textile fibres (1953 = 100)

Items (yarns)	1953			1959			1960		
	Price in d.	q	Total cost in d.	Price in d.	q	Total cost in d.	Price in d.	q	Total cost in d.
"Lucron" (lb)	22	5	110	36	10	—	49	10	—
"Dazon" (lb)	—	—	—	40	9*	360	55	8	450
Other yarns	—	—	2890	—	—	3140	—	—	3200
			3000			3500			3650

* $R = 10 \times \frac{36}{40} = 9$—the total cost is the same in the period (1959) splicing of both A and B takes place, i.e. $36 \times 10 = 40 \times 9$. "Lucron" ($A$) is replaced by a higher-quality product, "Dazon" (B), in that year.

The index (1953 = 100) for 1959 =

$$\frac{3500}{3000} \times 100 = 116.7.$$

In 1960, with the new commodity, the index becomes

$$\frac{3650 \times 100}{3000} = 121.7.$$

Without this switch the index in 1960 would have been

$$\frac{3620}{3000} = 120.6,$$

a lower figure, since the new product has risen more than Lucron in 1960.

If Dazon had been introduced without the quantity adjustment the figures for 1960 would have been:

$$\text{Dazon} \quad 55d. \times 10 = \quad 550$$
$$\text{Other} \qquad\qquad\qquad 3200$$
$$\underline{\qquad\qquad}$$
$$3750$$

giving an index of

$$\frac{3750}{3000} \times 100 = 125$$

but since this would include an increase of price accounted for by a change in quality, it could not be accepted.

SUMMARY

This chapter has indicated that changes in the base may be necessary, and has shown how to calculate such changes, either by periodic revision or by continuous chaining processes. In practice most indexes are of the fixed base type, revised at intervals or replaced by new indexes. Changes in quality are quite common and in most indexes such changes (unless of a temporary nature due to non-permanent shortages of materials) can quite easily be "spliced" into the index.

QUESTIONS AND EXERCISES

1. The following are the values of a cost of living index in Sweden from 1945 to 1952 with 1948 = 100: 93, 93, 96, 100, 102, 103, 119, 128. Shift the base of this index to 1951.

2. The following data relate to an "Index of Manufacturing Production Workers Employed" compiled by the U.S. Department of Labor for 1945–54, with 1947–9 = 100: 104, 97·9, 103·4, 102·8, 93·8, 99·6, 106·4, 106·3, 111·8, 101·8. Shift the base of this index to 1952.

3.

Item	Unit	Weights 1958	Prices in d.			
			1958	1959	1960	1961
A	lb	4	24	30	27	30
B	gal	3	30	36	33	36
C	oz	1	36	30	33	39
D	doz	2	12	9	15	18

Using 1958 = 100, calculate index numbers for each year, using the price relatives method and base weights but expressing each relative as to the previous year, and chaining the resultant index numbers.

4. It has been said that the technique of index number construction involves four major factors: (a) choice of items; (b) base period; (c) form of average; (d) weighting system. Do you agree with this view? If so, explain these four factors and discuss the problems to which they give rise. If you do not agree, give your views on the main problems involved in index number construction.   (I.O.T.)

5. What is meant by the "problem of quality changes" in index numbers? Consider methods of dealing with this problem in an index of retail prices.   (University of London 1959)

6. On 16th January 1962 the "all items" index of retail prices was 117·5, at which date a new index was commenced. The all items index figures given here (16th January 1962 = 100) should be rebased to 17th January 1956 = 100. June 1962, 102·9; December 1962, 102·3; February 1963, 103·6.

7. The U.S. Consumer Price Index (1947–9 = 100) was rebased to 1957–9 = 100. Show these indexes (1957–9 = 100) rebased to the earlier base date, using the conversion of 81·5 (i.e. divide by 81·5 and multiply by 100): yearly figure 1954, 93·6; yearly figure 1955, 93·3; yearly figure 1956, 94·7.

CHAPTER 8

TESTS FOR PERFECTION

IT is considered that a perfect index number can be compiled, and statisticians have devised a number of tests to which any index may be subjected.

We have already seen that certain calculations provided results which could not be calculated in reverse as well as forwards. However, if the price of a commodity in 1955 was £100, and in 1961 was £125, then the 1955 price (reversing our procedure) was 80% of the 1961 price. This can be checked for unity by reading Example 43.

THE TIME REVERSAL TEST

If we reverse the time subscripts of a price (or quantity) index the result should be the reciprocal of the original index.

EXAMPLE 44

Raw cotton increases from 20d. to 25d. between two dates, and consumption rises from four to eight units (one unit = 10,000 bales).

$$\text{Cotton} \quad \begin{array}{cc} p_0 & q_0 \\ 20 & 4 \end{array} \qquad \begin{array}{cc} p_1 & q_1 \\ 25 & 8 \end{array}$$

The index is

$$\frac{25 \times 8}{20 \times 4} \times 100 = 250 \quad (2\tfrac{1}{2} \text{ times as great}).$$

The reverse procedure should give the reciprocal

$$\frac{20 \times 4}{25 \times 8} \times 100 = 40, \quad i.e. \ \frac{1}{2\tfrac{1}{2}} \text{ times as great.}$$

This is one of the "tests" of the efficiency of an index, and it is called the time reversal test.

1. Effect of test on Laspeyres formula

EXAMPLE 45

Using the Laspeyres formula

$$\frac{\Sigma p_1 q_0}{\Sigma p_0 q_0} \text{ and reversing, we obtain } \frac{\Sigma p_0 q_1}{\Sigma p_1 q_1}$$

If this is to satisfy the test the original and the result should equal unity,

$$i.e. \qquad \frac{2\tfrac{1}{2}}{1} \times \frac{1}{2\tfrac{1}{2}} = 1 \text{ derived from } \left(\frac{25 \times 8}{20 \times 4} \times \frac{20 \times 4}{25 \times 8}\right)$$

but in the above instance

$$\frac{\Sigma p_1 q_0}{\Sigma p_0 q_0} \times \frac{\Sigma p_0 q_1}{\Sigma p_1 q_1} \neq 1 \text{ and the test is not satisfied.}$$

There are five methods which do satisfy the test:

1. Simple geometric mean of price relatives.
2. Aggregates with fixed weights.
3. $\dfrac{\Sigma p_1(q_0 + q_1)}{\Sigma p_0(q_0 + q_1)}$ (Marshall–Edgeworth).
4. The weighted geometric mean of price relatives if we use fixed weights.
5. The Fisher Ideal formula.

2. Effect of test on Fisher's Ideal formula

EXAMPLE 46

If we apply the test to No. 5 above:

$$\sqrt{\frac{\Sigma p_1 q_0}{\Sigma p_0 q_0} \times \frac{\Sigma p_1 q_1}{\Sigma p_0 q_1}}$$

which reversed is:

$$\sqrt{\frac{\Sigma p_0 q_1}{\Sigma p_1 q_1} \times \frac{\Sigma p_0 q_0}{\Sigma p_1 q_0}}$$

which is unity and thus meets the test.

To summarise, then, a (price) index should display the same *relative* movement from one year to another whichever one is taken as base, so that if an index based on 1947 is 150% in 1960, the same index using 1960 as base should equal $66\frac{2}{3}$.

THE FACTOR REVERSAL TEST

This test has the virtue of exclusiveness, since the only formula which stands up to it is the Fisher Ideal. The test applies to "value" indexes, *i.e.* those formed from the product of price and quantity indexes, if the result *is* a value index (v).

If value is found by $p \times q$, then if the p and q are interchanged the value should be constant. Naturally any formula containing prices only cannot qualify.

1. Effect of test on Laspeyres formula

EXAMPLE 47

$$p = \frac{\Sigma p_1 q_0}{\Sigma p_0 q_0} \qquad q = \frac{\Sigma q_1 p_0}{\Sigma q_0 p_0}$$

The product is $pq = \dfrac{(\Sigma p_1 q_0)(\Sigma q_1 p_0)}{(\Sigma p_0 q_0)^2}$

which does *not* give v.

2. Effect of test on Fisher's Ideal formula

EXAMPLE 48

$$p = \sqrt{\frac{\Sigma p_1 q_0}{\Sigma p_0 q_0} \times \frac{\Sigma p_1 q_1}{\Sigma p_0 q_1}}$$

which by interchange gives:

$$q = \sqrt{\frac{\Sigma q_1 p_0}{\Sigma q_0 p_0} \times \frac{\Sigma q_1 p_1}{\Sigma q_0 p_1}}$$

$$pq = \sqrt{\frac{\Sigma p_1 q_0}{\Sigma p_0 q_0} \times \frac{\Sigma p_1 q_1}{\Sigma p_0 q_1} \times \frac{\Sigma q_1 p_0}{\Sigma q_0 p_0} \times \frac{\Sigma q_1 p_1}{\Sigma q_0 p_1}}$$

$$= \sqrt{\frac{\Sigma p_1 q_1 \times \Sigma q_1 p_1}{\Sigma p_0 q_0 \times \Sigma p_0 q_0}} = \frac{\Sigma p_1 q_1}{\Sigma p_0 q_0}$$

$= v$, which is a true value ratio and satisfies the test.

The aim of this test is to find a formula which will solve a problem such as arises when prices and quantities both change in one period.

THE CIRCULAR TEST

This is an extension of the time reversal test over several years and is thus more searching than any single time reversal test which it contains. It involves fixed weights, *i.e.* the "basket of goods" which economists often quote as being a measure of comparative standards of living. Two formulae satisfy the requirements:

1. *Laspeyres formula*

$$\frac{\Sigma p_1 q_0}{\Sigma p_0 q_0}$$

i.e. base weights.

2. *Any aggregate index with fixed weights*

$$\frac{\Sigma w p_1}{\Sigma w p_0}$$

including the case where w is one in each item of the index (simple index).

To illustrate this test take the formula shown above and trace it over three years. Thus:

$$\frac{\Sigma w p_1}{\Sigma w p_0} \times \frac{\Sigma w p_2}{\Sigma w p_1} \times \frac{\Sigma w p_0}{\Sigma w p_2} = 1$$

or, if a series of three or more relatives of a single commodity is computed upon a fixed base, and a new series covering the same time periods and the same commodity is then computed on a different base, the two series will always be proportional.

EXAMPLE 49

In 1958 the price of x is £4; in 1959, £5, and in 1960, £6.

	1958	1959	1960
Relatives on 1958 base	$4/4 = 1{\cdot}00$	$5/4 = 1{\cdot}25$	$6/4 = 1{\cdot}50$
Relatives on 1959 base	$4/5 = 0{\cdot}75$	$5/5 = 1{\cdot}00$	$6/5 = 1{\cdot}20$
Relatives on 1960 base	$4/6 = 0{\cdot}67$	$5/6 = 0{\cdot}83$	$6/6 = 1{\cdot}00$

The relatives are in proportion to each other

$$\frac{4}{4} \div \frac{4}{5} = \frac{5}{4} \div \frac{5}{5} = \frac{6}{4} \div \frac{6}{5} = \frac{5}{4}$$

and

$$\frac{4}{4} \div \frac{4}{6} = \frac{5}{4} \div \frac{5}{6} = \frac{6}{4} \div \frac{6}{6} = \frac{3}{2}$$

and

$$\frac{4}{5} \div \frac{4}{6} = \frac{5}{5} \div \frac{5}{6} = \frac{6}{5} \div \frac{6}{6} = \frac{6}{5}$$

A useful characteristic is that the base of a series of index numbers can be shifted by dividing the old set of index numbers on the old base by the old number for the base period. Even if the correct formula is used, however, this still only has the merit of being the same as a new series computed from original price and quantity data (provided the old formula met the circular test). For example:

	Period 1	Period 2	Period 3
Relatives on base 1	$\dfrac{p_1}{p_1}$	$\dfrac{p_2}{p_1}$	$\dfrac{p_3}{p_1}$
Relatives on base 3	$\dfrac{p_1}{p_1} \div \dfrac{p_3}{p_1} = \dfrac{p_1}{p_3}$	$\dfrac{p_2}{p_1} \div \dfrac{p_3}{p_1} = \dfrac{p_2}{p_3}$	$\dfrac{p_3}{p_1} \div \dfrac{p_3}{p_1} = \dfrac{p_3}{p_3}$

or, in symbols again,

$$I_{2,3} = \frac{I_{1,3}}{I_{1,2}}$$

D

WHICH TEST?

Have we now discovered the perfect answer? Whatever the mathematical virtues of a formula the main considerations determining the choice are practical—ease of calculation and all-round reliability.

If reversal formulae are used there must be a regular flow of quantity and price information, which may be tedious and expensive to collect. Some of the suggested ideal methods are so time-consuming as to cancel out any other advantages.

Fisher's formula does not satisfy the circular test—indeed, Warren M. Persons, in *The Construction of Index Numbers*, has proved that no formula can satisfy both the factor reversal *and* the circular test. For a full discussion of the subject see Croxton and Cowden, and Mudgett.

QUESTIONS AND EXERCISES

1. What are the main difficulties in the construction of index numbers?

2. A and B are two commodities judged of equal importance, and they are priced as follows:

	Year 1	Year 2
A (£/ton)	10	15
B (s./yd)	3	2

Work out an unweighted price index taking Year 1 as the base; then work it out taking Year 2 as base. Do the results make sense? If not, give your observations.

3. Does the Marshall–Edgeworth formula meet the factor reversal test?

4. Describe the time reversal test.

Manufacture	Industrial production (Average 1948 = 100)		
	1956	1957	Weights
Engineering goods	151	156	160
Chemicals	185	192	47
Textiles	115	114	83
Metal goods	123	116	44

Calculate, for this group of manufactures, index numbers of production for 1956 and for 1957 respectively.

Test whether these indexes satisfy the time reversal test.

(*R.S.A. 1959*)

5.

Commodity	Price relatives			
	1945	1950	1955	1960
A	100	125	112·5	125
B	100	120	110	120
C	100	83	91	108
D	100	75	125	150

Calculate the index by geometric mean of the above years, and apply the time reversal test by using 1960 as base, to show that the simple G.M. of price relatives satisfies this test. (Solution: G.M. = 100, 98·4, 109·1, 124·9, which become 80·04, 78·74, 87·34, 100, when reversed.)

CHAPTER 9

VARIOUS ADJUSTMENTS

DEFLATING A SERIES

INDEX numbers may often be used to measure the degree of
price change over lengthy periods of time. One serious matter
which must be recognised is that upward price changes have
been so general for so many years as to cause the whole level of
prices to alter quite drastically. If we wish to measure changes
in consumer spending or wages, to permit realistic comparisons
between two dates, some form of adjustment must be made.
This adjustment may be of the kind known as "deflation,"
whereby index numbers are frequently used to reduce a series
expressed in money to real terms.

"Real" or "constant" money is money at the value it would
have been had it not been acted upon by the general change in
prices. For example, in Britain before 1939 a clerical wage of £3
a week was common. In 1964 a wage of £12 does not allow a
clerk to live in luxury. His "real" wage can be measured in
terms of the goods and services he can buy compared with the
equivalent at the earlier date.

Deflation, then, is the system used to adjust a *value* series for
price changes. Value series for which it is particularly appropriate include wages, income, and retail sales.

EXAMPLE 50

To measure "real" wages we must calculate:

$$\frac{\text{Total cash wages (or individual wage)}}{\text{A suitable price index}}$$

The main problem is, of course, which price index should be used?

Deflated wage rates for men (January 1956 = 100)

Year (April)	Average weekly wage (v)	Index of retail prices (p_p)	Real wages (r)
1956	242s.	100	242s.
1957	249s.	105	235s.
1958	261s.	109	240s.
1959	272s.	110	247s.
1960	296s.	111	267s.
1961	305s.	113	270s.

This expresses the aggregate worth of the weekly wage in terms of its command over goods and services, *i.e.*

$$r = \frac{v}{p_p}$$

where r = the real wage, v = the nominal value, and p_p is the deflating index (purchasing power).

A second major application of the technique is with production or sales series, where the value index is divided by a price index, leaving an adjusted quantity index.

EXAMPLE 51

If the records of Bladen's Stores Ltd show that sales for 1950 were £200,000 and sales for 1960 were £400,000, have the directors the right to claim that sales have doubled?

Prices have changed during the ten years, and one possible method of discovering the true position is to measure the volume of goods sold. A walk round a department store would convince the student that the variety of goods of all kinds and their varying quality would make this a formidable task. The better method is to adjust by means of an index for price changes.

Year	Value of sales in current money	A suitable price index	Real sales in £000's at 1950 level
1950	£200,000	100%	100/100 × 200 = £200
1960	£400,000	160%	100/160 × 400 = £250

Thus in real terms sales have increased from £200,000 to £250,000, and therefore have not by any means doubled.

When using published secondary data, the student must note carefully whether the series of index numbers has been adjusted if the span of time is at all great. If not, it is sometimes possible to obtain an adjusting factor from the publishers of the data. Thus, if it is estimated that rents in general are three times the level of those in 1939 for similar accommodation the adjustment would be made by dividing the current figures by three.

A second matter for careful consideration is that the qualities of the commodities being measured change, so that *true* comparison is never possible.

TIME SERIES ANALYSIS

The most common scale against which changes are measured is time; and time series analysis refers to the statistical analysis of such data in order to deduce certain regular movements from them.

The two major features of most series of commercial data, taken over months or years, are:

1. The "trend" or underlying movement of the data, often obscured by the irregular nature of the statistics.
2. The effect of seasonal influences.

These features are now considered in more detail.

1. The trend

If we study the sales figures of an established industrial concern we shall discover that over the years a regular trend is apparent. By simple arithmetic methods this trend can be calculated from any data, provided we can be assured that nothing cataclysmic has happened. The normal method of obtaining a trend from original data is by a process of overlapping averages—known as the "method of moving averages." This method may be applied to index numbers as easily as to the real data.

EXAMPLE 52 (a)

The following are the quarterly sales figures, in thousands of £, of "Gluggo," a cordial made by Threebee & Co. Ltd:

Year	Quarter 1	Quarter 2	Quarter 3	Quarter 4
1958	26	18	6	33
1959	24	12	7	32
1960	36	14	5	18
1961	20	11	4	10

The problem is, can this time series be used to help future years' production and sales preparations? By careful analysis much valuable information can in fact be obtained.

Step 1.—Tabulate the figures vertically, using each line (*i.e.* with no spaces between years).

Step 2.—Plot the data on a graph (*see* Fig. 2) and notice the seasonal peaks around Christmas and the "troughs" around mid-summer.

Step 3.—Calculate the trend by the moving-average method. The trend indicates the general movement of sales "on average" and is calculated by the use of the arithmetic mean, but on a moving or overlapping basis. This is easily understood if these instructions are followed, building up your own table as you go and numbering your columns for reference (*see* p. 90):

    (*a*) Choose the number of periods to average. This is determined by including one example of each regular rise and fall—in this case each consecutive four periods.

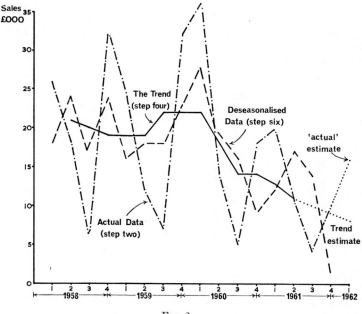

FIG. 2.

    (*b*) Sum the first four quarters and place the answer midway, in column 3 (this is the moving total):

26

18

Total 83

6

33

(*c*) Then move downwards one quarter and sum again:

18

6

Total 81

33

24

continuing to the final four quarters.

    Step 4.—Next, column 4. Find the average by dividing column 3 by four to obtain the trend and plot this on the same graph. The result

(Fig. 2) shows the pattern of business—a general decline apart from the cold-weather boost in 1959–60.

Sales of " Gluggo " (£000's)

Step 1		Step 2	Step 3	Step 4	Step 5	Step 6
					Seasonal variation	Deseasonal-
		Actual	*Moving total in*	*Moving average*	*Col. 2 minus*	*ised data*
Quarters		*sales*	*fours*	*(the trend)*	*Col. 4*	*(see Ex. 52 (b))*
1958	1	26	—	—	—	18
	2	18	—	—	—	24
			83	21		
	3	6			−15	17
			81	20		
	4	33			+13	24
			75	19		
1959	1	24			+5	16
			76	19		
	2	12			−7	18
			75	19		
	3	7			−12	18
			87	22		
	4	32			+10	23
			89	22		
1960	1	36			+14	28
			87	22		
	2	14			−8	20
			73	18		
	3	5			−13	16
			57	14		
	4	18			+4	9
			54	14		
1961	1	20			+6	12
			53	13		
	2	11			−2	17
			45	11		
	3	4	—	—	−7	14
	4	10	—	—	—	1

The student should now attempt to answer Question 5 at the end of this chapter.

2. Seasonal influences

Many industries show regular patterns of sales (and hence of production, employment, direct expenses, etc.) caused by "seasons" which may or may not coincide with the actual climatic seasons. For example, sea freights to Canada are low in winter because of the freeze-up of the River St Lawrence and the Great Lakes. In retailing, many items sell better during the pre-Christmas period than during the rest of the year. Hotels and catering establishments, especially at seaside resorts, reach a peak of activity in the same months each year. Seasons can be much shorter than this. The electricity-generating industry and passenger-transport services both face the problem at different times of a single day.

Many of these seasonal patterns are quite regular, especially in selling, and the trend analysis above can be extended to measure the average seasonal variations over several years, so giving an indication of the size of variations from the trend to be expected in the future.

Let us therefore now return to "Gluggo" and consider the seasonal variations.

EXAMPLE 52 (b)

Step 5.—Deduct the trend from the corresponding actual data (*see* table in Example 52 (a), column 5). For this purpose, the trend data will be dropped half a line to start against the third quarter of 1958, *i.e.*

$$\begin{array}{ll} \text{Quarter 3:} \quad \text{Actual sales} & 6 \\ \quad\quad\quad\quad\quad \text{Trend} & 21 \\ \hline \quad\quad\quad\quad\quad & -15 \end{array}$$

Notice that on the graph the actual data are 15 units below the corresponding trend.

The average amount of seasonal variation (plus or minus) can now be deduced, since we have about three years' data as evidence. For convenience, the calculation is extracted from the table in Example 52 (a).

Years	Quarter 1	Quarter 2	Quarter 3	Quarter 4
1958	—	—	−15	+13
1959	+5	−7	−12	+10
1960	+14	−8	−13	+4
1961	+6	−2	−7	—
Totals	+25	−17	−47	+27
Average seasonal variation	+8·3	−5·7	−11·8	+9
				Cross total = −0·2

Since variations above and below an average must cancel out in total, a check is thereby given. It is unlikely that the total will be exactly zero, since various approximations will have been made in the course of the calculations.

The figures represent the average variation which may be expected in the future from the projected trend.

The dotted line on the graph (Fig. 2) represents my estimate of the 1962 trend. If I were reporting my expected sales for the first quarter of 1962 I should calculate the trend as £7800 (from the graph) and would add to it about £8000 as being the positive seasonal variation for a first quarter; giving sales of £15,800, which Threebee's management would amend in the light of other information they might possess.

Step 6.—A final calculation should now be carried out, that of de-seasonalising the data of the table in 52 (*a*). Given actual data and average seasonal variation, the difference should be the trend. If there is still a residual of significant size the cause must be investigated—perhaps bad weather, a strike, a hold-up of material, or some other "non-recurrent" reason. Column 6 is obtained by taking our average S.V. away from (if +) or adding to (if −) the actual, *e.g.*

> 1958, Quarter 1: Actual sales   26
>   Seasonal variation   +8 (*i.e.* sales above trend)
>   Data without season   18

This is plotted on the graph, where it appears that a time lag is present from late 1960—the seasons as it were being pushed forward. The student must be warned that the foregoing is a fictitious example.

The seasonal variation data should be kept up to date, since the pattern of the movements may change. For instance in 1948 fewer than one in five of industrial workers in the Index of Industrial Production had a second week's holiday; by 1954 a second week's holiday was general.

Seasonally adjusted series are not claimed to be more accurate than the original data, but they do bring out the underlying trend. Many series are now issued by British Government sources, from the Index of Industrial Production (1956) to the Overseas Trade Figures (November 1959) and more lately the adjusted Retail Sales Index (January 1960).

CONTINUITY

Time series seasonal adjustments render long-period comparisons less important than formerly, when trends are under scrutiny. The passage of time affects many parts of the index, especially changes in fashion, income distribution, and prices (money values), but the point has been made that at present most index numbers have not been in existence long enough to worry users, who are mainly concerned with the present.

Changes in productivity may cause amendments in an index of industrial production, especially if the index is calculated as a ratio of quantity produced to input of production factors, *i.e.*

$$\text{Index} = \frac{\text{Quantity produced}}{\text{Factors input}}.$$

Changes in methods of production, engineering economics, or the arrival of new processes must be allowed for if they are fundamental. The same principles may be applied to most indexes but, as has been explained, the advantages of an up-to-date index may outweigh the benefits of continuity.

QUESTIONS AND EXERCISES

1. The average weekly wages (in $) for all manufacturing industries in the U.S.A. for the 14 months for November 1955–December 1956 were:

79·52	79·71	78·58	78·17	78·78	78·99	78
79·19	79	79·79	81·40	82·21	82·42	84·05

For the same months the Consumer Price Index was:

115	114·7	114·6	114·6	114·7	114·9	115·4
116·2	117	116·8	117·1	117·7	117·8	118

(*a*) Use these values of the Consumer Price Index to deflate the above wages.

(*b*) Calculate the actual percentage increase in these wages from November 1955 to December 1956 and compare it with the corresponding percentage change in real wages.

2. Calculate an index number which will show the change in the cost of housing repairs for the period 1954–8, using 1954 as the base year.

Consumer expenditure on housing repairs (£ million)

Year	Expenditure	Expenditure revalued at 1954 prices
1954	1053	1053
1955	1065	1029
1956	1124	1043
1957	1211	1054
1958	1374	1071

(*R.S.A. 1960*)

3. Explain how you would construct an index of real wages.

(*I.P.M. 1959*)

4. One of the statistical problems involved in the construction of a cost-of-living index is to keep the weighting base reasonably up to date. Consider methods of dealing with this problem.

(*University of London 1957*)

5.

Overseas finance: balance of payments current account
(£ million)

Quarters	1958	1959	1960	1961
Imports (f.o.b.)				
1	840	860	1020	1050
2	800	890	1030	1020
3	840	890	1005	1050
4	880	980	1060	1100
Exports (f.o.b.)				
1	880	840	970	980
2	820	890	940	980
3	830	830	860	920
4	870	950	950	990

(a) Plot these on two graphs, calculate the trends by table and insert them on the graphs.

(b) Insert both trends on one graph and advise the Government as to possible future events.

6.

Commodity	Marketing company's 1957 sales	Ministry of Labour index (15th October 1958)	Index of Retail Prices	
			Index (14/10/58)	Weights
Bread and flour, confectionery	£256,320	119	118	52
Meat and bacon	£223,200	99	108	89
Fish	—	110	114	9
Butter, margarine, and fats	£324,230	88	78	19
Other	£150,000	105	108	181
Total	£953,750	105	108	350

(a) Recalculate this index using weights corresponding to the departmental sales of food by the company. Compare the new index with the Ministry index for 1957 and 1958 and comment on the differences.

(b) How could you provide for continuity in this index if the range of products sold by the company changed from one year to another?

(*I.C.W.A. 1959*)

7.

Index of leather footwear sales (1954 = 100)

Quarter ending	1955	1956	1957	1958
March	105	110	117	114
June	101	108	109	101
September	87	91	93	
December	102	100	103	

Calculate the trend of footwear sales for the years 1955–8, using moving average in fours. Represent the data graphically and insert the trend line. Hence estimate the indexes for the third and fourth quarters of 1958. *(R.S.A. 1959)*

8.

British Railways passenger journeys originating

	1956 (millions)	1957 (millions)	Average seasonal variation (%)
Quarter 1	232	266	−4
Quarter 2	249	266	−2
Quarter 3	281	309	+14
Quarter 4	243	236	−7

Derive a series of quarterly index numbers corrected for seasonal variation, with Quarter 1 of 1956 = 100. *(I.O.T. 1959)*

9. Explain what is meant by a "moving average." Use the method of moving averages in order to obtain the seasonal variations in the following series:

Cost of Living Index Number

Month	1931	1932	1933
1	153	147	142
2	152	147	141
3	150	146	139
4	147	144	137
5	147	143	136
6	145	142	136
7	147	143	138
8	145	141	139
9	145	141	141
10	145	143	141
11	146	143	143
12	148	143	143

(London Chamber of Commerce 1950)

10. To what extent is it possible to reconcile the requirements that an index number should be revised so that it always "presents a reasonable picture of the present" and that it should "also fairly easily be made continuous" for use in time series and econometric analysis?

(University of London 1957)

11. Describe fully some practical applications, with examples and with discussion of their limitations (if any), of the following:

(*a*) Adjusting for seasonal variations.

(*b*) Fisher's Ideal index number formula.

(University of London 1961)

12. From the data in Question 9 draw, on the same diagram, graphs of the index numbers together with the smoothed series.

(London Chamber of Commerce 1950)

13. "Since statistics are always about the past, how can they tell us anything reliable about the future?" Discuss. *(B.S.I. 1962)*

Chapter 10

THE DEVELOPMENT OF INDEX NUMBERS

HISTORY

1. Bishop Fleetwood

Index-number calculation began with the attempt to measure changes in the value of commercial goods, with a view to comparing the state of the economy at the time with previous conditions. The earliest known attempt was by William Fleetwood, D.D., Bishop of Ely, whose book *Chronicum Preciosum*, published in 1707, was described by Edgeworth as "the earliest treatise on index numbers, and one of the best." Here is a short selection of quotations from this book:

"Since money is of no other use, than as it is the thing with which we purchase the necessaries and conveniences of life, 'tis evident, that if £5 in Henry VI days would purchase five quarters of wheat, four hogsheads of beer, and six yards of cloth, he who then had £5 in his pocket was full as rich as he who now has £20, if with that £20 he can purchase no more wheat, or beer, or cloth than the other. . . . You may safely conclude that £5 in the reign of Henry VI was of somewhat better value than £10 nowadays is. In the next place, to know somewhat more distinctly whereabouts an equivalent to your ancient £5 will come, you are to observe how much corn, meat, drink or cloth might have been purchased 250 years ago with £5 and to see how much of the modern money will be requisite to purchase the same quantity of corn, meat, drink or cloth nowadays. To this end, you must neither take a very dear year, to your prejudice, nor a very cheap one, in your own favour, nor indeed any single year to be your rule, but you must take the price of every particular commodity for as many years as you can (twenty if you have them) and put them all together, and then find out the common price; and afterwards take the same course with the price of things, for these last twenty years, and see what proportion they will bear to one another; for that proportion is to be your rule and guide."

"Sir H. Spelman complains, that the laws have not sufficient regard to the different price of things, when they condemn people to death for stealing things to the value of *twelve pence*, for though that is according to law, yet that law was made when 12*d*. would have purchased as much as you must give 20, 30, nay 40 shillings for today. . . ."

2. Charles Dutot

The work of Charles de Ferrare Dutot was the first statistical statement of price comparisons in a manner familiar today. Dutot was a French economist, who served as one of the principal officers of Law's Compagnie des Indes. His works offer clear theories of money and credit, and in 1738 he compared prices in the reigns of Louis XII (1462–1515) and Louis XIV (1638–1715), using index numbers calculated by the formula:

$$\frac{\Sigma p_1}{\Sigma p_0}$$

in other words his index used implicit weighting. His main work was *Political Reflections upon the Finances and Commerce of France* (translated 1739). Here are some brief extracts.

"The question is whether Louis XV with 100 millions is at this day richer than Louis XII was with 7,650,000 livres. To find out this we must have recourse to the prices of commodities under each of those reigns. . . ."

He studies several kings and several provinces in this way. Two of his tables, abbreviated, follow.

"In Bourbonnais

	Prices under Louis XII in 1508			Prices under Louis XV in 1735		
	Livres	Sols	Deniers	Livres	Sols	Deniers
Load of hay (12 quintals)	—	10	—	10	—	—
Tun of wine	—	30	—	50	—	—
Arpent of wood	—	2	6	1	—	—
Arpent of wine	—	30	—	12	—	—
Pound of butter	—	—	4	—	10	—
Pound of nut oil	—	—	4	—	7	—
Pound of tallow	—	—	4	—	6	—
	—	73	6	74	3	—

The cost in Bourbonnais in 1735 is upwards of twenty times more than in 1508."

King	Proportion of rise of the specie in the reign of Louis XV	Proportion of rise of commodities	Price compared with that of Louis XV's reign
Louis XII	1 to $5\frac{11}{16}$	1 to 22	$3\frac{79}{91}$ times more
Francis I	1 to $4\frac{19}{40}$	1 to 15	$3\frac{7}{20}$ times more
Henry III	1 to $3\frac{1}{3}$	1 to 8	$2\frac{2}{5}$ times more

The first American contribution came from the settlement in Massachusetts in 1748, whose people put forward the notion of a tabular standard of values to regulate the payment of debts. Little seems to have been written about it, however.

3. Count Gian Carli

The next recorded enquiry into index numbers was made by Count Gian Rinaldo Carli (1720–95). He succeeded in reforming the Florentine coinage system and is known for his major work, *Delle Monete e dell' Instituzione della Zecche d'Italia*, published in 1754–60. At that time he wished to measure the impact of large imports of silver from America on the value of silver as money and he compared the purchasing power of a unit of money at the time of the discovery of America with that of the same unit of money in 1750. He constructed a price index by averaging the price relatives of grain, wine, and oil between 1500 and 1750, using the simple arithmetic mean

$$\frac{\frac{\Sigma p_1}{\Sigma p_0}}{n}$$

By showing that the bullion content of the money unit had decreased, Carli refuted the theory of contemporary economists that the trebling of commodity prices signified a corresponding increase in the amount of metal in the country.

4. Sir George Evelyn

At the turn of the eighteenth century the problem that attracted interest in Britain was that of measuring the value of imports by more efficient means than actual prices. In 1798 Sir George Schuckburgh Evelyn, in a paper read to the Royal Society, concluded a discussion of

". . . the subject of prices of provisions and of the necessaries of life, etc., at different periods in our history and, in consequence, the depreciation of our money . . ."

with a general table, which was

"deduced from taking a mean rate of the price of each article, at the
particular periods, and afterwards combining these means to obtain a
general mean for the depreciation at that period; and lastly, by interpolation, reducing the whole into more regular periods, from the
Conquest to the present time: and however I may appear to descend
below the dignity of philosophy, in such economical researches, I trust
I shall find favour with the historian, at least, and the antiquary."

It was entitled "A Table exhibiting the Prices of Various
Necessaries of Life, together with that of Day Labour, in
Sterling Money, and also in Decimals . . . derived from respect-
able authorities. . . . (There are given decimal prices, whereof
those for the year 1550 may be taken for the integer, viz. 100)."

The table gives every fiftieth year from 1050 to the base year,
1550, and thereafter 1600, 1625, 1650, 1675, 1700, 1720, 1740,
1760, 1780, and 1795.

Evelyn takes the prices, as far as they could be ascertained,
of four groups of commodities: wheat, miscellaneous (horse, ox,
cow, sheep, hog; goose, hen, cock; butter, cheese, ale, and small
beer), meat (beef and mutton), and daily labour in husbandry.
Interpolating, as he points out, where information was not
available, he gives a mean depreciation for each group in
various years, and finally for all groups in certain years. Thus,
with 100 as the mean for 1550, it is 26 in 1050, 77 in 1350,
210 in 1673, 287 in 1740, 342 in 1760, and 531 in 1795.

He used the arithmetic mean of price relatives, and his
sources included Fleetwood and Adam Smith. Weighting was
not employed.

Other authorities who tried to solve the problem included
well-known writers such as Arthur Young, Joseph Lowe, G. P.
Scrope, and G. R. Porter.

5. Arthur Young

Weighting was used by Arthur Young, who published *An
enquiry into the Progressive Value of Money in England* in 1812,
when he was Secretary to the Board of Agriculture. He
criticised Evelyn's work, and weighted his commodities according to their importance, counting

". . . wheat five times, barley and oats twice each, produce of grass four
times, labour five times, and reckoning wool, coals and iron each but
once, while iron is considered the representative of all manufactures,"

and using $\quad\quad \dfrac{\Sigma w \frac{p_1}{p_0}}{\Sigma w}\quad$ *i.e.* a fixed weight aggregate.

Young estimates,

"the rise per cent from the prices of one century [the seventeenth] to those of the other [the eighteenth] will amount to no more than $22\frac{1}{2}\%$, or only the tenth part of the rise stated by Sir George."

A table is given of proportions in 20 (20 being the base, the seven years 1804–10), taken in some cases back to the thirteenth century.

6. Joseph Lowe

Our next writer, Joseph Lowe, contributed a plan for a sliding scale for wages, annuities, and so on. It will be found in *The Present State of England*, published in 1822, where a list of national expenditure is given; annuitants and other contracting parties should be able to use such a table by altering the sum in proportion to changes in the purchasing power of the pound. He suggests changes should be made every three, five, or seven years, averaging changes over the whole period. Evelyn comes in for some criticism:

"Butcher's meat is put on a par with wheat, although with the mass of the population it does not form a fifth part of the consumption. Each of the twelve miscellaneous articles is considered of equal importance and manufactures of every sort omitted."

A number of interesting tables are given, to prove that the "lower orders" spend different proportions of their income from the upper and middle classes. Thus, on p. 94 (appendix):

	Family of agricultural labourer ($5\frac{4}{5}$ members)	Family of middle class (4 members, 2 maids) living in London on £500 p.a.
Provisions	74	$33\frac{1}{3}$
Clothes and washing	13	$18\frac{1}{3}$
Rent	$4\frac{1}{2}$	$11\frac{2}{3}$
Fuel and light	7	6
Contingencies	$1\frac{1}{2}$	—
Assessed taxes and Poor Rate	—	5
Servants' wages	—	$3\frac{2}{3}$
Education, charity, repair of furniture and all contingencies	—	22
Total	100	100

His "tabular standard" device follows the ideas of Evelyn, but with a considerable improvement in technique. Its use would have given a uniform value over time to a given money income.

7. G. P. Scrope

Very soon after Lowe's book appeared, a further explanation of the tabular standard of value was published by G. Poulett Scrope, M.P., 1797–1876, who gave the system a name and introduced the subject into a general treatise for the first time. Scrope wrote a pamphlet in 1833 called *Examination of the Bank Charter Question, with an enquiry into the Nature of a just standard of Value and suggestions for the Improvement of our Monetary System*, followed by a book, *Principles of Political Economy*, proposing periodic issue of a price list of commodities in general use, about a hundred of them, whose quantities should correspond to relative consumptions. They were intended to be used voluntarily as a basis for monetary contracts. The idea received attention much later from Jevons, who forecast its future use, and intended that his own work on index numbers should develop it. Further support came from Marshall, Keynes, and lesser but still important economists. Today Scrope's system is still the basis for selecting items for most cost of living indexes.

8. G. R. Porter

In 1838 appeared the first edition of a much-quoted book, *The Progress of the Nation*, by G. R. Porter (1792–1852). Porter was the first to use the term "index prices," and his book contains the first calculations of prices on a monthly basis, beginning with January 1833 and (in the first edition) carried on for five years. The calculations are on fifty articles of commerce, including wheat, based on the average of prices in the first week of January 1833 and using an unweighted arithmetic mean.

Porter's ideas on index numbers are explained in the first edition. He begins by commenting on the difficulty of measuring price levels caused by the various units of measurement. "Some are sold by the pound or gallon . . . by the hundredweight . . . or by the pipe . . ." He would overcome the problem by reducing prices to a common element. "The index price, whether it is 5d., 50s., or £100, being expressed by unity, or 1·0000, the supposed variations . . . would in each case be expressed by the figures 1·1000 . . ." He gives a table showing his index for fifty articles, monthly, to four decimal places, using the main kinds of goods entering foreign commerce. Thus, January 1833, 1·0000; January 1834, 1·1094.

By the middle of the nineteenth century, after much discussion of the measurement of prices, regular price indexes were soon to be established for the use of economists, businessmen, and others.

9. William Newmarch

William Newmarch (1820–82) is known for his co-operation with the famous Tooke in the *History of Prices*. Newmarch was a member of what is now the Royal Statistical Society and is remembered as the originator of the *Economist* index number. In 1859 he published an index number for nineteen articles, starting at 1st January 1851, in the *Journal of the Statistical Society*, vol. XXII, in an article on "The Report of Trade of the U.K., 1858."

Newmarch later calculated his numbers on a plural base of 1846–50, and from 1864 he published his indexes in *The Economist*, beginning with their Annual Review. In 1849 the Californian gold rush began, followed in 1850 by the Australian one; in the next few years new gold poured into Europe and prices rose. The current question was whether rising prices correlated closely with this influx of new gold. Newmarch's index covered the average prices of twenty-two leading articles of commerce, using the arithmetic mean of price relatives; it may be regarded as the beginning of regular published index numbers in Great Britain. The name "total index number" (which was taken over by Jevons and thence passed into general use) was applied in the earlier index to the total of all the columns for the given year. *The Economist* pointed out that weighting was not attempted—wheat, for instance, reckoned no more than indigo.

10. W. S. Jevons

One of the more remarkable economists of the century was William Stanley Jevons (1835–82), who is regarded by some as the "father" of index numbers.

He called attention to the problems involved in the construction of index numbers, especially in his pamphlet *A Serious Fall in the Value of Gold*, where he goes into the use of the geometric mean, which he particularly advocated, and considers weighting and the problem of components. His theory was developed in another paper *On the Variation of Prices and Value of Currency since 1782.* With the backing of reporting in *The Economist*, Jevons's index numbers were calculated regularly. He had discussed indexes and the best average to use with Laspeyres, and used the geometric mean "for no strong logical reasons, *i.e.*, it lies between the A.M. and the H.M., one can use logs, etc. . . ." (Gayer, Rostow and Schwartz). The method of weighting is to include varieties of some commodities.

Jevons's work kindled interest among others, but the next major step forward was made twenty years later by Edgeworth. Jevons's *A Serious Fall* compiles tables of 39 articles from price lists in *The Economist* at mid-month, reducing them to an arithmetic mean. It is impossible to reproduce his tables here, but those interested will find the pamphlet useful. Weights are discussed on pp. 32 ff.

11. Frank Edgeworth

Frank Ysido Edgeworth (1845–1926) was fellow of many societies, President of the Royal Statistical Society and joint editor of the *Economic Journal*. A man of wide interests, index numbers attracted his attention between 1887 and 1890, and the result was papers H–N of *Papers Relating to Political Economy* (1925). Papers H and I were prepared for the British Association for the Advancement of Science in 1887–9 and form a comprehensive analysis of the purpose of index numbers, although not for the student with only a slight knowledge of mathematics. The later papers consist of comments on other writers, some favourable, some not; they constitute an early but important approach to the value of money, which engaged the attention of leading economists between 1870 and 1914 and after.

12. Augustus Sauerbeck

The bulk of the early index numbers were inevitably wholesale price numbers—reliable retail prices were not available until recent years, and indeed even today their use is more often due to popular demand than to statistical justification.

An index of continuing publication (now in *The Statist*) was designed by Augustus Sauerbeck in 1886. He collected new data on the "unprecedented fall in prices in the last twelve years" and chose an average of the years 1867–77 (the same base is still used) in preference to the years generally used at that time (1872–3), which were a time of inflation. The article gives both weighted and simple index numbers. On one table he weights three chosen years, 1849, 1873, and 1884, according to the importance of each article in the United Kingdom on the average of 1848–50, 1872–4, and 1883–5, to obtain a real average percentage of prices. His results are (on the base 1867–77) 72·5, 115·2, and 71·2.

In another he gives his best-known table, which consists mainly of primary commodities, using simple A.M., classifying 45 articles into six groups, and displaying the fall in prices very clearly. The data (by then 46 items) were published up to 1908 in pamphlet form, with full tables and graphs. The present index is fully discussed in Part II of this book.

1867–77 = 100

	1846	1848	1857	1867	1877	1885
Vegetable food	106	92	105	115	100	68
Animal food	81	83	89	89	101	88
Sugar, coffee, tea	98	69	119	94	103	63
Minerals	92	78	108	87	84	66
Textiles	77	64	92	110	85	65
Sundry materials	86	77	119	100	94	76
Grand total	89	78	105	100	94	72
Silver	97·5	97·8	101·5	99·7	90·2	79·9

Readers who like controversies should look up the article by Sauerbeck in the *Economic Journal* mentioned in the Bibliography. In an article called "Scarcity of Gold" in the Dutch periodical *De Gids* in 1895, Mr N. G. Pierson had compared Sauerbeck's index unfavourably with that of Soetbeer, since the former has only 41 articles to Soetbeer's 114. Sauerbeck defends his index at length, showing how carefully he chose his items on the basis of reliable price quotations and good standards, whereas Soetbeer's are mainly average values as declared by agents. Pierson's case was reinforced in an article by Edgeworth, who showed that in fact the fall in prices in 1881–3 was "due" to Sauerbeck's small coverage.

"If we compare the period 1886–93, with the period 1861–70 taken for the base, we shall find from Mr Heinz's materials the index number 88·8; from Mr Sauerbeck's 69·5. According to Mr Pierson the former measure of appreciation is more trustworthy; but the latter is more convenient for the advocates of bi-metallism."

The Mr Heinz quoted here continued Soetbeer's work.

13. C. M. Walsh

Walsh, an American writer, had much influence on proposals for formulae and tests of good index numbers. In 1901, in *The Measurement of General Exchange Value*, he approved the time-reversal test of a good index number. In this volume Walsh named the Laspeyres and Paasche index formulae after their originators. His name is also linked with others in the advocacy of the arithmetic mean of the Laspeyres and Paasche indexes —although this method has less in its favour than the Marshall–Edgeworth method. His volume *Problems of Estimation* (1921) should be read by those interested in the development of index numbers.

14. Fisher, Laspeyres and Paasche

A line of distinguished economic theorists have played, and continue to play, a dominant part in the index-number field. They have postulated the basic ideas on value, although statisticians have been responsible for much of the practical details of calculation. The major U.S. contribution has been that of Professor Irving Fisher (1867–1947) in *The Making of Index Numbers* (1923). This work formulated certain conditions which a number should satisfy (you will remember the Ideal index number in an earlier chapter). An earlier volume showed his concern with the use of the price index to measure changes in the concept "purchasing power of money" (see—if available —*The Purchasing Power of Money* published in New York in 1911). Fisher is known far beyond the realm of statistics, through his studies in the Quantity Theory of money ($MV = PT$).

Étienne Laspeyres (1834–1913), German statesman and economist, explained his method in two issues of the *Jahrbücher für Nationalökonomie und Statistik* for 1864 and 1871. He defended the use of the arithmetic mean and proposed the formula (No. 10) which was discussed in Chapter 5, although he was never able to apply it because insufficient data prevented him from "ascertaining the quantities of every good consumed in the country."

In 1874 H. Paasche, in *Jahrbücher für Nationalökonomie*, proposed the use of current weights as discussed in Chapters 5 and 6. Moritz Drobisch (1802–96), mathematician and philosopher, is known to us mainly for his suggestion to mix Paasche and Laspeyres (see *Königlich Sächsiche Gesellschaft der Wissenschaften*, 1871).

15. Other writers

Difficulties abound for the student of index-number history, since so much work is found in Continental volumes, many of which have not been translated. The student who wishes to pursue the findings of the economists of Europe on this topic will find Schumpeter's book of the greatest value. He defends Evelyn, incidentally, against the strictures of earlier writers such as Young and Lowe:

"Economists even failed to avail themselves of the most primitive devices for presenting figures . . . Moreover there is no excuse for the hesitation with which fact-finding economists took to the use of price index numbers or theoretical economists to the task of providing a theory for them. We have seen that the idea emerged before Adam Smith. A great step forward towards full realisation of the importance of the method was made in 1798 when Sir George Evelyn presented a paper . . ."

Members of the Cambridge School discussed index numbers in various works, notably Alfred Marshall (1842–1924), who suggested the system of chaining. Marshall was well schooled in mathematics and his articles (unlike his *Principles of Economics*) do not make easy reading for the layman. A. C. Pigou (1877–1945), who succeeded Marshall and whose main work was in the sphere of welfare economics, explained the system in his *Economics of Welfare* (1920). Finally, J. M. Keynes (1883–1946), Britain's greatest economist, used index numbers in his *Treatise on Money* in 1930, but left them completely out of his greatest work.

Other economists who contributed are: W. Lexis, who made theoretical developments in a paper in *Zeitschrift für die Gesamte Staatswissenschaft* in 1886, although they were little noticed; Léon Walras (1834–1910), the French economist (see *Études d'économie politique appliquée*); Knut Wicksell (1851–1926), the Swedish writer on money (see *Interest and Prices*, Chapter 2), and Friedrich von Wieser (1851–1926), an Austrian economist who was leader of the Austrian school of thought (see *Schriften des Vereins für Sozial Politik*, 1910). He was the only member of the Austrian school of economists who supported the index idea for measuring purchasing power. The others (*e.g.* Böhm-Bawerk, Menger, and von Mises) appear to have denied that the price level could be measured.

For a very positive contribution of a critical nature, reference should be made to the writings of Gottfried von Haberler, who stresses the subjective (or non-statistical) nature of consumers' choice. He maintains that "for a given individual of unchanging tastes, the price level has fallen between time T_0 and time T_1 if (his money income being the same) the individual can buy at T_1 a collection of goods which he prefers to the one he could buy at T_0."

(vice versa applies, of course). This interpretation links index numbers with welfare economics, but the chief importance of his thought lies in its basing of index numbers on the "theory of choice," which is an important feature of modern value theory.

Schumpeter summarises his survey of index-number development by remarking that sectional price levels appear to be of more significance to the future than an overall one. In fact, all modern indexes are sectional, devoting their attention to wholesale prices, retail prices, shares or some other section of the level of prices.

The present century has seen many writers devote their energies to the problem of index numbers, and references are made in most chapters of this book.

FUTURE TRENDS

This brief survey has shown how index numbers were developed as an aid to the measurement of price levels, a problem which has engaged the attention of economists in each century from the eighteenth to the present.

In the future two trends seem likely. First, index-number "specialists" will continue to argue details of their construction and use in the journals of statistics and economics. This is territory into which most of us cannot follow, but when they reach conclusions of importance we hope that competent interpreters will be available to translate their "models" into useful methods which can be applied by practical statisticians. Secondly, index numbers will be compiled in increasing numbers by newspapers, international bodies, and governments, especially for investment and wage-policy purposes.

CRITICISMS

The following suggestions and criticisms are culled from writers whose expertise commands great respect.

"Index numbers are just a special kind of average. Everyone has them—the Board of Trade, the Ministry of Labour, the economist—they are a corporate way of keeping up with the Joneses."

Mr Moroney, who can be recommended to all who appreciate a lively attitude to statistics, suggests that we might scrap the lot. So many are antiquated, out of date, unreal and (worst of all, I suspect) of no practical value. He claims that they are "academic tomfoolery." A standard family is invented with all the normal "bad habits"—it drinks quite heavily, smokes, is not vegetarian—and this "family" is tracked at regular intervals to measure changes in "the cost of living."

Mr Moroney's strictures are justified, but they apply with equal force to any average, whether on the basis of 100 or natural numbers. Industrial engineers are more guilty of creating Mr Everyman than the economic statisticians, since an essential preliminary in work study is to create a standard time for every job or task, that is, the time taken to perform a carefully identified task by an average trained person. But during several years in industry and commerce I have never met an "average" typist or machinist (nor after several years in further education have I met the "average student").

However, provided the limitations of indexes are recognised, we can appreciate their advantages—such as their flexibility, adaptability, and wide field of application. Even on this latter point, however, there is disagreement. Two schools of thought exist, the first consisting of those who wish to see more and more "general indexes" which would eventually comprise one huge international index; the second, of those who feel that too general an index is of much less force than sectional ones. For example, a single number to represent the change in all retail prices can hardly be truly meaningful.

Much writing has been devoted to the mathematical concepts of index numbers and the selection of data. Ferger feels not enough attention has been paid to the phenomena of economics behind them, especially in measuring the value of money, which has been regarded as simply the reciprocal of price changes.

The purpose of this volume is not to comply with Ferger's demands but to present the statistical side of the problem. We are still very far from a solution to the economic question of the value of money and it is perhaps unfair to expect the statisticians to design indexes (or any other kind of technique) to fit in perfectly with an undecided theory of money value.

On the practical side, index numbers should not be calculated unless they help to illustrate or solve a particular problem. As Slonim remarks,

"With the exception, perhaps, of stilts for a serpent, there is nothing more useless or ridiculous than a mass of figures collected at great travail, added, multiplied, divided by the cube root of π and converted to homogenised index numbers, that have no bearing on the problem."

Robin Marris, in his excellent book *Economic Arithmetic,* assembles several sceptical views of index-number theory (pp. 262 ff.) and it ought to be read. The points he raises mainly concern index numbers used in connection with cost-of-living measurements and the attempt to determine consumer "indifference curves" despite the fact that tastes, techniques, and incomes are always changing. However, as Marris says of them,

"As arguments, each on its own is clearly legitimate and effective, but nevertheless there is a considerable danger that in carrying them too far one arrives at a position where no quantitative measure of economic progress is possible whatsover, either precise or imprecise."

He concludes:

"It is safe to wager that if the reader continues to maintain interest in economic affairs at all, he will continue to make use in one way or another of economic measurements in index number form."

He ends Chapter 9 with the perfect nutshell summary:

". . . the reader should never forget that essentially the whole, or nearly the whole, of the index number 'problem' arises from the Achilles heel of positive economics itself, that is, from the fact that the thing which it is the objective of political economy to improve—economic welfare—is a thing which cannot be directly measured."

The lack of material in this section may be taken to illustrate the paucity of criticism of index numbers. Perhaps we may simply conclude that index-number calculation and compilation is an important part of economic statistics as a service to commerce.

QUESTIONS AND EXERCISES

1. Explain the statistical basis of an index number, and discuss the particular problems which arise when constructing an index of wholesale prices.

2. An important customer says to you, "The index number of retail prices is derived from basic prices per pound, per hundredweight, per bushel, and per yard. How can an average derived from such a mixture of unit prices be compared with changes in the retail prices of the goods you are selling?"

Draft a note to convince him how differences of unit are normally overcome in computing price index numbers and why, in a hypothetical or real example, you feel that the index discloses a general trend of prices against which movements in the retail prices of your goods may be compared.   (*I.M.S.M. 1955*)

3. "There is no satisfactory method of constructing a composite index of a country's level of living, nor would such an index serve any useful purpose." Discuss.   (*University of London 1957*)

4.   *United Kingdom imports of dutiable beverages*

	1906		1919	
	Quantities	Value £	Quantities	Value £
Beer and ale (bls)	58,600	158,650	450	4,060
Raw cocoa (lb)	51,670,321	1,335,100	246,623,200	8,943,000
Coffee (cwt)	765,600	2,024,600	1,066,000	5,988,800
Tea (lb)	321,190,100	9,904,085	494,353,500	33,050,900
Wine (gal)	13,103,300	4,214,870	25,252,400	18,167,000

Compute: (*a*) a volume index for 1919, using 1906 as base date, and (*b*) a price index for 1906, using 1919 as base date.

5.   *Index of retail prices at 13th May 1958*
            (17th January 1956 = 100)

Group	Group weight	Group index number
Food	350	108·5
Drink and tobacco	151	106·8
Housing	142	116·9
Household goods	66	100·2
Clothing	106	103·1
Transport	68	112·9
Miscellaneous goods	59	112·7
Services	58	114·4

Compute the index number for all the items combined, and for all items except Transport.   (*I.O.T. 1959*)

6. The six items of information listed below can be found in the official series of statistics. State for each:

(*a*) the series and the Department responsible,
(*b*) the frequency with which the figures appear.

(i) A general measure of changes in the level of industrial activity.
(ii) Average changes in the rates of pay of manual workers.
(iii) The numbers of skilled workers in different areas.
(iv) Gross margins in retail shops.
(v) Detailed figures of exports by quantity and value.
(vi) Changes in the turnover of different types of shop.

(*I.C.W.A. 1960*)

7. Show the percentage change in the following statistics in the most concise form of diagram:

Monthly economic indicator	Unit	Latest monthly figure available*	
		1957	1958
Index of Industrial Production	Average 1948 = 100	136·5	136·0
Coal †	000 tons	4,667	4,555
Steel †	000 tons	432	427
Passenger cars †		11,910	20,865
Commercial vehicles †		5,246	6,871
Total in civil employment	thousands	23,103	23,057
Registered unemployed	thousands	363	433
Imports	£ millions	321	288
Exports	£ millions	278	265
Gold and dollar reserves	£ millions	789	989
Import prices	1954 = 100	111	99
Export prices	1954 = 100	110	111
Wholesale prices	30th June 1949 = 100	159·8	141·3

* The latest monthly figure for 1958 and the corresponding month of 1957.
† Weekly averages.

(*I.M.T.A. 1958*)

8.   *Production of steel sheet*

	1951		1954	
	Quantity (000 tons)	Value (£000's)	Quantity (000 tons)	Value (£00's)
Black sheets of non-alloy steel	1,357	48,466	1,524	68,073
Stainless and heat-resistant steel	22	6,715	25	9,769
Other sheets of non-alloy steel	67	4,174	71	5,439
Flat galvanised sheets	63	3,349	105	5,907
Corrugated galvanised sheets	83	4,880	215	13,900
Other plates or sheets	42	1,879	46	2,412

Calculate an index number of production for the steel sheet industry in 1954 (1951 = 100). Describe how you would proceed to calculate an index number for 1951 on a 1954 base.

(*University of Manchester 1959*)

CHAPTER 11

CHOOSING WITHOUT PICKING: THE THEORY OF SAMPLING

INTRODUCTION

SINCE index numbers are averages derived from a selection of data, it will be a profitable digression to study in outline some of the principles of selecting (or, more accurately, sampling) these data. This chapter aims at providing the reader with such an outline, although for a full statement recourse will need to be made to some of the volumes listed in the Bibliography.

The market for gramophone records is highly competitive, and producers must keep abreast of consumers' tastes by constant research into the market. The number of people who attend concerts, listen to the radio, watch televised performances, or buy records must be several millions in the United Kingdom, and the task of a producer who wishes to "quiz" these listeners would be impossible if he approached every one (even supposing a complete list of names and addresses were available). He would need a large staff to post question forms or deliver them by hand, or his workers would have to visit every household concerned with music and ask the occupants various questions. I cannot deal with the questionnaire technique in detail here, but the following points should be noted.

(a) The mortality rate of forms sent by post is high. How high depends on whether inducements are provided, such as the offer of free gifts. In general, to obtain a response of above 40%, strenuous efforts must be made—by gifts, provision of stamped envelopes, interesting questions, and appeals to professional pride, etc. (Moser). There are exceptions, the most obvious being O.H.M.S. correspondence, which often has the force of law behind it.

(b) If door-to-door visits are made response will be much higher but, as will be shown, a sample survey may be almost as reliable. Complete coverage is expensive, and in a residential district will be impossible because some will be at work or away from home for longer periods.

(c) If the questions were to be accompanied by a free gift the double cost would be prohibitive.

For reasons which will be explained, the preferred course is to "sample" the market and use the results of the sample in place of the results of the "census"—which is the term used when coverage is complete. A "sample" is that part of a population which is chosen according to statistical principles to be representative of the whole, in other words, "any sub-aggregate which is taken from the population aggregate." The term "universe" is also used to signify the complete quantity. The "frame" is the term used for the schedule, list, directory, table, or other source of the complete population, from which the sample must be chosen with care to ensure that the contents correspond with the population being studied and that the components are up to date. This is impossible in the literal sense, but the longer the frame has been in existence the less reliable will any sample drawn from it become.

Sampling has certain major advantages over a census:

(a) A complete survey or census may be impracticable, even if money and other resources are available. Where complete data are inaccessible or have passed into history, sampling is the only possible method to use.

(b) The process of sampling may involve the destruction of the article. Steel bars may be stressed to destruction before acceptance for a given purpose: a highly uneconomic proceeding if applied to the whole batch of steel bars (the "population").

(c) The cost of a survey, the time involved, and the labour required to obtain the information and analyse it make it impossible unless the population is quite small—as in a survey of the students of a university—or the surveyors are wealthy—a government, for example. Speed may be all-important, as in samples of opinions about television programmes. However, if the sample is cheaply organised it may be useless.

(d) A survey may be large yet have to be carried out rapidly. This leads to the paradox that a sample may be more reliable than a survey if it is carefully designed and taken. For example in the U.S.A. the Bureau of the Census uses samples to check the accuracy of certain items of the population census.

More time and effort can be expended on each item of a sample. In the case of non-response it would be possible to return at a later date; if queries arise, there is more time to solve them.

It has been justly observed (by Slonim) that "Anyone who

is of the notion that a 100% count automatically provides the true figure should try counting and re-counting a heap of boiled peas the size of a dunce's cap until he gets the same total twice."

(e) If a survey be perfectly taken, and a sample also taken, the sample will show an error; the results will not be identical. If the error is small it is usually unimportant and the advantages mentioned above should outweigh minor errors. In practice, the degree of error can be measured and the size of the sample can be governed according to the requirements of precision.

(f) Often the population is so large that a sample is the only practical method of discovering the qualities of the whole. This is the basis of contracts for the sale of most raw materials—wheat, cotton, timber—all of which are sold "by sample." Naturally, both seller and buyer must act in good faith and not put "all the best ones on top" as fruit sellers in street markets have been known to do.

Certain limitations of sampling have already been mentioned. One complaint is its lack of individuality. If names are drawn out of a hat every item in the group has an equal chance of being chosen and for some purposes this may be *too* "unbiased." We shall therefore go on to consider the various kinds of sampling.

THE METHODS AVAILABLE

Much of statistics depends on the laws of mathematical probability. The laws of probability affect samples, but only those which are taken "at random."

Each member of the frame is a sampling unit (a person, company, village, or town) and the frame itself must be chosen with great care. The classic example of wrong use is the choice of the telephone directory for an investigation into householders' opinions. More useful frames include registers of voters, census returns, school pupil lists, trade directories, and jury lists—but all must be used while still up to date.

Care must be taken, of course, that any conclusions are made only about the particular population sampled. An enquiry using the telephone book as its frame should not be extended to cover people outside that frame.

E

1. Random sampling

The process has been defined by Kendall and Buckland thus:

"A sample, size N, is a random sample if it was obtained by a process which gave each possible combination of n items in the population the same chance of being the sample actually drawn. The laws of mathematical probability apply only to random samples."

To be precise it is not the sample which is random but the method of selecting the items from the frame. "Random sampling" must have a frame which is very carefully chosen indeed to avoid all bias. This may involve greater costs than haphazard selection, but the money will be well spent, since no reliability can be placed on the latter type, while the former can be planned to give any required degree of accuracy.

A simple method is to sample from tables of random numbers, which are lists of numbers selected by proper random methods so that all numbers have an equal chance of appearing in the tables; most books on statistics give examples and explain how they work.

Deliberate selection must be avoided, and this involves guessing numbers. The student may care to experiment, if he has time, by calling out several sets of ten numbers, and he will probably find that certain digits recur more often than others: his "favourite" numbers are being used; some are uttered more readily than others, especially those beginning with s, and bias like this must be avoided.

Another failure may occur during the actual investigation. The enquirer is instructed to visit houses 15, 37, 42, 61, and 89 in a certain road. He calls at 42, but no reply is obtained, so he substitutes No. 44. It may seem a minor matter to him, but none the less it introduces bias.

An equally important cause of bias would arise if the investigation were terminated before the full sample had been taken. If after 600 replies had been obtained from 1000 originally planned the investigators felt that enough data had been obtained and closed the sample it is certain that the error would be much higher than had a sample of 600 been planned from the start.

Simple random sampling is of great value, but it is not used to any extent in practical work in its simple form, mainly for reasons of economy. Sampling experts have developed a wide selection of alternatives which have good theoretical *and* practical advantages. A selection of better methods is given below (the terminology is not yet standardised).

2. Stratified sampling

Ideally, random samples should be made from a homogeneous group (*e.g.* male university graduates). If the population consists of two or more recognisably homogeneous groups, stratified sampling may be used. In a survey of British university students the group might be (*a*) females, (*b*) males, and for each group we might select arts, science, and social science students. A random sample would then be taken of each group to ensure that all are represented. Weighting can be introduced. If, for example, Redbrick has twice as many science as arts students the sample can be 2 : 1. Another reason for taking a larger sample of one than the other would arise if one group varied around the average (in age, height, or intelligence, etc.) more than the other. The higher the standard deviation, the greater might be the sample.

In public-opinion surveys and commercial market research an adaptation of the stratified method known as "quota sampling" is common. Each interviewer is given a selection of streets or an area to cover. He is told how many interviews to make and then left to select the "victims" as experience guides him, according to instructions about the ages or classes of person he must cover.

This method is only partially random and is not necessarily very reliable—although it is probably efficient in commercial research because mathematical accuracy of a high order is seldom required. Ultimately, the success of the method depends on the efficiency of the interviewer.

Stratification ensures that the various groups are properly represented, and thus has an advantage over random sampling.

3. Systematic sampling

"A starting point in the first *i* observations is chosen at random, then every *i*th observation thereafter is chosen. Here every observation has the same probability of being included as in a simple random sample, but the probabilities are not independent" (Wallis and Roberts). Thus every tenth house in certain streets may be visited during the course of a market survey, but the first house number should be selected at random. If No. 1 is always chosen as the first house bias will be present: in a terrace No. 1 may be the only semi-detached or corner house.

This method can be very efficient, unless by mischance there happens to be a pattern in the frame which coincides with the sampling interval.

4. Cluster sampling

This is also known as multi-stage sampling. If a survey is to be made covering a large geographical area such as the whole country the selection may be carried out in two or more stages. The country is subdivided into districts and a random sample of a given size taken from among those districts. Then a sample of the characteristic required is taken from each selected district.

Wallis and Roberts use as an example a study of family incomes in a large city. Instead of a random sample of 1000 families from one frame (Chicago) a smaller error and greater economy might result if a sample of 100 blocks in the city is selected and 25 families taken from each to give 2500 families. The authors mention that the family incomes in each block may be homogeneous, but there can if required be a deliberate selection of districts to ensure a heterogeneous distribution.

THE USES OF SAMPLING

1. We have already referred to quality control: during production a regularly timed sample of items is taken from the work-place and measured for the characteristic it is wished to control. From a graph of the data, note is taken of the average and dispersion of the sample as compared with the accepted standard. If there appears to be a trend on the graph approaching the established "rejection limits" action will be taken.

2. In Part II of this book will be found details of sampling applications for index numbers. It is very seldom that the population can be used, and the reasons given above apply therefore to the construction of indexes.

3. The best-known use of sampling is in the sphere of market research and public opinion polls. Every imaginable difficulty occurs in conducting a survey of public attitudes, but if the job *has* to be done, then sampling is the method to use.

4. Social scientists make use of sampling, although for their purposes high degrees of accuracy may not be needed. One of the most famous social samples in history was that made by Noah as reported in Genesis VII, 2–3, when he selected clean beasts by sevens, male and female, and unclean beasts by twos.

Government agencies often conduct social surveys to learn more about the welfare of the people in such matters as housing, food, and health so that they can legislate for improvements.

5. The accountant will use samples when auditing company

accounts. One illustration is the practice of sending copies of their individual accounts to debtors selected at random from the sales ledgers, with the request that any disagreements be reported.

6. We have discussed sampling from quantities of raw materials such as grain, cotton, and bulk liquids. With articles of a homogeneous nature and considerable bulk, sampling is the only practical means of ensuring that the terms of a contract have been fulfilled.

7. When a census like the Census of Population is taken, the results take years to edit. So that more immediate use can be made of the data, a 1% sample is often extracted from the returns. Today this is less necessary than it was before the advent of electronic data processing equipment enabled results to be obtained rapidly. Samples are still needed, however, if the census is taken at ten-year intervals, so that data are available for the intervening years.

ACCURACY OF SAMPLING

1. Why does sampling work?

The laws of probability apply to random samples and we must remember that if a sample departs from the principles of randomness the advantage of being able to predict the variability of the sample will be lost. This type of sampling bears the name "probability sampling," *i.e.* where every single unit in the population has a chance of being selected.

Many terms in sampling theory have specific meanings which must be carefully noted and used. To obtain the greatest benefit from samples, various measures are calculated from the distribution obtained from the sample which if the entire population were available would be derived from that. A measure computed from a sample is known as a "statistic" and includes such measures as the mean, median, standard deviation, and other summaries. When similar measures are obtained from a population they are known as "parameters." Thus, if the average heights of men and women were calculated the averages would be parameters if they were obtained from a survey of *all* men and women in the population, and statistics if obtained from samples. You will appreciate that one problem of sampling is to estimate the nearness of statistic and corresponding parameter.

In American volumes and often in others the convention is for parameters to be shown in Greek letters or capitals and statistics in Roman or small letters. Thus S or σ stands for population standard deviation and s for the statistic.

Suppose we calculate a parameter, say the S.D. We then calculate the same measure from samples of that population, and obtain from each several sample statistics, s. Each sample deviation will be slightly different, and the distribution of such values is the "sampling distribution." Of course, we cannot usually tell what the parameters are. We may wish to test a new drug to combat a disease. During the test we measure the results on a sample and decide on the efficacy of the drug accordingly. Obviously to treat the population instead of the sample might be unfortunate, to say the least.

Since it can be shown by test how reliable the sample is, there would be no need to submit the whole group to testing. The tests involve knowledge of a variety of equations, all connected with the probability theory and the normal curve of distribution. The following explanation is much simplified.

2. Errors of technique

If a random sample is drawn and statistics derived from it, there will be differences of size between the statistics and the corresponding parameters. The difference in size is called the "sampling error," and it should be carefully noticed that "error" in this connection does *not* imply mistake. Errors in the normal sense do occur at times, and before we go on to discuss the sample tests it might be as well to list the more likely ones. The first is the commonest.

(a) *Errors of bias*

In quota sampling, where the enumerator is responsible for the selection of his "questionees," his selection may be less than perfectly random.

(b) *Errors caused by non-response*

From a population of 100,000 a sample is drawn by postal questionnaire of 1000. Of these, 250 reply and 200 of them are in favour of your proposal. What reliability would you expect? Since 80% of your respondents are in favour you might deduce a favourable reply from the population. But what of the 750 who did not reply?

(c) *Errors in preparation*

A survey requires much forethought and preparation—in deciding the kind of sample and the scope of the questions—and bad preparation can easily be a source of errors. So can sloppy field work, as was explained earlier.

(d) *Errors in response*

These are difficult to deal with. People are not always ready to tell the truth if they think it will reflect unfavourably on them. Slonim illustrates the problem with his example of age paradox. It is remarkable that when returned forms are analysed the average age of women over 40 is found to be under 40! The "halo" effect is quite common. If the interviewer accidentally indicates the answer he expects or prefers, the response may often be sympathetic, for most people are unwilling to offend.

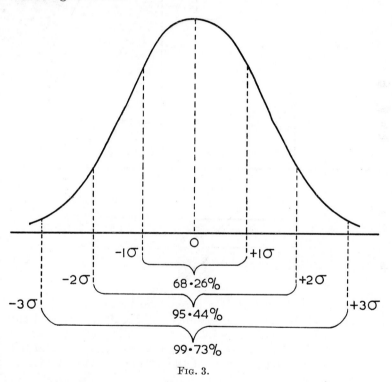

Fig. 3.

3. Sampling errors

(a) *Confidence*

Random sampling error then is the difference between two values and arises because one value derives from the population and the other from a sample. Since the parameter cannot always be obtained, the theoretical method of calculating the size of the error is of great importance.

We cannot be certain of the exact size of the error (under the assumption above), but we can set limits either side of the sample mean within which the exact data should lie. A further complication is that even having marked off limits we cannot be one hundred per cent certain of the pattern of the population. So we calculate the reliability in terms of "confidence intervals" which represent the "goodness" of the statistic. This interval

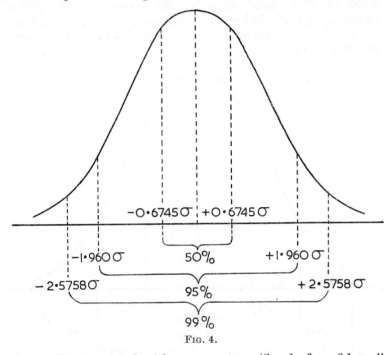

$$-0 \cdot 6745\,\sigma \quad\vdots\quad +0 \cdot 6745\,\sigma$$

$$-1 \cdot 960\,\sigma \qquad 50\% \qquad +1 \cdot 960\,\sigma$$

$$-2 \cdot 5758\,\sigma \qquad\qquad 95\% \qquad\qquad +2 \cdot 5758\,\sigma$$

$$99\%$$

Fig. 4.

is usually associated with a percentage "level of confidence" in terms of the laws of probability. If the distribution of the sample will provide a graph approximating to the normal curve of distribution (*see* Fig. 3) the percentage confidence level can be given in terms of the average, plus or minus so many standard deviations.

In terms of areas 68·26% of a distribution will be found within 1 σ $\pm$ of the mean, 95·44% within 2 σ, and 99·73 within 3 σ. But confidence intervals are usually expressed as 95% (5% limits) or as 99% of the area (1% limits), and the distribution in Fig. 3 may be converted to show these exact percentages (*see* Fig. 4). Thus in a normal curve 95% of the area is found within 1·960 σ $\pm$. The confidence limit in that case is 5%, which signifies that only 5% of the sample means (that is, the means we obtain by successive sampling, giving a sampling distribution) will be outside 1·96 σ of the mean. This brings us to consider the standard error of the mean.

(b) *Standard error of the mean*

If we take successive samples from one population and plot the distribution of the means, we obtain the sampling distribution of the means of samples. The mean of these means should be closely related to the population mean. If we then calculate the standard deviation of these means the result will be the standard error of the mean. The standard error gives an indication of the spread of the sampling distribution from the sample mean, in exactly the same way that the S.D. does from the population mean.

An interesting aspect of this is that the mean and standard error, which are calculated from the distribution of sample statistics, tend to be normally distributed, even though the original population distribution shows some bias. This applies provided the number of cases in a series of samples is thirty or more. With fewer than thirty in each sample it is found that the distribution will not be close to normal. Thus, as might be expected, a larger sample is better than a smaller one. The benefits of accuracy will increase, but at a diminishing rate —in inverse proportion to the square root of the size of the sample. The idea is worth restating:

It is better to sample *more*, rather than less, because a sample of over thirty cases gives greater accuracy. But if one takes the percentage

$$\frac{\text{sample}}{\text{population}} \times 100$$

it is found that no appreciable advantage is gained by a large percentage rather than a smaller.

The notion persists that a high percentage of the population gives the best results when used as a sample. No agreement exists as to the definition of a "high" percentage, and some samplers use 5%, others 40%. Wallis and Roberts justifiably criticise this indecision: "It is like asking an expert cook, 'What percentage of the flour in the bin should I put in my cake?' The answer is 'A certain amount,' depending on what sort of cake you are going to make."

Given that the sample contains more than thirty units, the standard error of the mean is:

$$\sigma_{\bar{x}} = \frac{\sigma}{\sqrt{n}}$$

i.e. the standard deviation of the population, σ, divided by the square root of the sample size $\sqrt{n}$.

EXAMPLE 53

From a large population a bus operator samples 80 buses for oil consumption tests. He discovers that the mean oil consumption is 25 quarts, with a standard deviation of 5 quarts. What assurance has he that these figures would apply to the population?

$$\sigma_{\bar{x}} = \frac{5}{\sqrt{80}} \text{ or } 0\cdot6 \text{ quarts approx.}$$

A common confidence limit is 5% which, you will remember, means that only 5% of the sample means should lie outside 1·96 $\sigma_{\bar{x}}$ of the true mean (a 1 : 20 chance that we are wrong will still remain, of course). Therefore the upper and lower confidence limits regarding the value of the estimated mean are 25 $\pm$ (1·96 $\times$ 0·6) quarts, and he can be sure the oil consumption mean lies between 26·2 and 23·8 quarts. You should now calculate the 1% confidence limits.

EXAMPLE 54

Moroney measures the height of 90,000 military servicemen. Since they are all of similar age and are all males, the curve of distribution should be normal. The mean height statistic is 67·5 inches and the sample deviation is 2·62 inches. How closely will this resemble the population?

$$\sigma_{\bar{x}} = \sqrt{\frac{2\cdot62}{90,000}} = 0\cdot0087 \text{ in.}$$

Using 5% confidence limits, the true result for all servicemen would be 67·5 $\pm$ (1·96 $\times$ 0·0087) inches, or within the range 67·52 and 67·48 inches.

If you refer to the second part of this book you will find details of the sampling methods used in the compilation of some published indexes. Each of them relies on the theories explained above.

Many writers explain the treatment necessary when the sample is taken from a small population and the items are not replaced after selection (the population being finite); then

$$\sigma_{\bar{x}} = \frac{\sigma}{\sqrt{n}} \times \sqrt{\frac{N - n}{N - 1}}$$

where N is the number of items in the population and n the number in the sample. They explain further that in common practice it is not possible to discover σ, the deviation of the population, nor can we afford to sample frequently to obtain $\sigma_{\bar{x}}$. As a rule one sample must suffice and we estimate σ by using

$$s = \sqrt{\frac{(X - \bar{x})^2}{n - 1}}.$$

Since the standard deviation of a sample is usually less than that of the population, we divide by $(n - 1)$. s is the estimated standard deviation and thus, to obtain the standard error of the mean, we use

$$s_{\bar{x}} = \frac{s}{\sqrt{n}}.$$

4. Size of the sample

We have discovered that the size of the sample is more important than the proportion of the sample to the population size. We should use the random sample to obtain reliable results but must remember that not all distributions are "normal" in the sense of the classic normal curve. Some populations are always "skewed" (*i.e.* the average is off centre), and care should be taken that the extremes of the group are represented.

The purpose of the survey will influence the size of the sample. For every 100 additions to a sample the cost will, of course, increase. Since the reliability will not increase to a similar extent, a compromise will be reached according to whether precision or estimation is required. In market research the characteristics of the group being studied are often very varied. On the other hand, some groups may be homogeneous by nature: the consumer habits of patrons of high-class department stores, for example. A smaller sample of the latter would give results as reliable as a larger sample of the former population.

The size of the sample should be calculated in advance because the errors caused by "adding in" more later on would cost more than the effort of calculating the right sample in the beginning. With a sample of more than thirty from a large population

$$\sigma_{\bar{x}} = \frac{\sigma}{\sqrt{n}} \quad \text{and thus} \quad n = \frac{\sigma^2}{\sigma_{\bar{x}}^2}.$$

To calculate this we must know the dispersion of the whole, which may be obtainable from an earlier survey or from government or market research agency data. $\sigma_{\bar{x}}$ will be determined by the confidence interval we wish to incorporate.

EXAMPLE 55

We will accept a 5% confidence unit (*i.e.* 1·960). The interval on either side of the mean is to be £2; then

$$\sigma_{\bar{x}} = \frac{£2}{1\cdot96} = £1\cdot02.$$

We learn that the standard deviation is £10 and wish to calculate the number to sample (assuming a simple random sample will be used); then

$$n = \frac{\sigma^2}{\sigma_{\bar{x}}^2} = \frac{10^2}{1\cdot02^2} = 98$$

and the sample will be of 98 items.

With samples in commerce more advanced methods are used because simple random sampling is not always adopted. A sample of hundreds or even thousands may not give the required precision in some cases, although it has been observed that in a famous instance one single case showed (quite conclusively) that atomic bombs sometimes explode.

QUESTIONS AND EXERCISES

1. Examine the contention that randomness is the essence of all good sample design. In what circumstances might you be inclined to propose non-random designs? (*University of London 1960*)

2. Discuss, with examples, the problem of sampling a population when there is no available list of the individuals comprising the universe of study. (*I.P.M. 1960*)

3. "Random sampling is the mathematician's imposition on the practical man; it opens the door to the most unrepresentative of samples, and offers only theoretical advantages in return." Explain and discuss. (*University of London 1958*)

4. Discuss the ways in which published economic statistics are based on sample material. Indicate the type of sampling involved, saying whether you think it could be improved.

(*University of London 1959*)

5. Compare the relative merits and demerits of quota sampling and simple random sampling. (*I.P.M. 1958*)

6. The need for speed in the publication of official statistics is evident. Discuss, with appropriate illustrations, how sampling can assist in achieving speed of publication. (*University of London 1958*)

7. What are the meaning and purpose of stratification in sampling design? In a study of labour mobility a sample of the employees of a large undertaking are to be interviewed to ascertain their previous employment history. What basis of stratification (if any) would you suggest for the design of the sample? (*I.P.M. 1957*)

8. "When a sample is regarded as a population with a frequency function, the mean, variance, etc., of this function are called the sample

mean, variance, etc. These have some relation to the mean, variance, etc., of the whole population but should not be confused with them."

Discuss the relationship between sample means and the mean of the whole population, and show how this relationship may be used to provide a confidence interval for the true mean of a population from sample data. (*I.P.M. 1956*)

9. What do you understand by a confidence interval? A random sample of 87 employees were asked whether they would be willing to receive payment of wages by cheque. The replies were: yes, 36; no, 34; don't know, 17. The company has 5000 employees. Write a brief report advising the managing director of the number of employees who might be willing to accept cheques. (*I.P.M. 1957*)

10. A simple random sample of 100 households was drawn from an area containing 25,724 households, with the following results:

Number of persons per household:	1	2	3	4	5	6	7
Number of households:	4	16	40	21	10	6	4

Estimate the total number of persons in the area and give 95% confidence limits for this total. (*University of Manchester 1956*)

11. An intelligence test was given to a sample of children aged 11 years in Scotland in 1947. The data show scores obtained by children whose fathers were in the professional and managerial class. Find a 99% confidence interval for the mean score of all children in the class from which the sample was taken.

Score	Number of children
20–	6
30–	7
40–	28
50–	51
60–	43
70–76	8

(*I.P.M. 1958*)

12. A military supply department, buying army boots, specified that no more than 3% of an order for 100,000 pairs should be "defective." In a random sample of 100, four pairs are found to be defective. What can be said about the quality of the order as a whole? Given that the department wishes not to have more than a 5% chance of accepting a low-quality delivery (3% or more defective), what number of defective pairs (*a*) in a sample of 100, (*b*) in a sample of 200, (*c*) in a sample of 2000 would cause it to reject delivery? (*University of Bristol 1960*)

13. A random sample of sixty employees from the staff of a large firm was found to have an average length of service with the firm of 10·4 years and a standard deviation of 5·82 years. Prepare confidence limits for the mean length of service of all the firm's employees.

(*University of Liverpool 1962*)

Chapter 12

CORRELATION

THE SIGNIFICANCE OF CORRELATION

THIS chapter has been included because comparisons are a vital part of most statistical techniques; yet many compilers of index numbers are not aware of the value of correlation analysis as a means of spotlighting connections between the series they are interpreting.

Before entering into the theory of the subject it may be useful to discuss the significance of the measures of correlation.

1. In commerce and industry action may have to be taken before its results can be known with certainty. A new marketing campaign may be inaugurated and the management must be kept informed of the results. In such a case correlation can be measured between the degree of advertising applied and the orders coming in. It might be possible to over-advertise and cause an inverse correlation if the public weary of the product. Or say that in industry a new bonus system is introduced. The result should be increased production, fewer rejections, and higher earnings. These factors are carefully watched to see that correlation is present.

Some banks and manufacturing concerns run courses for executives, trainee managers, and others. The costs are usually high, and the management may try to correlate the marks gained on the course with future performance and career. This of course is a lengthy matter and might be difficult to compute statistically.

2. The Government publishes many index numbers applicable to the whole country. An employer may wish to use a retail price index or index of wage-rates as the basis of an agreement with his workers or a contract with his suppliers. Can he be sure that the index he chooses is reliable in his given area? He could conduct a survey in his town (through local shops, Ministry of Labour offices, etc.), and correlate the results with the Government data for the same period. If correlation is strong he can use the Government data with some confidence.

3. In social work, as in commerce, we may wish to estimate "cause and effect." For example, smoking has been correlated statistically with lung cancer: is there causal proof?

In industrial and commercial statistical studies the possibility of a connection between two or more variables often needs investigation: "correlation" is that part of statistical method which attempts to discover the connection (if any) and to measure it. In the analysis which follows, we shall assume that only two variables, X and Y, are involved and that their relationship (if any) is of the linear kind. To interpret more than two variables is possible but involved (and might even need the use of a computer): it is more relevant here to consider only two.

It may be helpful to summarise roughly the treatment usually accorded to two variables which we suspect may be related. Any new terms will be explained soon.

1. Plot both X and Y on a scatter diagram and study the pattern of the plots.

2. If the impression given is of definite connection, ensure that it is not of the "nonsense" kind.

3. Calculate an equation and draw a regression line (or two regression lines) of "best fit."

4. Tabulate and compute the coefficient of correlation, plus or minus.

5. Consider the significance of the results obtained, either on their own or by comparison with similar correlations.

We are looking for a causal relationship between X and Y. Correlation may be found even though one has no direct effect on the other, because a third variable influences both. In most cases in index number analysis, we shall be seeking correlation of the "X causes a change in Y" type such as that between changes in income levels and spending on consumer goods.

TYPES OF CORRELATION

Correlation relationships may be described in these ways:

1. Positive correlation (+)

An increase in one variable is associated with an increase in the other. One need not *cause* the other, but both must be associated.

Example: in recent years more and more people in modest income groups have been holidaying abroad. The consumption of wines per head has steadily increased. There is some evidence that the two are associated in a positive manner.

2. Inverse correlation (—)

As one variable increases, a decline takes place in the other.
Example: the longer and better the induction of workers, the smaller will be the turnover of labour.

3. Zero correlation (0)

We may suspect that two variables are associated, but after collecting data we discover that in fact there is no relationship at all.
Example: advertising media may suggest that cleaning the teeth with "Dentrose" toothpaste will lessen the risk of decay. Dental experts, however, assure us there is no benefit beyond that of cleaning the teeth with any toothpaste.

4. Nonsense correlation

Where it occurs this is confusing. There is in fact no correlation at all, but appearances are that correlation (+ or —) is high.
Example: a writer discovered an apparent relationship between size of feet and quality of handwriting among a group of schoolboys. The boys with the larger feet were on the average older (Wallis and Roberts).

Fortunately the experienced user of statistics can usually decide whether the correlation is apparent rather than real.

THE MEASUREMENT OF CORRELATION

1. The scatter diagram

Given a series of data for two variables, X and Y, the aim is to measure the degree of relationship between them. A useful start is to show the two plotted on a graph, calling the determining variable X and that caused by it Y. In some cases of correlation both may be largely independent, in which case either may be called X.

EXAMPLE 56

The table below shows the monthly index of inland goods transport (column Y) and the monthly index of industrial production (column X) for 1959, the monthly average for 1958 being taken as 100.

	Y	X
January	95	101
February	104	104
March	98	103
April	106	108
May	101	105
June	100	109
July	100	96
August	95	92
September	106	110
October	111	115
November	112	117
December	103	109

(Adapted, I.M.T.A. 1960)

We wish to discover the relationship, if there is one, between them. Plot the data on a graph (*see* Fig. 5). We assume that X represents industrial production, since presumably the

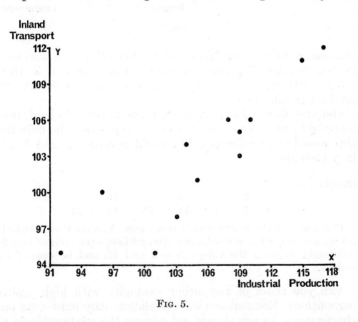

Fig. 5.

quantity of goods produced determines the amount of inland transport used. Make the points quite boldly and examine the result. If the dots appear to follow a pattern there is some evidence of correlation. If the trend is upwards and to the right it is positive; if downwards to the right it is negative (*see* Fig. 6).

The significance of this of course is that if the dots follow a positive pattern one variable is high when the other is, and vice versa.

With this graph for reference the reader should now try Question 1 at the end of this chapter. Note that the rules of graphic presentation (*see* Chapter 19) apply to scatter diagrams with certain modifications, for example there is no need to

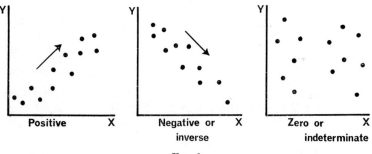

FIG. 6.

commence either scale from zero where the data are much larger. Scatter diagrams are not normally an end in themselves, although they may be useful in elementary and preliminary analysis.

One step forward is to show the trend of the data by drawing a straight line more or less through the points. The only time this would be literally possible would be where X and Y were in perfect step.

EXAMPLE 57

X	2	4	6	8	10	12
Y	3	7	11	15	19	23

Plot and join the points with a ruled line. You see that correlation is high and linear (*i.e.* it results in a straight line)—the "line of best fit" is straight between the values $X = 2$ and 12, and between $Y = 3$ and 23.

Can you think of any other examples with high positive correlation? Remember that correlation may exist over only short ranges, so you should not assume the relationship in the above example would necessarily give, say, $X = 20$ and $Y = 39$. There is a strong connection between the sales of a particular commodity and the revenue received, but as sales increase larger discounts will be offered and the line will become less straight. In manufacturing, economies of scale may cause the cost–output relationship to vary.

2. Regression lines

The line we have drawn in Example 57 is a regression line. Except in the isolated case of fully perfect correlation, a line can only be drawn by inspection (which would require someone with great experience) or calculation by the "method of least squares." The latter is the one we shall use, and the resultant line provides a simple method by which X and Y can be related visually.

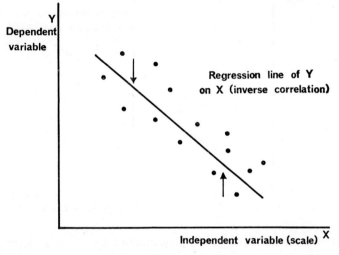

Fig. 7.

The method of least squares

In this method each point of a scatter diagram is measured in distance from the proposed line. This distance is squared and the squares are averaged to give a line which best fits the data. A common cause of confusion is that some writers show two lines labelled "X on Y" and "Y on X," which are obtained by taking Y or X in turn as the dependent variable. In general, X will be the independent variable, where known, and in that case changes in X cause changes in Y and the description will be "the regression line of Y upon X," which will provide the user with the expected value of one variable at any value of the other, within the span of the measures (*see* Fig. 7).

You will see by the (illustrative) arrows that the dots are measured vertically to the X axis. For the record, if we were to calculate the regression line of X on Y we should be measuring horizontally to the X axis (*see* Fig. 8).

The line of best fit

To fit the best line, use is made of the equation (sometimes called the estimating equation): $Y = aX + b$, where Y is the dependent variable and X is the independent variable. a and b are special constants, of which a fixes the point where the line crosses the Y axis (known as the Y intercept) and b determines

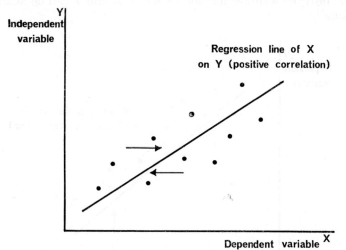

Fig. 8.

the slope of the line—that is, the amount by which Y decreases or increases when X changes by one unit. Having a and b, we can determine the regression line, but remember that the best line in the world cannot ensure that the two variables *are* actually correlated! (*See* Fig. 9.)

To obtain the regression line, given X and Y, we must find values for a and b. There are various formulae for different circumstances. Here is a simple one using the original data values.

X and Y are given in the data; a and b are given by:

$$a = \frac{(\Sigma X)(\Sigma X Y) - (\Sigma Y)(\Sigma X^2)}{(\Sigma X)^2 - n(\Sigma X^2)} \quad \text{(the Intercept formula)}$$

and $\quad b = \dfrac{\Sigma X Y - \dfrac{(\Sigma X)(\Sigma Y)}{n}}{\Sigma X^2 - \dfrac{(\Sigma X)^2}{n}} \quad$ (the Slope formula)

Using the simple Example 57:

X	Y	XY	X²
2	3	6	4
4	7	28	16
6	11	66	36
8	15	120	64
10	19	190	100
12	23	276	144
$\Sigma X = 42$	$\Sigma Y = 78$	$\Sigma XY = 686$	$\Sigma X^2 = 364$

$$n = 6$$

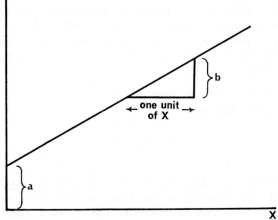

Fig. 9.

The calculation proceeds:

$$a = \frac{(42 \times 686) - (78 \times 364)}{(42 \times 42) - (6 \times 364)} = \frac{420}{-420} = -1$$

$$b = \frac{686 - \dfrac{(42 \times 78)}{6}}{364 - \dfrac{42 \times 42}{6}} = \frac{140}{70} = +2.$$

Therefore $Y = -1 + 2X$, which you can test on the data. This is the regression equation that gives the best of several possible fits.

3. The coefficient of correlation

Those who use statistics often require a further measure than the scatter diagram and regression line can provide. We have a "line of best fit," but must now measure the strength of the relationship between the points plotted and the line drawn. It may be calculated in a variety of ways, each leading to the "coefficient of correlation" (r).

The methods provided below are for examples of linear correlation. r shows whether the correlation is positive or inverse and is a reasonably reliable guide to the strength of the relationship. Four measures are given here. The formulae and symbols may vary from book to book, according to the author's estimate of his readers' experience!

The methods are: (a) simple formula—ungrouped data; (b) short method—ungrouped data; (c) short method—grouped data or "the product moment coefficient of correlation"; (d) rank coefficient of correlation. Remember that whichever method is most apposite the same result will be obtained, namely a single number which (irrespective of units) will represent the two variables in terms of the strength of their relationship.

(a) *Simple formula with ungrouped data*

This is the formula:

$$r = \frac{\Sigma xy}{\sqrt{(\Sigma x^2)(\Sigma y^2)}}$$

where x and y are the deviations of the units from the respective averages $\bar{X}$ and $\bar{Y}$. The result may range from $+1$ through 0 to -1. The top line of the formula, Σxy, is known as the "covariance," which has a limited use by itself, since it shows whether the relationship is positive or inverse or nil, as may be seen from this example:

X	Y	x	y	xy	x^2	y^2
£3	£20	−5	+10	−50	25	100
6	14	−2	+4	−8	4	16
8	7	0	−3	0	0	9
9	6	+1	−4	−4	1	16
14	3	+6	−7	−42	36	49

$\bar{X} = 8$ $\bar{Y} = 10$ $\Sigma xy = -104$ $\Sigma x^2 = 66$ $\Sigma y^2 = 190$ $n = 5$

The covariance is £ -104, which shows inverse correlation (one rises as the other falls). The size £104 may give some clue as to the strength of the relationship, but it should not be relied on, since it depends on the sizes of X and Y, which may be in very different units—shillings and tons, perhaps.

To improve the measure we divide by the geometric mean of the sums of the squared deviations of X and Y,

$$\sqrt{(\Sigma x^2)(\Sigma y^2)},$$

obtaining the correlation coefficient r, which gives:

$$\frac{-104}{\sqrt{(66 \times 190)}} = -0.93,$$

which may or may not be high. We cannot tell without a similar distribution for comparison. It should be remembered that much of statistics is the art of comparison, and the student should avoid deciding the size of any number without a relevant comparison.

At this stage turn to the examination questions and try some for yourself.

(b) *Short method with ungrouped data*

The previous formula is commonly applied, but it can lead to larger numbers than are convenient to handle. A rather startling but basically simple formula is:

$$r = \frac{\Sigma XY - \dfrac{(\Sigma X)(\Sigma Y)}{n}}{\sqrt{\left\{\Sigma X^2 - \dfrac{(\Sigma X)^2}{n}\right\}\left\{\Sigma Y^2 - \dfrac{(\Sigma Y)^2}{n}\right\}}}$$

where X and Y are original units. It can be illustrated with the help of the example in (a) above.

X	Y	XY	X^2	Y^2
£3	£20	60	9	400
6	14	84	36	196
8	7	56	64	49
9	6	54	81	36
14	3	42	196	9
40	50	296	386	690

Then

$$r = \frac{296 - \dfrac{(40 \times 50)}{5}}{\sqrt{\left\{386 - \dfrac{(40)^2}{5}\right\}\left\{690 - \dfrac{(50)^2}{5}\right\}}} = -0.93.$$

(c) *The product moment coefficient of correlation*

With grouped data, this is an adaptation of the method above, but allowing for class intervals and frequencies. The calculation is best carried out in class intervals in a similar manner to the assumed mean method of calculating the arithmetic mean. Anyone who is interested can refer to the larger texts, such as Dornbusch or Croxton and Cowden, for details of the methods and proofs.

(d) *Rank coefficient of correlation*

It may happen that full data concerning the X and Y variables are not available although the order of size may be. A measure of correlation is possible, either by (i) Spearman's rank correlation or (ii) Kendall's τ method. For simplicity's sake the first of the two will be dealt with here.

Rank the variation in order of size, the highest or "best" being number 1. The formula is:

$$r = 1 - \frac{6\Sigma d^2}{N(N^2 - 1)}.$$

This is the product moment formula modified by C. Spearman in 1906, where d is the rank difference.

EXAMPLE 58

Baseball teams in the U.S. National League ranked thus on June 24th and July 22nd:

	24th June	22nd July
1. Milwaukee	1	1
2. St Louis	2	4
3. Cincinatti	3	2
4. Brooklyn	4	3
5. Pittsburgh	5	5
6. New York	6	8
7. Philadelphia	7	6
8. Chicago	8	7

The calculation proceeds:

Team	Deviations in rank (d)	Squared deviations (d^2)
1	0	0
2	2	4
3	1	1
4	1	1
5	0	0
6	2	4
7	1	1
8	1	1
		$\Sigma d^2 = 12$

then

$$r = 1 - \frac{6(12)}{8(8^2 - 1)} = 0{\cdot}857.$$

In a series it may happen that two or more members are ranked equal. If, say, Robert and Alan are equal first in an examination they are both ranked at the mean, 1·5, and the next student is ranked third, not second.

It now remains to consider the significance of the measurement of the coefficient of correlation. In a great deal of industrial, social, and commercial investigation, action may be taken which it is hoped will lead to specific desired results. In due course measurements are made and the two sets of data inspected for a connection, which may or may not be present. Other examples include things such as length of apprenticeship and efficiency of trained workers, quantity of fertiliser and yields per acre, advertising expenditure and sales revenue.

In psychology, statistics can help determine the results of experiments such as results of intelligence tests as against real abilities. Beware of false interpretations, especially in attempting to decide which (if either) of the variables *causes* changes in the other.

CASUAL AND CAUSAL RELATIONSHIPS

1. External influences

Frequently two series correlate closely, although they prove to be independent, because they are both influenced by general external conditions. Flourishing business conditions will affect retail sales indexes as well as production indexes. Both are rising independently because of general prosperity. In a time series you should remove the external influence if possible, by removing the trend upwards (or downwards) for both series and correlating the two trend-free series. It is best to refer to the chapter on time series in a good textbook (see especially Karmel and Tippet).

2. Nonsense correlation

"Correlation" may be pure chance, especially in a small sample. The only satisfactory remedy is to study the data as closely as possible, bearing in mind the possibility of coincidence, chance, and external factors; and to think hard about your conclusions.

3. Misinterpretation of correlation coefficient

Tuttle discusses and criticises the use of the coefficient of correlation as very liable to misinterpretation. In any pair of variables, X and Y, in which there is some degree of correlation, the term "explained variation" can be used for the variations in Y which occur in step with X; in the case of perfect correlation all variations are explained. "Unexplained variations" therefore occur where X and Y are not absolutely in step with each other.

In spite of Tuttle's interesting arguments r is now very likely to continue to be the measure most used.

QUESTIONS AND EXERCISES

1. The gross income of families and their weekly expenditure on food (to the nearest shilling) are shown by these figures:

Gross income	Expenditure on food
£3–6	43s.
6–8	61s.
8–10	72s.
10–14	83s.
14–20	100s.
20–30	123s.
30–50	137s.

Plot a scatter diagram using mid-points of gross incomes and decide: (a) whether there is correlation, and (b) if so whether positive or negative.

(*Adapted, I.P.M. 1959*)

2. The following figures show fuel consumption (in gallons per 100 miles) and weight (in cwt) of three groups of buses with diesel engines of one basic type. The groups refer broadly to the age of the engine.

Group 1		Group 2		Group 3	
gal/100 miles	cwt	gal/100 miles	cwt	gal/100 miles	cwt
9·96	153·75	9·71	154·50	10·05	155·25
9·46	153·25	10·12	154·00	9·76	154·25
10·04	153·75	10·15	155·00	9·91	154·50
9·77	154·25	9·64	154·25	10·17	152·50
10·55	153·25	9·71	152·00	10·16	154·25
9·66	152·75	9·99	151·75	9·84	154·50
10·13	148·00	9·72	153·25	10·06	154·25
9·37	152·50	9·81	152·25	10·32	154·75

Plot these data on a scatter chart and comment on what the chart reveals.

(*I.O.T. 1956*)

3. The number of grammes of a given salt which will dissolve in 100 g of water at different temperatures is:

Temperature ($x°$ C)	0	10	20	30	40	50
Weight of salt (y g)	53·5	59·5	65·2	70·6	75·5	80·2

Temperature ($x°$ C)	60	70	80	90	100
Weight of salt (y g)	85·5	90	95	99·2	104·0

Use the method of least squares to find the linear formula $y = a + bx$, which best fits these observations.

(University of London, quoted in Loveday)

4.   *Index Number of Import Prices 1950–7 (1954 = 100)*

Source	1950	1951	1952	1953	1954	1955	1956	1957
(a) C.S.O.	88	114	108	100	100	104	105	107
(b) B. of T.	85	113	111	101	100	103	105	107

(a) is a current weighted index of average values of imports of goods and services.

(b) is an index of import prices weighted in accordance with the 1954 pattern of merchandise trade.

Calculate the correlation coefficient. How would you interpret the figure you get?   *(University of London 1961)*

5.

Country	Average wool consumption per head (lb)	Average real income per head (international units)
United Kingdom	5·27	1069
New Zealand	4·65	1202
Australia	4·63	980
Belgium	4·55	600
Sweden	3·55	653
Czechoslovakia	2·04	455
Japan	1·26	353
Italy	1·22	343
U.S.S.R.	0·87	320

Y = wool consumption $y = Y - \bar{Y}$ $\Sigma y^2 = 24·7716$
X = real income $x = X - \bar{X}$ $\Sigma xy = 4,262·88$
$\bar{X} = 663·9$ $\bar{Y} = 3·116$
$\Sigma x^2 = 919,321$

On the assumption that there is a linear relation between wool consumption and real incomes, obtain the least squares estimates of the parameters of that relation.   *(University of Manchester 1960)*

6. Illustrate the difficulties of using a correlation coefficient by calculating it for:

Great Britain:	1951	1952	1953	1954	1955	1956	1957	1958
(a) Number of proved murder charges	51	72	55	69	55	69	79	73
(b) Men unemployed (000's)	162	228	218	184	147	169	217	321

(University of London 1960)

7. What statistical information would you use, and how would you analyse it, in examining the relationship (if any) between wage-rates and unemployment since the war?   *(University of London 1958)*

8. It is known that the average number of days' absence per employee per year varies with the age of the employee. It is believed that the relationship can be described by a regression equation of the form: $\log y = a + bt$, where $y =$ the number of days' absence and $t =$ age in years. A small sample from the personnel records provides the following data for 1954:

Age	Number of days' absence	Age	Number of days' absence
21	4	35	7
42	14	24	3
38	10	44	30
64	38	50	28
53	19	27	7
61	34	59	34
47	17		

Fit the regression equation to these data and illustrate both the raw data and the regression equation on one graph.   *(I.P.M. 1956)*

9. Ten shades of green, when arranged from light to dark, are numbered 1–10 respectively. An observer, when asked to arrange the shades from light to dark, gave 3, 1, 5, 2, 6, 4, 10, 9, 7, 8. What is the value of Spearman's coefficient in this case? (Answer: 0·78.)

(London G.C.E., quoted in Loveday)

10. In a drama competition ten plays are ranked by two judges, X and Y, thus:

Play	A	B	C	D	E	F	G	H	I	J
Rank given by X	5	2	6	8	1	7	4	9	3	10
Rank given by Y	1	7	6	10	4	5	3	8	2	9

Calculate the coefficient of rank correlation. Is there any reason for saying that there is a significant agreement between the two judges? (Answer: 0·62.)   *(London G.C.E., quoted in Loveday)*

11. Discuss the usefulness of the correlation coefficient and calculate it for the following data:

    A represents the *Statist* index of wholesale prices.
    B represents the number of incomes exceeding £2000.

	1935	1936	1937	1938	1939	1940	1941	1942	1943	1944
A	83	88	102	90	94	128	142	151	155	160
B	93	100	107	105	103	103	111	123	133	144

(*London Chamber of Commerce 1959*)

12. The figures below show for coalmines in Great Britain *X* output per manshift and *Y* average real earnings per manshift (*i.e.* average money earnings deflated by a cost of living index). Find the coefficient between *X* and *Y*, and the regression coefficient of *Y* on *X*.

	1944	1945	1946	1947	1948	1949	1950	1951	1952	1953
X	1·00	1·00	1·03	1·07	1·11	1·16	1·19	1·21	1·19	1·21
Y	1·12	1·19	1·23	1·43	1·53	1·54	1·55	1·54	1·55	1·60

(*University of Bristol 1958*)

PART II
APPLICATIONS OF INDEX NUMBERS

	I.—OUTPUT			II.—PRICES			
	C.S.O. Industrial Production			M.L. Retail Prices	B.T. Wholesale Prices		F.T Indust Ordin Shar
DATE	All industries	Textiles, leather, and clothing	General chemicals	All items	Basic materials and fuel used: mfg. ind.	Manufactured products: home sales	Pric Ind
Years	Average 1958 = 100 Months seasonally adjusted			16th Jan. 1962	Average months 1954		1st J 193
1958	100	100	100	—	100·8	111·1	181
1959	105	107	111	—	101·7	111·5	250
1960	112	113	123	94·2	101·8	113·0	318
1961	114	111	125	97·4	100·6	116·0	319
1962	115	109	130	101·6	100·6	118·6	285
1963	119	112	140	103·6	103·0	120·2	317
19—							
1962 Jan.	113	107	124	100·0	101·6	117·8	305
Feb.	114	109	126	100·1	101·7	118·1	303
Mar.	115	108	125	100·5	101·6	118·3	296
Apr.	114	106	127	101·9	101·6	118·2	301
May	116	108	128	102·2	100·9	118·3	293
June	116	107	130	102·9	100·0	118·5	264
July	115	108	131	102·5	100·3	118·7	265
Aug.	116	109	131	101·6	99·0	118·8	276
Sept.	117	111	131	101·5	99·0	119·0	275
Oct.	116	109	130	101·4	99·5	119·1	275
Nov.	116	109	131	101·8	100·4	119·1	28
Dec.	113	111	131	102·3	101·5	119·3	28
1963 Jan.	109	107	130	102·7	102·4	119·4	28
Feb.	113	106	130	103·6	102·0	119·7	29
Mar.	116	110	133	103·7	101·8	119·7	30
Apr.	116	108	139	104·0	102·2	119·8	30
May	118	110	137	103·9	104·6	120·5	31
June	118	113	140	103·9	99·6	119·5	30
July	120	113	140	103·3	101·2	120·1	31
Aug.	121	116	141	103·0	100·2	120·0	32
Sept.	121	113	141	103·3	103·0	120·6	32
Oct.	123	116	146	103·7	106·4	121·0	33
Nov.	124	118	146	104·0	105·7	120·8	34
Dec.	125	115	146	104·2	106·3	121·5	34
19— Jan.							
Feb.							
Mar.							
Apr.							
May							
June							
July							
Aug.							
Sept.							
Oct.							
Nov.							
Dec.							

SOME SELEC

In November 1962 a new series of statistics appeared in
tors." In a rather similar fashion several important series
since different base dates are used, but they should p

B.T. Retail Sales		B.T. turnover catering	B.T. change in Retail Stocks (at cost)	B.T. Unit Value Indexes —Exports and Imports		Bank of England currency circulation (average)	M. of L. All workers manufacturing		DATE
Food shops	Durable goods shops	Restaurants, cafés, etc.		Imports	Exports		Weekly wage rates	Normal weekly hours	
Weekly average 1961		Weekly average 1960 = 100	End 1956 = 100	1961 = 100		1954	31st Jan. 1956		Years
—	—	—	109	103	99	122·8	113·7	99·8	1958
—	—	—	115	102	98	127·0	116·5	99·6	1959
—	—	100	120	102	100	133·0	119·4	97·3	1960
100	100	106	125	100	100	138·7	124·2	95·4	1961
103	102	109	133	99	101	139·3	128·0	95·1	1962
107	107	114	137	103	104	143·1	131·8	95·0	1963
									19—
102	99	92	124	100	102	139·3	125·3	95·2	Jan. 1962
103	100	93	128	100	101	139·1	125·4	95·2	Feb.
104	99	96	135	99	101	139·3	126·4	95·2	Mar.
104	98	104	137	100	101	140·6	126·8	95·1	Apr.
104	104	107	139	99	101	138·3	127·2	95·1	May
103	104	123	135	100	101	138·6	127·4	95·1	June
104	104	130	132	100	101	139·9	129·2	95·1	July
105	108	141	130	99	101	140·4	129·3	95·1	Aug.
105	104	120	133	100	102	137·8	129·5	95·1	Sept.
104	103	106	144	101	102	137·7	129·6	95·1	Oct.
105	103	100	151	100	101	138·2	129·8	95·1	Nov.
105	103	100	133	100	102	143·1	130·1	95·1	Dec.
108	98	89	130	101	102	138·5	130·3	95·1	Jan. 1963
108	97	92	134	102	103	138·7	130·3	95·1	Feb.
107	101	99	142	102	103	139·5	130·6	95·1	Mar.
107	102	108	142	102	103	141·9	131·0	95·1	Apr.
108	109	110	143	103	103	141·5	131·3	95·1	May
104	106	129	139	104	104	142·5	131·6	95·1	June
106	108	134	135	103	104	146·8	131·9	95·1	July
108	114	147	133	103	104	145·6	131·9	95·1	Aug.
108	110	125	135	103	104	143·8	132·0	95·0	Sept.
108	110	112	147	105	105	143·6	131·9	95·0	Oct.
109	110	106	157	106	105	144·4	132·5	95·0	Nov.
108	114	109	137	106	105	150·5	135·6	95·0	Dec.
									Jan. 19—
									Feb.
									Mar.
									Apr.
									May
									June
									July
									Aug.
									Sept.
									Oct.
									Nov.
									Dec.

Column headers above tables: III.—EXPENDITURE | IV.—STOCKS | V.—OVERSEAS TRADE | VI.—FINANCE | VII.—LABOUR

ICATORS

rd of Trade Journal, called "The Economy—Selected Indica-
a selected and are given above. These are not comparable
·resting.

F

CHAPTER 13

INDEX NUMBERS OF PRICES

SOME of the best known index numbers are described in this chapter, since prices (or costs) to the public, businessmen, and Government authorities represent tangible economic factors of great importance.

Price changes have been studied by many historians and can be traced back to the thirteenth century, but most price indexes published at present have a more topical aim, that of providing useful data by which trends can be studied and individual items measured against the performance of a group.

The Index of Retail Prices and, to a lesser extent, the Index of Wholesale Prices are used as measures of the cost of living (or value of money). They are imperfect for this purpose, but within their restricted fields can certainly indicate whether money values are changing appreciably. The wholesale price indexes are useful measures of input costs and output values for many industries; commodity price indexes are guides to trends in raw-material prices.

This chapter deals with wholesale and retail prices, stocks, and commodity price indexes. Investment indexes are self-contained and are described in Chapter 14.

STOCKS

Considerable interest is shown by economists in figures relating to stocks held and changes in inventories from period to period. For an informative article see "The Estimation of changes in stocks in manufacturing, wholesaling and retailing" in *Economic Trends* for March 1959. More recent articles have appeared in bank reviews and such weeklies as *The Economist*.

In an industrial country large stocks must be maintained to satisfy customers' demands, and changes in the outlook of manufacturers regarding future events can cast long shadows before on their suppliers of raw materials or cause trouble at wholesale and retail level as they unload their finished goods.

At the end of 1957 stocks in the United Kingdom (including work in progress) were valued at £9000 million, of which 53% was held by manufacturing industry, 10% by retailers, and 11% by wholesalers. Of the manufacturing figure, £620 million was held by the food, drink, and tobacco group, £360 by the chemical industry, and roughly equal amounts by metal and textile manufacturers of the £4620 million. £2020 million were in materials and fuel, £1560 million in work-in-progress, and £1040 million in finished goods. The article deals with the efforts of the Board of Trade to obtain the speediest, most accurate, and most comprehensive data on stocks. For an analysis of the whole economic situation, including stock changes, see *N.I.E.S.R. Economic Review*, especially the January issue.

Manufacturers' stocks were discussed in *Economic Trends* for August 1960. Information comes from annual censuses of production and sample enquiries conducted by the Board of Trade.

MINISTRY OF LABOUR: INDEX OF RETAIL PRICES

The most widely known index in Great Britain has a long history, but is far from antique: the latest revision was made in 1962.

The first official Index covered the period 1877–1900 and measured the price changes of nine articles in London. In 1904 its range was increased after a Board of Trade enquiry covering 1,944 working-class households in urban areas, the new Index being on the base 1914 = 100. This index was due to be replaced after a Ministry of Labour enquiry of 1937–8 into the budgets of 10,762 working-class households, but because of the war years it "soldiered on" until June 1947, changes being made from time to time. In 1916, for example, it was expanded by the addition of food, rent, fuel and light, cloth, and a "miscellaneous" group. The index was strictly "working class" and was known as the Cost of Living Index, which title it still proudly—but unofficially—bears today. Its original purpose was apparently to spotlight poverty by tracing the price movements of a "basket of goods" bought by the abstemious poor. Today there is a diminishing correspondence between "the poor" and the bulk of the population, which means that the old working-class basket of goods would be unrepresentative of the majority.

After the 1938 enquiry an interim index was created, based on 17th June 1948 = 100. This was an improvement on previous ones; but the criticism levelled at it is still heard: that, since the average consumer does not exist, no index can be representative.

Honor Croome considered that no single index could perform

the function of an economic measure. No improvements can cure one basic popular error, that of regarding the cost of living as a mirror image of the standard of material consumption. There have been violent discrepancies between the one and the other since 1939; those caused by rationing and other physical controls, for instance. The figures for rents gave no indication of the difficulties of finding a place in which to live.

Recent and current versions of the Index

"The Retail Price index is not intended to be a cost-of-living index, because it does not take into account everything people spend their money on nor does it cover spending by the whole population. But over short periods, at any rate, changes in retail prices are likely to reflect similar changes in the cost of living" (Council on Prices, Productivity and Income).

In 1953–4 the Cost of Living Advisory Committee made an enquiry into the spending of 12,911 households, using random sampling of the population and not restricting the sample to the "working classes" as did earlier studies. Their report was published in 1957, followed by a new Index of Retail Prices on the base of 31st January 1956 = 100. The coverage was wide but two classes of household were excluded: those whose head had a recorded income in 1953 of over £20 gross weekly; and those households in which at least three-quarters of the total income was derived from National Insurance, retirement or similar pensions and/or National Assistance. 11,638 households remained, of which 7% consisted of one person, 54% contained two or three persons, and 39% contained between four and fifteen persons. Household budgets were kept voluntarily for one year and formed the main source of information, although certain items (drinks and confectionery) were recorded elsewhere. The budgets were comprehensive, but in the compilation of the Index certain spending was excluded, namely: income tax, subscriptions to trade unions, church collections, other cash gifts, betting payments, National Insurance contributions, and "capital items" such as house purchase. An explanatory booklet was published by the Ministry of Labour for the new Index, much of which applies to the 1962 Index. Because patterns of consumer spending change rapidly, the Government has decided that yearly enquiries into spending shall be conducted instead of highly elaborate ones every so many years.

The first enquiry began in 1957, the results being published late in 1961, and a new Index was foreshadowed in a report in 1962 (which the student should obtain). It was fully reported

4 {

in the press, the *Financial Times* commenting that the latest items of consumer spending to be included were: "fish fingers and potato crisps, jeans and thick-knit sweaters, sherry and wallpaper, panties and girdles and of course scooters: it reads remarkably like a stockbroker's list of growth stocks." The new Index is based on 16th January 1962 = 100 and is expected to continue for at least ten years. Weighting has been modified as mentioned in terms of new consumer habits and, as a very new development, each year weighting will be changed (and noted in the *Ministry of Labour Gazette*). The weights for 1962 (February to January) were given in the *Gazette* for March 1962, those for 1963 in the March 1963 issue. To obtain these weights, information obtained from the Family Expenditure Survey for the three years ended the previous June will be used and it should result in an up-to-date Index, consisting as it does of continuous surveys of 9000 households.

Compilation and calculation

The Index is calculated from a combination of percentage changes in the prices of a large number of selected commodities and services, each weighted. Every month price changes are

Index group	Weights in old index (Jan. 1956 = 100)	Survey 1958–61 Weight for 1962 (Jan. 1962 = 100)	Weights for 1963 (Jan. 1962 = 100)
I. Food	350	319	319
II. Alcoholic drink	71	64	63
III. Tobacco	80	79	77
IV. Housing	87	102	104
V. Fuel and light	55	62	163
VI. Durable household goods	66	64	64
VII. Clothing and footwear	106	98	98
VIII. Transport and vehicles	68	92	93
IX. Miscellaneous goods	59	64	63
X. Services	58	56	56
All items	1000	1000	1000

averaged for each item, the method varying according to the type of item. The items from various retailers are averaged for each town, having been collected by local Ministry of Labour officers on personal visits or (in the case of proprietary foods) by taking a small sample. For food prices five shops are usually visited for each item, including a Co-operative if possible, a branch of a chain store, and a self service store. Some prices come direct from the manufacturer of the items (especially confectionery). Two hundred local Ministry offices collect prices.

The ten groups are made up from 92 sections covering the whole field of goods and services, prices being collected monthly. Within each section are individual items, and reference to Cmd.* 1657 should be made for the complete list, a selection of which is given here.

I. Food, Section 121: Coffee, cocoa, proprietary drinks

  1. Coffee, ground or roasted
  2. Coffee extract, powder
  3. Coffee essence, liquid
  4. Cocoa
  5. Proprietary drinks   (Total weight 3)

IV. Housing, Section 401: Rent

Rent, rates, and water charges for privately owned and local authorities' dwellings let unfurnished in a selection of urban and rural areas throughout the United Kingdom.

                    (Total weight 86)

X. Services, Section 007: Boot and Shoe Repairing

  1. Men's shoes, soling and heeling
  2. Women's shoes, heeling   (Total weight 4)

Thus, in Group II, Alcoholic drink, prices are those of different makes sold in public-houses. Beer is liable to changes in strength and when this happens an adjustment in the price relative is made. In Group III, Tobacco, prices are normally obtained direct from the manufacturer. In Group V, Fuel and light (coal, coke, electricity, and oil), coal and coke prices are for common qualities from retailers; gas coke prices are submitted by area Gas Boards. Gas prices include the cost of certain heating and cooking apparatus. There are many tariffs for electricity, so the Index prices are the average cost per unit of: (*a*) 750 units used each year (*i.e.* only for lighting, radio, etc.), and (*b*) 3000 units (an "all-electric" household).

In Group VI, Durable household goods, are such items as furniture, hardware, and soft furnishing. Prices for furniture, floor coverings, and domestic ware are obtained by Ministry

---

* *i.e.* Command (of the Government). Blue books and other reports to Parliament are numbered in series, and presented "by command of Her Majesty."

representatives who visit large retail stores in twenty-three urban areas. It is known that prices, qualities, and styles of all these items change quite rapidly. Prices for drapery, soft furnishings, and china hardware are obtained by post from a large sample of retailers.

Prices in Group VII, Clothing and footwear, are obtained by correspondence between the Statistics Department of the Ministry of Labour and many hundreds of retailers, special note being taken of changes in quality. This group covers all men's, women's, and children's outer and under wear.

Because of considerable changes in consumer habits, Group VIII has been considerably revised and an additional item, motor scooters, inserted. Used-car prices are the recognised average prices at relevant dates of specified cars of a given age; insurance costs come from insurance companies; public transport fares from the operators; tyre prices from the manufacturers.

In Group IX, Miscellaneous goods, book and periodical prices are obtained from the publishers; manufacturers supply those for chemists' shop goods and retailers give prices of cleaning articles.

Under Group X, Services, the G.P.O. give details of postal services, as well as radio and television licence costs. Laundry charges are supplied by certain national firms; prices of hairdressing, shoe repairs, and dance-hall admissions are obtained by observation.

When prices have been obtained in various areas of the country they are averaged for each item in each town and a price index calculated. In each of the five categories of towns a price index is obtained by calculating the unweighted arithmetic mean of the price indexes for the various towns within the group. These are then combined by calculating the unweighted mean of all five—the result being the price index for that item for the whole of the country.

Town indexes are not calculated for items sent direct to headquarters (e.g. clothing and hardware), but the prices are grouped into multiples, department stores, Co-ops, and other. In the case of multiples a weighted average is calculated, the weights being proportional to the estimated relative importance of each undertaking. For the other three an unweighted average is worked out. The four are then combined, using weights proportionate to the estimated relative importance of each outlet.

The above results should reflect the percentage change in price since the base date, as adjusted for changes in quality or quantity. When quality changes, the measurement is taken of price changes (quality for quality) by substituting a new item of similar quality to the old and using the chain base method.

Thereafter the data are grouped into sections and an average of the 92 is calculated. Finally, after each group weight is used, an all-items figure is calculated.

In the past the official Index figure has always been rounded to the nearest whole number (although shown to one place of decimals in the *M.L.G.* as well). This is not now regarded as satisfactory, and the Index is now being rounded to the nearest first place of decimals (from January 1963).

Prices are normally collected on the Tuesday nearest the 15th of the month and the result is available during the third week of the month following. It is issued to the press and later published in the *Ministry of Labour Gazette*.

The new Index can be linked to provide a continuous series and the conversion factor is 1·175, *i.e.* current figures should be multiplied by 1·175 to obtain the data based on 17th January 1956 = 100.

The Index is of great value as a measure of inflation or deflation if we assume that consumer spending reflects such economic events without too serious a time lag. Again, many sliding-scale agreements are based on the Index. It is regularly published in the *Ministry of Labour Gazette*, the *Monthly Digest of Statistics*, the *Annual Abstract of Statistics*, *Economic Trends*, and newspapers.

The Family Expenditure Survey

From 1957 a sample of 5000 households is being taken yearly. They are visited and asked to keep detailed expenditure records for fourteen consecutive days and to give details of longer payments, such as rent and insurance. The Ministry states that approximately two-thirds of households co-operate; it is considered that for the purposes required no other sources of data are available and that reliability is high. The kinds of household sampled are similar to those taken in earlier surveys, except that the income limits of the head of the household were raised in 1957–8 to £25 and in 1959–60 to £30 weekly. As noted earlier, the Index is to be re-weighted annually in January on information obtained from the survey in respect of "index households" over a period of three consecutive years ended the previous June. Processing is done in six months, and a regular revision is thus possible.

Commentaries

Since this is such a commonly reported index, the Ministry of Labour takes special care in its commentaries on it. Each year an interpretative essay is published in the *Gazette* which considers the reasons for changes in the previous year and gives tables showing increases and decreases in each section. An article covering the first four years of the 1956 = 100 Index is in *Economic Trends* for May 1960. During those years the Index rose 10 points, but naturally this covered many greater rises and some falls.

Housing rose 29 points, fuel and light 18—but clothing and footwear only 3 points, and durable household goods *fell* by 2 points. The article also shows how uneven are many price movements because of seasonal influences, changes in taxes and subsidies, and import changes.

INDEX OF RETAIL PRICES

1. *Detailed figures* (16th January 1962 = 100)

	Mid-Apr. 1962	July	Oct.	Mid-Jan. 1963	April	July	Oct.	Mid-Jan. 19—
I. *Food:*								
Bread, flour, cereals, biscuits, and cakes	102	103	103	103	103	104	105	
Meat and bacon	101	101	101	102	98	101	105	
Fish	99	97	98	99	100	98	101	
Butter, margarine, lard, and cooking fat	99	102	103	106	106	109	110	
Milk, cheese, and eggs	95	97	103	113	109	101	108	
Tea, coffee, cocoa, and soft drinks, etc.	99	103	103	103	103	103	103	
Sugar, preserves, and confectionery	100	111	111	114	115	114	122	
Vegetables: fresh, dried, and canned	143	132	88	106	138	108	95	
Fruit: fresh, dried, and canned	101	94	85	84	88	95	82	
Other food	100	105	105	104	104	104	104	
Total food	104·1	104·6	100·5	103·8	106·5	103·7	104·2	
II. *Alcoholic drink*	100	100·3	100·6	100·9	101	103	103·2	
III. *Tobacco*	100	100	100	100	100	100	100	
IV. *Housing*	103·3	104·1	104·9	105·5	107·7	109·1	109·8	
V. *Fuel and light:*								
Coal and coke	100	98	99	109	109	100	100	
Other fuel and light	101	102	103	104	105	108	109	
Total fuel and light	100·8	100·2	101·1	106·5	106·8	104·2	104·9	
VI. *Durable household goods:*								
Furniture, floor coverings, and soft furnishings	102	103	103	103	104	104	104	
Radio, television, and other household appliances	98	98	98	96	96	96	96	
Pottery, glassware, and hardware	100	100	100	100	101	101	101	
Total durable household goods	99·8	100·6	100·8	99·8	99·8	100·1	100·3	

	Mid-Apr. 1962	July	Oct.	Mid. Jan. 1963	April	July	Oct.	Mid-Jan. 19—
VII. *Clothing and footwear:*								
Men's outer clothing	102	104	104	104	105	105	105	
Men's under clothing	100	103	104	104	105	105	105	
Women's outer clothing	101	101	102	103	103	103	103	
Women's under clothing	102	104	104	104	104	104	104	
Children's clothing	100	101	101	101	101	101	102	
Other clothing including hosiery, haberdashery, and materials	100	102	101	102	102	102	102	
Footwear	101	104	105	105	106	105	106	
Total clothing and footwear	100·9	102·6	103	103·2	103·5	103·5	103·7	
VIII. *Transport and vehicles:*								
Motoring and cycling	100	100	99	96	98	98	96	
Fares	101	104	105	105	105	107	108	
Total transport and vehicles	100·4	101·4	101·1	99·6	100·4	101	100·5	
IX. *Miscellaneous goods*								
Books, newspapers, and periodicals, matches, etc.	101	102	102	103	104	105	107	
Medicines, toilet requisites, soap, photo and optical goods	100	100	100	100	100	100	100	
Stationery, toys, travel, and sports goods	101	101	101	102	102	103	103	
Total miscellaneous goods	100·2	100·7	101·1	101	101·7	101·8	102·6	
X. *Services*								
Post and telegraph	100	100	100	100	100	103	103	
Entertainment	101	101	102	102	102	101	102	
Other services including domestic help, hairdressing, boot and shoe repairing, laundering and dry cleaning	102	103	104	104	106	107	107	
Total services	101·4	102	102·9	102·3	103·5	104·1	104·9	
Total: all items	101·9	102·5	101·4	102·7	104	103·3	103·7	

2. *All Items* (17th January 1956 = 100, linked)

	1956	1957	1958	1959	1960	1961	1962
Jan.	100	104	108	110	110	112	117
Feb.	100	104	108	110	110	112	118
Mar.	101	104	108	110	110	113	118
Apr.	103	104	110	110	110	113	120
May	103	105	109	109	110	114	120
June	102	106	110	109	111	115	121
July	102	107	109	109	111	115	120
Aug.	102	106	108	109	110	116	119
Sept.	102	106	108	109	110	115	119
Oct.	103	107	109	109	111	116	119
Nov.	103	108	110	110	112	117	120
Dec.	103	108	110	110	112	117	120

BOARD OF TRADE: SEASONALLY ADJUSTED INDEX
OF RETAIL SALES

A Census of Distribution was taken under the Statistics of
Trade Act, 1947, and the 1961 census was made during 1962,
using information available from those engaged on the 1961
Census of Population. The census was conducted by post in
early January 1962 and satisfactory returns were received from
87% of establishments, accounting for 93% of total turnover.
A National-Elliott 405 computer was used for checking
individual returns and checking the classification of the more
detailed returns, and both computer and punched-card
machinery are being used to compile the final results report.

A variety of index numbers are prepared to cover the retailing
field, and the aim of the Index of Retail Sales is to show in good
time changes in the economic climate, for which reason sales
are seasonally adjusted. The tables published monthly in the
Board of Trade Journal are elaborate and classified mostly into
types of outlet, such as multiples, Co-operatives, or independent
retailers. They are useful indicators of short-term trends in
retailers' trade.

On the computer the unadjusted data are subjected to a
rigorous analysis which enables underlying movements to be
effectively separated from such seasonal movements as
Christmas shopping. However, the Board of Trade points out
that non-seasonal influences are still present, such as public
anticipation of changes in purchase tax, hire-purchase regulations—and the effect of weather on shopping! Changes in
data from one month to another should not be too minutely
interpreted, since the method of seasonal adjustment itself is
based on past experience.

Each month a selection of tables is given in the *Board of
Trade Journal*, some in terms of index numbers. These are
given weights to give due measures of relative importance to
different sizes of contribution, different regions, and different
kinds of organisation. A table is regularly given in the *Monthly
Digest of Statistics*, and the *Journal* has a summary table giving
both adjusted and unadjusted data. Since the tables are
elaborate, I cannot reproduce them here, but give instead one
example and summary tables.

With the available early census results the Board of Trade
rebased the Index from (average weekly sales 1957) to the new
(average weekly sales 1961 = 100), thus modernising it. As
more information is available, the Index will be adjusted, and
readers should refer to the *Board of Trade Journal* for details.

The turnover information from the 1961 census was used to provide data for the new 1961 base, and this rebasing has been applied to derived statistics such as the estimates of volume of sales at constant prices and seasonally adjusted estimates of both the value and volume of sales.

The information comes from returns from independent retailers, multiples, Co-operatives, and general department stores. In the case of independent retailers, multiples, and department stores, information is extracted by types of goods sold. The Co-operative sales are extracted on a departmental basis. The periods covered consist of either four or five weeks, each quarter consisting of three months of four, four, and five weeks. The data given are based on the value of sales, and so price movements affect them (including purchase tax changes). Reference should be made to the published results of the 1961 Census of Distribution; the *Board of Trade Journal* for 10th November 1961, 6th July 1962, 8th February 1963, and 10th May 1963; *Economic Trends*, May 1962.

The tables given from time to time in the *Board of Trade Journal* include:

1. *A summary table*, value (at current prices) showing monthly, quarterly, and annual data for major groupings, as follows:

		1961	1962	1963	19—
All kinds of business	(£9095 million)	100	103	108	
Non-food shops	(£4923 million)	100	103	108	
Food shops	(£4171 million)	100	104	107	
Clothing and footwear	(£1395 million)	100	102	107	
Durable goods	(£956 million)	100	102	107	
General department stores	(£451 million)	100	103	108	
Miscellaneous non-food stores	(£2121 million)	100	103	109	

2. *Volume (at average 1961 prices)*. This gives in brief fashion an interesting corrective to possible price reasons for apparent increased sales as shown above. It appears monthly, and shows quarterly and annual data.

		1961	1962	1963	19—
All kinds of business	(£9095 million)	100	101	103	
Food shops	(£4171 million)	100	102	103	
Non-food shops	(£4923 million)	100	100	104	

3. *Index numbers of values of sales per week (in detail):* several pages of information, expanded from Table 1 above. For example, "Food shop sales" is divided into Food, Grocers, Butchers, Greengrocers, Fishmongers, Bread and Flour, Off-licences, Dairymen, Other food shops; and separate values are shown for each group in terms of outlet: Co-ops, Multiples, etc.

4. Two other tables show *Retail sales, seasonally adjusted*; one at current prices, the other at average 1961 prices. The former is given below.

RETAIL SALES, SEASONALLY ADJUSTED AT CURRENT PRICES
(1961 = 100)

Quarter		All kinds of business	Food shops	Non-food shops			
				Total	Clothing and footwear	Durable goods shops	Others
1961	1	99	98	99	100	98	98
	2	100	99	100	99	102	99
	3	101	101	101	100	103	101
	4	101	102	100	101	97	102
1962	1	102	103	102	100	99	102
	2	102	103	102	99	102	102
	3	105	105	105	105	105	104
	4	104	105	103	104	103	105
1963	1	106	108	104	102	99	106
	2	106	108	105	101	105	107
	3	109	107	110	112	111	110
	4	110	109	111	111	112	112

(Source: *Board of Trade Journal*)

COMMONWEALTH ECONOMIC COMMITTEE: INDEX OF RETAIL SALES OF BUTTER

The Commonwealth Economic Committee publishes a monthly journal, the *Intelligence Bulletin,* and among the statistics of Commonwealth trade given is the Index of Retail Sales of Butter. The purpose of the Index is simply to indicate the trend of the product's sales, without showing the total butter sales in the United Kingdom. It is based on the average of the four weeks ended 10th February 1962 = 100 and uses data of weekly butter sales provided by some of the larger Co-operative Societies and multiple stores. Data given weekly are shown here at the end of the month.

INDEX OF RETAIL BUTTER SALES

Year	Jan.	Feb.	Mar.	Apr.	May	June	July	Aug.	Sept.	Oct.	Nov.	Dec.
1962	109	102	103	95	103	101	101	102	103	103	102	109
1963	102	93	96	98	99	98	97	98	98	99	108	96
19—												

GOVERNMENT OF NORTHERN IRELAND—MINISTRY OF COMMERCE: INDEX OF RETAIL SALES

The aim is to describe an important sector of the Northern Ireland economy and enable individual traders to check their situation by comparison with the trade as a whole.

The Index indicates the movements in sales for eleven different kinds of business group, using similar methods to the Board of Trade index, and with the same base date: (average weekly sales 1961 = 100). Each current month the average weekly sales are expressed as a percentage of the weekly average for the year as a whole.

The Ministry depends on the co-operation of 760 volunteer retail establishments, representing Grocery, Butchers, Other food sellers (*e.g.* greengrocers, fishmongers, bakers), Dairymen, Shoe retailers, Clothing and drapery shops, Hardware, Chemists, Tobacconists, Newsagents, and others. Monthly information submitted includes: (*a*) total value of sales monthly; (*b*) the number of persons employed.

Information is received from the panel of retailers within four weeks of the actual date, and this is related to a "standard month" (of which there are two of four weeks and one of five in each quarter). Then follows grouping of results, and the percentage change in total sales is calculated for each group in comparison with the same month a year ago. The percentage change is applied to the group index number for the same month last year to obtain a new index number, the link method used excluding seasonal elements. Each group index is weighted by a figure appropriate to that group, derived from the 1957 Census of Distribution and later changes. The index number of all retail sales is calculated by summing the resultant figures and dividing by 100.

This index was first published in March 1960 and is given in part in the *Board of Trade Journal* and as a leaflet released by the Northern Ireland Government. The Ministry points out

NORTHERN IRELAND INDEX OF RETAIL SALES

Quarterly data (actually published monthly). (Average weekly sales of each group in 1961 = 100.)

Quarter	All kinds of business (weight 100)	Grocery (25·4)	Butchers (5·5)	Other food* (10·5)	Milk (4)	Foot-wear (3·1)	Clothing and drapery (16·7)	Hard-ware† (9·1)	Phar-macy (2·6)	Dept. and variety stores (9·1)	Confec-tionery‡ (11·3)	Misc. non-foods§ (2·7)
						1961						
1	93	97	102	97	101	85	89	92	95	81	90	79
2	98	98	98	99	101	106	101	99	96	97	92	89
3	98	98	93	100	97	94	92	102	97	102	102	92
4	111	106	106	104	101	114	118	106	111	120	112	140
Year	100	100	100	100	100	100	100	100	100	100	100	100
						1962						
1	93	103	102	101	104	72	85	95	93	80	92	70
2	102	106	98	107	103	113	90	105	99	99	92	99
3	100	104	93	108	101	97	92	100	98	100	100	93
4	117	112	111	109	108	119	126	116	115	125	114	151
Year	103	103	101	106	104	100	100	104	101	101	99	103
						1963						
1	97	108	106	104	105	74	91	106	94	81	92	73
2	105	113	103	109	106	113	103	102	101	97	98	99
3	104	108	97	112	100	105	99	108	104	102	101	103
4	121	119	114	113	111	126	133	121	113	129	112	160
Year	107	112	105	110	106	104	106	107	103	102	101	108

* Includes greengrocers, fishmongers, bakers, ice-cream sales.   † Includes furniture, ironmongers, hardware, radio, and electrical.
‡ Includes confectionery, tobacco, newspapers, books, stationery.   § Includes jewellery, fancy goods, sports goods.

that any single year's results do not in themselves provide particularly useful information about trends, since many of the monthly movements are seasonal, but the main value of the index develops as previous years' comparisons become available.

BOARD OF TRADE: INDEX NUMBERS OF HIRE PURCHASE BUSINESS

A vast amount of trade in shops is paid for on "easy terms," ranging yearly from about £600 million to £1000 million of new credit. In effect, the goods are hired and the property changes hands on payment of the last instalment. This system is especially common with the larger durable goods. With credit sales agreements, property passes to the buyer on delivery and payments extend (usually) over nine months or less. This system is used with some clothing purchases.

Credit comes from two sources. In one case the dealer extends it to the customer. In the other (especially where large sums are involved), money comes from finance houses. The Board of Trade assembles and publishes statistics from both sources in monthly statistics in its *Journal*. Monthly returns are made by two types of contributor, household goods shops and finance houses. The former supply the value of goods sold on credit, including the initial deposits or down payments as well as the credit during the period, and index numbers are derived from these values. The figures are inclusive of finance house credit and are reported by public utility showrooms, Co-operatives, department, multiple, and independent retailers, but not by clothing shops, mail-order houses, or credit traders calling on customers for orders. Finance houses themselves send in the returns of the value of new credit *excluding* down payments.

Up to the present the published tables are based on estimates derived from the 1957 Census of Distribution. Four tables are regularly given, the last two in the form of index numbers:

1. Estimates of hire purchase and other credit instalments outstanding, in £ million.

2. Hire purchase and other instalment credit extended and repaid, to show the change in hire purchase debt from month to month, in £ million.

3. New business of household goods shops.

4. New business of finance houses.

The first collection of statistics of hire purchase business by the Board of Trade was made in 1955 and first published in the

TABLE 3: NEW BUSINESS OF HOUSEHOLD GOODS SHOPS

Index numbers of value of goods sold on hire purchase and other instalment credit per week
(monthly average 1957 = 100)

Year	Jan.	Feb.	Mar.	Apr.	May	June	July	Aug.	Sept.	Oct.	Nov.	Dec.
Furniture and furnishing shops												
1960	122	113	111	121	102	90	101	92	102	112	120	124
1961	97	90	98	102	104	104	121	102	106	117	126	132
1962	98	96	94	100	105	104	115	108	113	124	131	140
1963	93	87	94	105	114	102	121	110	122	128	140	148
19—												
Hardware, radio, electrical goods, cycle and pram shops												
1960	126	130	126	124	105	96	92	90	98	109	108	114
1961	92	96	97	99	104	104	125	96	99	105	105	113
1962	89	86	93	88	98	116	118	112	116	120	127	136
1963	97	97	102	96	112	119	118	118	128	129	135	140
19—												
Department stores (household goods departments)												
1960	140	116	120	140	121	101	128	100	117	137	143	138
1961	133	119	117	123	124	111	156	109	119	141	143	146
1962	142	114	111	117	120	121	148	122	134	153	160	155
1963	138	109	111	116	129	112	155	119	134	158	172	162
19—												

TABLE 4: NEW BUSINESS OF FINANCE HOUSES

Index numbers of new hire purchase and other instalment credit extended direct to hirers
per calendar month (selected items only; monthly average of 1957 = 100).

Year	Jan.	Feb.	Mar.	Apr.	May	June	July	Aug.	Sept.	Oct.	Nov.	Dec.
Used private cars												
1960	160	191	250	240	178	155	150	149	129	121	113	92
1961	131	179	204	183	218	201	195	143	110	118	108	79
1962	96	121	134	138	179	162	169	152	126	133	111	78
1963	81	104	151	168	188	160	181	162	149	163	141	112
19—												
Caravans, new and used												
1960	113	162	233	254	264	168	156	148	126	108	83	54
1961	74	137	220	219	242	248	226	188	146	159	123	80
1962	95	127	172	175	222	205	217	198	160	153	115	76
1963	74	98	178	242	235	216	231	209	177	173	136	93
19—												
Household goods												
1961	138	114	126	120	136	123	133	115	107	118	119	104
1962	118	98	90	88	110	105	120	115	107	120	117	110
1963	128	96	108	107	124	105	120	120	118	133	127	128
19—												
All goods												
1960	180	188	244	232	201	170	169	151	139	138	132	110
1961	148	168	297	190	220	204	207	150	123	131	128	96
1962	121	133	147	142	179	160	168	143	127	140	126	94
1963	115	116	164	177	201	169	189	162	154	175	157	129
19—												

Journal of 21st April 1956. In July 1957 the scope was extended to include credit sales as well.

Tables 3 and 4 are based on the average of 1957 = 100. Table 3 shows the progress of new business of retailers in terms of the new credit they extend to customers; Table 4 covers new business of finance houses. For full data reference should be made to the appropriate *Board of Trade Journal* each month, but in outline form the tables are shown herewith.

The Census of 1957 gave the following values in £ million: *Furniture and furnishing shops* £138·3, of which multiples accounted for £58·8 and independents £59·8. *Hardware shops:* total credit sales £153·9, of which radio and electrical goods were £81·1 and cycle shops £17·7. Credit from *department stores* was valued at £22·4, and the total of all household goods shops' credit was £314·6 million.

From the Census of 1957 the following data are extracted (in £ million):

New private cars £56	Caravans £7
Used private cars £122·4	Farm equipment £7·5
Commercial vehicles £46·3	Industrial equipment £17
Motor cycles £32·3	Household goods £49

All goods £350·6 million (including items not listed above).

The tables show clearly the seasonal influence of most items, and in addition there are the effects of credit "squeezes" (governmental stipulations as to the length of time credit can be extended or amount of deposit necessary). See the *Board of Trade Journal*, 17th August 1962, and *Economic Trends*, September 1961.

BOARD OF TRADE: TURNOVER IN THE CATERING TRADES

Each month a sample enquiry is made into retailers' turnover; in recent years it has been extended to cover the catering trades, this having been made possible by the Enquiry into Catering held in 1960. The aim is to provide estimates of current changes in this important sector of the service trades and to give up-to-date indications of changes in consumers' spending on, for example, accommodation and meals away from home. To give an impression of the relative importance of this sector of the economy, total turnover in 1960 was £1300 million (including sales in public-houses and fish and chip shops), total retail trade being valued at £8500 million.

The monthly enquiry covers items in Minimum List Heading 884 of the Standard Industrial Classification, *i.e.* those mainly engaged in providing meals, drink, and accommodation (excluding catering in hospitals, schools, or registered clubs unless provided by outside caterers). Service canteens, cinema restaurants, and railway hotels and catering services are covered.

Catering index numbers are given in that issue of the *Board of Trade Journal* following the one giving the latest estimates for total retail trade. Two tables are provided, one giving turnover index numbers and the other value information.

Fairly marked seasonal sales patterns are noticeable in the summer months (especially where holiday camps are included) and again in December. To obtain the index numbers a sample of caterers is taken, to cover large multiple traders, hotels, and smaller businesses. Each month about 300 caterers provide the Board of Trade with statistics.

CATERING TRADES: INDEXES OF TURNOVER PER WEEK

Showing kinds of business; turnover in £ million (1960 = 100)

Year	Jan.	Feb.	Mar.	Apr.	May	June	July	Aug.	Sept.	Oct.	Nov.	Dec.
				Total all caterers (£1290)								
1960	100	82	81	85	96	98	111	118	120	107	97	91	111
1961	107	87	88	94	101	108	115	124	130	118	106	98	117
1962	112	93	94	96	108	109	125	131	136	121	112	102	119
1963	117	94	93	100	101	113	130	136	142	126	118	109	126
19—												
				Licensed hotels and holiday camps (£169)								
1960	100	65	65	72	91	97	123	141	150	128	105	77	86
1961	107	66	68	78	95	107	130	149	161	138	113	82	91
1962	113	71	74	84	98	109	143	161	169	146	117	87	93
1963	118	69	72	85	103	113	149	169	184	151	128	94	100
19—												
				Restaurants, cafés, fish and chip shops (£307)								
1960	100	82	82	86	94	97	115	124	130	108	95	91	94
1961	106	88	88	94	100	108	117	127	138	116	101	97	98
1962	109	92	93	96	104	107	123	130	141	120	106	100	100
1963	114	89	92	99	108	110	129	134	147	125	112	106	109
19—												
				Public-houses (£711)								
1960	100	82	81	85	98	97	108	114	114	102	95	91	126
1961	109	89	90	95	103	109	112	120	126	115	106	99	133
1962	114	97	97	98	113	110	124	128	132	118	113	104	135
1963	118	98	94	101	115	113	128	133	137	122	119	112	141
19—												
				Canteens and catering contractors (£102)								
1960	100	105	106	102	95	102	94	94	85	99	106	110	103
1961	105	109	108	105	104	104	102	103	87	105	110	115	109
1962	108	113	114	111	104	111	104	103	90	109	112	118	110
1963	115	119	122	120	111	119	111	108	96	112	118	125	115
19—												

For interest the results in summary form of the 1960 enquiry are given (£ million 1960 approx.):

Total turnover	Sale of meals	Sales of alcoholic drink	Residents' accommo- dation	Cigarettes and tobacco	Other goods and services
		Total, all caterers			
1290	380	623	83	163	41
		Licensed hotels and holiday camps			
170	45	41	71	6	6
		Restaurants, cafés, fish and chip shops			
310	233	21	4	28	22
		Public-houses			
710	33	560	7	103	8
		Canteens and caterers			
100	70	1	1	26	5

U.S. DEPARTMENT OF LABOR, BUREAU OF LABOR STATISTICS: WHOLESALE AND CONSUMER PRICE INDEXES

These indexes attempt to measure changes in the purchasing power of money in terms of the goods and services one dollar will buy at various dates. The Bureau of Labor Statistics calculates two basic price indexes, the Wholesale Price Index and the Consumer Price Index. In both cases the purchasing power of the $ is calculated by:

$$\frac{\text{Index number for the base period}}{\text{Index for the date to be compared}}$$

and the result is expressed in $.

The Wholesale Price Index

This is a general-purpose index, providing a continuous monthly series showing price changes for all commodities dealt in on primary markets of the U.S.A. It measures real price changes, excluding influences caused by differences in quality or quantity over time.

From December 1960 the base was revised to 1957-9 = 100. Three measures are issued, those published daily (based on 22 items), a weekly estimate, and a comprehensive monthly index. The original monthly index contained 250 items. Now 2200 commodities are included from 6300 quotations.

The main uses the Index serves can be classified as:

(a) An important indicator of changes in the economy as shown by basic price movements.

(b) An aid to measuring the purchasing power of the dollar. The Index is used as the bases for sliding-scale agreements, especially for rentals and long-term purchases. For example, a long-term contract may be subject to adjustment when raw-material prices are shown by the Index to change. In the payment of royalties, use of the Index can protect both parties against wide fluctuations in price levels.

(c) A measure of general and specific price trends, used in Government and industrial budget making and reviews, as well as in L.I.F.O. accounting by some organisations.

The prices used are obtained at the time of the first commercial transaction in the product. Retail prices are not involved, but those of the raw materials which enter its manufacture are.

Each commodity series has its own weight (in terms of the direct sales), to which is added the weight of other commodities which are not in the Index but are known to move usually in similar fashion. New commodities are included only when they are established both technically and in the market. Net weights are based on the values of shipments from the 1958 censuses of manufactures and mineral industries.

Prices are obtained where possible at the point of price determination: thus machinery prices are ex-works; grain prices are obtained from organised exchanges. Transport costs are included only in so far as they are directly regarded as part of the primary market price.

The items are chosen after consultation with experts (i.e. not by probability sampling) and are carefully specified, e.g. $\frac{15}{16}$ in. cotton; No. 2 hard winter wheat. Calculation is facilitated by use of modern electronic equipment. Price changes and percentages are worked out, after which chain relatives are compiled for each commodity, i.e. (current monthly percentage change/100) × the previous index.

These relatives are weighted and the aggregates totalled by product classes, sub-groups, special combinations, and "all commodities." These aggregates are then reconverted into indexes. The formula involves a chain of relatives, each calculated by Laspeyres:

$$\frac{\Sigma p_1 q_0}{\Sigma p_0 q_0}$$

The daily index involves changes in the prices of 22 items and is designed to measure the price trend of these sensitive items. The calculation is based on an unweighted geometric mean of the individual commodity price relatives. No weights are used; each commodity tends to reflect experts' appraisal of both current and future economic forces affecting the organised markets, and this is the main purpose of the index.

The items in the daily index are:

Food

1. Hogs (100 lb)	Good to choice	Chicago
2. Steers (100 lb)	Good	Chicago
3. Wheat (bushel)	No. 2, Hard Winter	Kansas City
	No. 1, Dark N. Spring	Minneapolis
4. Corn (bushel)	No. 3 Yellow	Chicago
5. Cocoa beans (lb)	Accra	New York
6. Butter (lb)	Grade A	Chicago
7. Cottonseed oil (lb)	Crude	Memphis
8. Lard (lb)	Prime Steam	Chicago
9. Sugar (100 lb)	Raw 96°	New York

Natural fibres

10. Cotton (lb)	$\frac{15}{16}$ in. Middling Staple	10 markets
11. Print cloth (yd)	39 in. 80 × 80 count 4 yds/lb	New York
12. Wool tops (lb)	Spot Market	New York
13. Burlap (yd)	40 in. 10 oz/yd	New York

Metals

14. Copper scrap (lb)	No. 1 heavy copper and wire	New York
15. Tin (lb)	Grade A	New York
16. Lead scrap (lb)	Battery plates, flat price	Chicago
17. Zinc (lb)	Prime Western pig	New York
18. Steel scrap (ton)	No. 1 Heavy Melting	Chicago

Rubber

19. Rubber (lb)	Plantation ribbed smoked sheets	New York

Other

20. Rosin (lb)	W G Grade	New York
21. Tallow (lb)	Packers' prime inedible	Chicago
22. Hides (lb)	Cow, Light Native packers	Chicago

The Consumer Price Index

The full title is "Index of changes in prices of goods and services purchased by city wage-earner and clerical worker families to maintain their level of living." The Index does not indicate changes in quantities bought, how much families spend, or the differences in living costs in different places.

The Index includes the retail prices of food, clothing, furnishings, fuel, rent, and services, using retail prices including sales and excise taxes, and is based on 1957–9 = 100. It covers 64% of all urban dwellers and 40% of the American population, using reports from families of two or more persons (excluding those with incomes of more than $10,000 after taxation).

Each item is weighted and an "all groups" figure is derived after combining the total expenditure weights for all cities, large cities carrying greater weights than those with smaller populations.

The items (at 1958 revision)

Groups	Number of items priced	Value weights 1935–9 based on Family Survey 1934–6	December 1958 value weights adjusted for price changes since 1950 Survey
All items	310	100	100
Food	87	35·4	28·7
Housing	66	33·7	32·7
Apparel	73	11	8·9
Transport	18	8·2	11·7
Medical care	18	4	5·4
Personal care	13	2·4	2·2
Reading and recreation	31	2·9	5·3
Other goods and services	4	2·4	5·1

The Index has extensive use in labour–management contracts to adjust wages. It is estimated that the wages of more than 4 million employees are adjusted according to changes in this Index. Other types of contract incorporate adjustments based on the Index—long-term rentals, royalties, pensions, and even alimony payments. Government and private research agencies also use the Index as an economic indicator of retail price movements and to show trends.

The Index is designed to measure a specific thing, *i.e.* the average change in certain goods and services prices, so care must be taken if the Index is used for other purposes—to study high-income groups, for example.

U.S. Consumer Price Index. All items from 1913 onward

based on the previous (1947–9 = 100) annual average

1913	42·3	1929	73·3	1945	76·9
1914	42·9	1930	71·4	1946	83·4
1915	43·4	1931	65	1947	95·5
1916	46·6	1932	58·4	1948	102·8
1917	54·8	1933	55·3	1949	101·8
1918	64·3	1934	57·2	1950	102·8
1919	74	1935	58·7	1951	110
1920	85·7	1936	59·3	1952	113·5
1921	76·4	1937	61·4	1953	114·4
1922	71·6	1938	60·3	1954	114·8
1923	72·9	1939	59·4	1955	114·5
1924	73·1	1940	59·9	1956	116·2
1925	75	1941	62·9	1957	120·2
1926	75·6	1942	69·7	1958	123·5
1927	74·2	1943	74	1959	124·6
1928	73·3	1944	75·2	19—	

These data might well be plotted on a chart on a log scale to show the varying rates of change in fifty years. Some of the major events that influenced the changes were the first world war, the depression of 1929–35, the second world war, and the Korean war.

A revision began in January 1964 which extends the coverage to include single people and to increase representation in other directions. Weighting will shift—less weight will be given to food, for example. For full details see the Memorandum of 17th June 1963. On the new base, the December 1963 data were All items 107, All food 105, All services 113.

FEDERAL RESERVE SYSTEM: INDEXES OF TOTAL DEPARTMENT STORE SALES AND STOCKS

The two indexes are weighted averages of the twelve individual Federal Reserve district indexes and are published monthly, with seasonal adjustments, and weekly, unadjusted. The base date is 1957–9 = 100.

The Sales Index

The Index was first constructed early in the 1920s, and has been changed over the years to reflect changes in the character of consumer spending and in the number, location, and character of department stores. It now covers almost every important department store in the various areas—nearly 1700 stores for sales, 1300 for stocks. Weighting is done on the basis of total sales (or stocks) in each district compared with the total for the U.S.A. in the base period. Sales are measured on the daily average amount to avoid fluctuations due to varying month lengths. Department stores deal in goods which are highly affected by seasonal demands and the weather—for example, Christmas accounts for 40% of the year's sales of toys and games, and a high proportion of handkerchief sales. The time of the year preceding "back to school" also greatly affects clothing sales. Equally it is obvious that stocks will rise during the few weeks before these times of high sales. Both seasonally adjusted and unadjusted indexes are published.

The Sales Index provides an interesting illustration of seasonal fluctuation:

NEW YORK FEDERAL RESERVE DISTRICT
SALES OF DEPARTMENT STORES IN 1955
(1947–9 = 100)

Jan.	Feb.	Mar.	Apr.	May	June	July	Aug.	Sept.	Oct.	Nov.	Dec.
				Without seasonal adjustment							
87	86	98	105	108	107	82	86	117	122	146	205
				With seasonal adjustment							
112	108	112	109	111	110	113	111	114	115	114	116

The Stocks Index

This is similarly the weighted average of the indexes for the twelve Federal Reserve districts, based on the *retail* value of stocks at the end of each month.

BOARD OF TRADE: INDEX OF WHOLESALE PRICES

The word "wholesale" in the title is rather misleading. The Retail Price Index is accurately named, in that it measures changes in prices charged by shops to customers; but the Wholesale Price Index does not measure changes in prices charged by wholesalers to retailers. It measures changes in costs of inputs to British industry and the prices of their major products, and therefore it would be more accurately termed a manufacturers' cost/price index. The information appears in four tables:

1. Materials purchased by broad sectors of industry.
2. Output of broad sectors of industry.
3. (a) Commodities produced in the United Kingdom.
   (b) Commodities wholly or partly imported into the U.K.

These tables are fully described in the *Board of Trade Journal*, which should be referred to for any changes that take place.

According to H. S. Phillips the Index is useful for two broad purposes:

1. *Official and academic:* as an aid to forecasting future price changes, the Index supplies information about the structure of prices; and it supplies "long" runs of data which will be useful to economists and social scientists.

H. S. Phillips also mentions the usefulness of the Index in the task of deflating value series, but hints at certain difficulties in its application for this purpose.

2. *Commercial:* the Wholesale Price Indexes have the advantage of regular (monthly) publication and standard terminology and compilation; thus they provide a suitable source of market intelligence.

There are various ways of interpreting price changes, and Phillips suggests some:

1. The actual price movements of any product may be compared with price movements on average or changes in prices of similar products.

2. Users of raw materials may compare changes in prices of home-produced materials with similar imported materials. The lifting of tariff barriers in Europe will make this exercise even more vital than formerly.

3. The Index can be used as a standard by which wages may be negotiated. There is no reason why sliding-scale wage agreements should not be linked to wholesale prices, although the Retail Price Index is the one more commonly used. In a similar way, business contracts may be linked to changes in the Index, so that a change in price of a certain percentage would lead to a revision of the terms of the contract.

The indexes

These are published by the Board of Trade and appear mid-monthly in their *Journal* and in the *Monthly Digest of Statistics*. The four tables are based on (annual average 1954 = 100), having been changed from the earlier 30th June 1949 = 100, which was considered too near the end of the war to be normal. It is claimed for the latest version that it has greater scope than versions between 1871 and 1955. Whereas the earlier indexes tried to measure changes in money relative to other things, the current index seeks to measure price changes relative to major economic groups and money flows in the economy.

The first issue on the new base appeared in the *Journal* on 21st March 1958. Like many Government index numbers it is linked with the Standard Industrial Classification, which is useful when comparing individual items with those in other indexes. In spite of this, comparisons should only be made with care because the definitions of such terms as "wholesale" and "retail" are not always the same in each index being compared. For example, retail prices include profit margins and taxes levied on the goods. It has been suggested that three valid useful comparisons would be:

1. The wholesale price of manufactured personal consumer goods (excluding fuel, food, drink, and tobacco) with the same base, for several years.

2. The Wholesale Price Index of clothing and footwear (excluding materials) with retail prices for the same, remembering that the latter include clothing materials, weighted 6 out of 98.

3. The Wholesale Price Index for basic materials with a similar non-Government index, such as the *Financial Times'*, Sauerbeck–*Statist*, Reuter's, or Moodies'.

The Index covers some 7000 materials and products representative of goods bought and sold by industry in the United Kingdom, whose prices are the annual average home market prices based on 1954 equivalents.

The data are obtained largely from voluntary informants such as businesses, trade associations, and industrial undertakings. When there are changes in quality and information is received by the Board of Trade, new items are substituted for old, with suitable adjustments to ensure comparability.

Prices

For finished goods, selling prices are used, but no account is taken of "negotiated" prices or special discounts such as trade-in allowances, since these are probably exceptional.

For Table 1, "Materials purchased by broad sectors of industry," the prices used are "delivered" where possible, that is, the prices charged by the suppliers including delivery expenses to the user's premises.

In Table 3 (*a*), "Commodities produced in the U.K.," the prices are "ex-works" where possible, that is, the prices which would be charged if the buyers collected the goods at the factory. If, however, it is the trade custom to deliver, then "delivered" prices are used.

In each case prices exclude purchase tax, but where a subsidy is paid to, or duty paid by, the producer, this is included.

Weighting

The indexes are formed by using weighted averages of price relatives, the data being combined in proportion to the value of sales or purchases in 1954: for Tables 1 and 2 each commodity price index number of materials purchased by (Table 1), and of the output of (Table 2) broad sectors of industry. Net weights (*i.e.* excluding transfers between two undertakings within the same sector) are used to combine the commodity index numbers into sector indexes.

No comprehensive index number is calculated, *i.e.* there is no "index number of wholesale prices" in one figure, since the components of the tables are disparate. No seasonal adjustments are made to the data.

1. Materials purchased by broad sectors of industry

This series covers the major basic materials used by a variety of industries. The Index shows clearly the effect of world conditions on prices paid by the home manufacturer for new materials, effects which become very evident in times of crisis such as Suez or Korea. Any attempt to compare movements of raw material prices with those of finished products should be done carefully—costs of manufacture in Britain are several times greater than the costs of imported raw materials, so that a wage increase or a higher coal bill can often offset a fall in raw-material prices. On the other hand, the raw-material proportion of the costs of certain industries is great—the cotton textile industry is an obvious example.

A sub-index "Basic materials and fuel" has weights of 88·5 and 11·5 respectively and aims at measuring the price movements of purchases by undertakings in divisions 2–4 in the Standard Industrial Classification (all manufacturing) bought from outside the sector, such as imported coal, minerals, raw foods, timber, textiles, and "imports" from other parts of the U.K. economy such as gas and electricity.

The sub-index "Materials and fuel used in the food manufacturing industries" (Minimum List Heading 211–229) was introduced in 1959 and measures prices of materials bought from outside this sector, weighted in proportion to 1954 purchases. Imported commodities (weight 46·8) include wheat, raw sugar, and cocoa; home produce (29·3) includes wheat, pigs, milk, barley, and beet; home manufactures (23·9) include packing materials and oils.

The sub-index shows sensitivity to world price movements, since half of its components are imports and much of the rest are produced in competition with overseas countries. This input index corresponds with that of Table 2, "Products of Food Manufacturing Industries."

The third sub-group covers most of M.L.H. 331–349 excluding 342, Mechanical Engineering Industries. 55% of the weights relate to iron and steel; other items are wood, rubber, non-ferrous metals, fuel and electricity. The fourth is M.L.H. 361, Electrical Machinery Industries, including wires and cables, electrical sheets, and steel ingots. The fifth sub-group covers Textiles, the major items being raw cotton, raw wool, packing materials, and dyes. The sub-group Construction Materials covers such materials as bricks, steel, sand, and gravel. A separate sub-group relates to house building materials.

MATERIALS PURCHASED BY BROAD SECTORS OF INDUSTRY

For regular data see *B.T.J.* each month
Annual averages (given annually in *B.T.J.*) 1954 = 100

	1955	1956	1957	1958	1959	1960	1961	1962	1963	19—
Basic materials and fuel used in manufacturing	103	107	107	101	102	102	101	101	103	
Materials	103	105	105	97	98	99	96	96	99	
Fuel	106	117	123	129	128	128	133	136	138	
Materials and fuel used in food manufacture	98	100	97	97	99	96	93	95	100	
Materials and fuel used in mech. engineering	110	117	122	124	125	126	128	130	131	
Materials and fuel used in elect. machinery industry	110	114	115	115	116	117	118	120	121	
As above in textiles	96	98	103	89	88	92	93	91	97	
Construction materials	105	109	114	114	113	115	118	120	122	
House building materials	105	109	112	112	111	114	118	120	122	

2. Output of broad sectors of industry

This is basically comparable with Table 1 and can be so used if applied carefully. For most sub-groups two series are shown: Total Sales and Home Market Sales.

OUTPUT OF BROAD SECTORS OF INDUSTRY

Annual averages only (1954 = 100)

	1955	1956	1957	1958	1959	1960	1961	1962	1963	19—
All manufacturing:										
total sales	103	107	110	111	111	113	116	118	120	
home market sales	103	107	110	111	112	113	116	119	120	
Food manufacture:										
home sales	102	106	107	105	107	107	107	111	114	
Chemicals: total sales	100	103	106	105	105	104	103	103	103	
home market sales	100	103	107	106	107	106	105	105	105	
Iron and steel:										
total sales	104	112	124	128	125	126	126	129	129	
home market sales	105	113	125	130	129	129	130	133	134	
Textiles other than clothing:										
total sales	98	98	101	99	97	101	104	104	106	
home sales	98	98	101	98	96	101	103	103	104	
Clothing and footwear:										
home sales	100	102	104	106	105	107	109	110	111	
Paper industries:										
home sales	105	109	110	110	108	108	110	111	112	
Index: new construction	106	110	114	115	113	114	118	122	126	

3. (a) Commodities produced in the United Kingdom

The items selected (some 100 in number) generally relate to the "principal product" or group of products of an industry; the weights used include the value of sales of the principal products of an industry. To give an idea of the scope, the following is a selection: coal, beer, soap, steel tubes, paper bags, Harris tweed, cotton cloth, cutlery, toys and games, cement (delivered).

3. (b) Commodities wholly or partly imported into the United Kingdom

There are nine main groups: Hides and skins, Non-ferrous metals, Oils, Resins, Gums, Pyrites, Rubber, Sulphur, Textiles, Timber and woodpulp. To aid comparison with non-official indexes, this table is given in full below.

For complete analysis, monthly data must be used, as many of the above items show a highly seasonal pattern and twice-yearly data is too arbitrary.

Many of the sub-items in Table 3 (a) are incorporated regularly into the Index of Industrial Production and some of them are published individually in occasional issues of the *Board of Trade Journal*. These include the Index of Leather Footwear, the Index of Production and Sales of Hosiery, and the Index of Sales of Carpets and Rugs. The great majority of such sub-indexes are not included here owing to the demands on space.

COMMODITIES WHOLLY OR PARTLY IMPORTED INTO
THE UNITED KINGDOM

Reclassified in approximate order of the unofficial commodity indexes (1954 = 100)

| | 1960 | | 1961 | | 1962 | | 1963 | | 19— | |
	Jan.	July	Jan.	July	Jan.	July	Jan.	July	Jan.	July
Natural fibres										
Coir yarn, c.i.f. U.K. ports	128	129	138	157	159	157	156	154		
Cotton, raw	74	76	76	73	75	73	72	71		
Jute, raw "Mill Lightnings," c.i.f. Dundee	108	147	207	112	138	112	134	117		
Wool, raw, cross-bred fine c.i.f. U.K.	83	80	74	79	74	79	86	91		
Metals										
Copper *ex*-ship	103	101	89	94	93	94	94	94		
Tin ingot, min. 99·75%, settlement price	110	110	109	120	132	120	118	125		
Zinc *ex*-ship	122	116	101	85	90	85	86	95		
Aluminium, virgin ingot	117	119	119	115	119	115	115	115		
Nickel, refined delivery	123	123	123	132	136	132	132	132		
Oils, etc.										
Linseed oil, crude	136	142	129	133	147	133	110	110		
Palm oil, c.i.f. bulk	102	97	98	92	100	92	93	97		
Whale oil, soft *ex*-works	116	116	116	72	69	72	56	69		
Rubber, etc.										
Rubber, I.R.S.S. Imo. future	169	180	124	111	118	111	117	107		
Pyrites, c.i.f. U.K. ports	68	61	62	59	63	59	59	59		
Sulphur, crude c.i.f.	77	75	72	74	75	74	68	66		
Timber										
Imported hardwood	106	110	113	109	111	110	110	110		
Imported pulp wood	96	98	101	94	100	98	94	96		
Hides and skins										
Imported	127	110	107	101	108	101	95	83		
Native	97	98	87	85	88	85	76	66		

The indexes are published in the *Board of Trade Journal* together with comments describing the significance of changes in various items since the last published date. Each year (usually in February) notes are published together with charts and yearly comparisons.

Several articles have discussed them in economic journals, and although opinions vary as to the efficiency of the Indexes, they are in general highly regarded. Some writers have commented on an interesting phenomenon—applicable not solely to wholesale price indexes. To maintain them in an up-to-date condition changes in weights are made when the compilers think

is prepared by the Ministry with the assistance of other agricultural departments. The series is divided into two parts, indexes of output and input prices.

Output price index

The aim is to measure changes in the prices farm producers receive from the sale of their products; they are not appropriate for assessing the effect on a farmer's revenue of changes in the average values of output.

The indexes cover the whole of the United Kingdom and follow broadly Minimum List Heading 001 of the Standard Industrial Classification, excluding the output of flowers and nursery stock and agricultural services.

There are two calculations. For some products the United Kingdom is treated as a homogeneous market, combining prices from each country by current weights (the quantities sold in each of the countries in the current period), e.g. cereals, fatstock.

For others, separate price relatives are calculated for each county and combined into United Kingdom indexes by using fixed weights as if supplies in each county formed a constant proportion of the whole, e.g. milk.

Annual average prices are normally derived from the current weighted average of twelve months' prices—although for some seasonal products (fruit and vegetables) the prices for the season are used.

The groupings are as follows:

1. *Farm crops*. Weekly growers' prices are obtained from the Corn Returns in Great Britain or Northern Ireland. For potatoes: (i) early: weighted averages for June and July are used; (ii) main crop: weighted averages for January–December for the calendar year data; or seasonally weighted August–July prices for harvest year data. Sugar beet and hops: fixed annual prices.

2. *Fatstock*. United Kingdom weekly average market prices, if sold under the Fatstock Guarantee scheme, are used. For those not under the scheme, prices are obtained from sixty auction markets.

3. *Livestock products, poultry*. Milk, eggs, and wool are at gross prices paid to the producers by the Marketing Boards. Eggs are divided into three grades, large, standard, and medium.

The seasonal index for wool is based on the average price paid to producers of fleece wool by the British marketing board.

4. *Fruit and vegetables*. Prices come mainly from wholesale markets.

INDEX NUMBERS OF AGRICULTURAL PRICES

Agricultural products (based on prices after the addition of subsidies, where payable)

Average of 1954–5 to 1956–7 (July–June years) = 100

| | Weights | 1954–5 | 1955–6 | 1956–7 | Harvest (July–June) year averages | | | | | |
					1957–8	1958–9	1959–60	1960–1	1961–2	1962–3
All products	1000	99·7	102·2	98·1	101·6	101·2	96·4	93·5	97·4	97·2
Farm crops	187	98·6	106·6	94·9	112·6	117	96·9	93·6	105·7	108·8
Fatstock	318	99·7	98·7	101·6	98	100	99·3	98·1	99·1	98·0
Livestock products and poultry	409	100·7	101·8	97·5	96·7	95·4	92·1	90·2	86·1	87·7
Fruit and vegetables	86	97·8	107·4	94·7	113·7	98·1	104·8	91·8	127·3	114
Agricultural materials										
All feedingstuffs	100	98·4	99·8	101·7	89·8	90·3	90·8	87·2	90	90·1
Straight	25	98·8	100·2	100·9	88·7	91·9	89·9	84	91	83·9
Compound	75	98·3	99·6	102	90·2	89·8	91·1	88·2	89·7	92·2
Fertilisers*	91·5	97·8	101·6	100·6	95·8	91·9	89·2	86·7	87·4	85·9
Lime*	8·5	109·1	93·4	97·5	100·3	96·1	93·8	90·8	89·7	89
Fertilisers and lime*	100	98·8	100·9	100·3	96·2	92·3	89·6	87	87·6	86·2
Fuel	—	94·7	96·8	108·5	103·4	104·2	104·9	105	112·9	113·9

* Based on net prices to the farmers after deduction of subsidy.

Input price index

The purpose is to measure average changes in the prices paid by farmers for their materials. The present index includes feedingstuffs, fertilisers, lime, and fuel. Fertiliser and compound feedingstuff prices are taken from manufacturers' lists; the prices of most other feedingstuffs are measured as at the main ports. The statistics are published in the monthly pamphlet issued (on subscription) by the Ministry of Agriculture. There are two series, annual and monthly.

1. *Annual Series*: this consists of three tables:

(*a*) Product-group and all-products indexes (gross prices): farm crops (weight 187), fatstock (318), livestock and poultry (409), fruit and vegetables (86). Total weights = 1000.

(*b*) Products: sugar beet, hops, poultry, wool, fruit, and vegetables.

(*c*) Materials: straight feeding stuffs, *e.g.* whole wheat, whole barley; fertilisers; lime; fuel.

2. *Monthly Series*: this consists of three tables:

(*a*) Products (excluding fruit and vegetables) comprising farm crops, fatstock, livestock, and poultry.

(*b*) Materials, *i.e.* compound feeds, fertilisers.

(*c*) Fruit and vegetables, by types: outdoor fruit, outdoor vegetables, indoor vegetables (*e.g.* tomatoes, cucumbers, and mushrooms).

Other agricultural price indexes

Other index numbers closely related to agriculture are:

1. *Wholesale Price Index for the Food Manufacturing Industries*. This index is a component of the Board of Trade Wholesale Price Index, and is divided into two sections: (*a*) Materials and Fuel; (*b*) Products. For a description see the *Board of Trade Journal* for 16th January 1959 and *Economic Trends* for September 1958 and September 1959.

2. *Annual Index Numbers of Consumer Food Prices*. This index, based on 1958 = 100, includes the main food groups and is published in the C.S.O. Blue Book on *National Income and Expenditure*. It is part of the National Income Statistics; reference should be made to *Economic Trends* for March 1960 and to the book *National Income Statistics: Sources and Methods*.

U.S. DEPARTMENT OF AGRICULTURE: PRICE INDEXES

The Department issues three price indexes:

1. The Index of Prices Paid by Farmers.
2. The Index of Prices Received by Farmers.
3. The Parity Ratio.

The Index of prices paid by farmers for commodities used for production and for living, including interest, taxes, and farm wage-rates

The short title is "The Parity Index." It measures the average changes in the prices of representative foods and services most important in farm living, producing, and financing, and is thus the counterpart of the Prices Received by Farmers index. It is used when calculating parity prices for farm products, since it has been accepted for many years as a major criterion of satisfactory returns to farmers.

It must not be thought that the Index gives a reliable guide to a farmer's costs of production, for the input quantities are not measured, *e.g.* as fertiliser prices increase, the farmer may possibly offset the extra cost by reducing his purchases. Again, changes in technology may alter the patterns of expenditure: a common one is the substitution of machinery for unskilled labour.

The base chosen was the average of the five years 1910–14 = 100. Indexes are prepared for suitably homogeneous periods of time, using the most representative weights available. Thereafter these indexes are chained together, thus keeping the index up to date but allowing reference back for a considerable number of years. Each group is calculated separately and the final index for each one only is linked into the main index. The formula used is discussed in the section on the Prices Received by Farmers index.

In 1959 a revision of weights was instituted, based on the 1956 Farm Expenditure Survey. The group weights assigned about 2500 items to categories: (*a*) family living groups, *e.g.* food and clothing; (*b*) production groups, *e.g.* feed, livestock. There are now 389 items, of which 120 were completely new (such as cake mixes, television, and nylon slips). From time to time substitutes are made, for example instant coffee was included in 1958.

The base date for the latest section is 1955, so the Index is based on this but can be linked back by formulae to earlier periods. Data are collected through mailed questionnaires. These are used in spite of known drawbacks, for economy reasons. Response is voluntary and sometimes very much less than 100%. Another problem is that styles and qualities of goods change.

The Index roughly compares in purpose with the Consumer Price Index, one being mainly aimed at rural, the other at urban householders.

The Index of prices received by farmers

This aims at measuring, from month to month and year to year, changes in the general level of prices of agricultural products. It is the only composite measure of U.S. average prices for farm products at the point of sale by the farmer. The first index was published in 1909, based on 10 commodities; there are now 55.

Various groups of indexes are calculated for farm product prices and they cover 93% of all receipts from the sale of farm products, excluding forestry, nursery, and greenhouse products.

The base for the weights is 1953–7 and the calculation uses a modified fixed-weight aggregate formula. The individual commodity prices used measure the *average* price at the local market for all grades and quantities of that product. Quantities sold affect the index: when steers and heifers predominate at local markets at certain times of the year average prices of beef cattle rise. When cows, for which the price is lower, predominate the average falls. This average price received, multiplied by the quantity (*i.e.* cash receipts), is represented in the index.

The base aggregates were provided for the period 1953–7 by multiplying average marketings by average prices, *i.e.* $p \times q$. Each month the current month's group aggregate is worked out, using 1953–7 marketings and current prices; the result is then divided by the five-year average aggregate to give the monthly index on the 1953–7 base. Here is an example.

Food grains

Commodity	Av. quantity sold 1953–7 (millions)	Av. price 1953–7	Av. aggregate	Av. price Jan. 1964	Aggregate Jan. 1964
Wheat (bushel)	913	$2.00	1826	$1.71	1561·2
Rye (bushel)	17	1.12	19	0.967	16·4
Rice (cwt)	52	4.93	256·4	4.85	252·2
			2101·4		1829·8

The index at January 1964 (1953–7 = 100) is

$$\frac{1829\cdot8}{2101\cdot4} \times 100 = 87\cdot1.$$

The monthly group indexes are then combined into: (a) All crops; (b) All livestock and (c) Livestock products. Index and group weights are computed. The Laspeyres formula is modified to allow for changes in the importance of commodities or to substitute commodities. The problem of changes is solved by chaining. Thus for the periods:

(i) 1910–January 1935, the weights are based on 1924–9.

(ii) For January 1935–September 1952 they are based on 1937–41 weights.

(iii) For September 1952–present they are based on 1953–7 weights. A revision is likely to rebase the Index on 1957–9 = 100.

The complete current link formula is:

$$I_1 = \frac{\Sigma p_{J35} q_{24-9}}{\Sigma p_0 q_{24-9}} \times \frac{\Sigma_{S52} q_{37-41}}{\Sigma p_{J35} q_{37-41}} \times \frac{\Sigma p_1 q_{53-7}}{\Sigma p_{S52} q_{53-7}}$$

where I_1 is the Index for any date 1 after September 1952; J_{35} represents January 1935 and s_{52} September 1952; q's are quantity weights in total; and p_0 represents the average price of the several commodities during 1910–14.

The weights derive from official estimates of production, marketing, and sales of farm products as collected by the Department. 1953–7 was chosen as being reasonably free from major abnormalities. Information is collected regularly from voluntary reporters, e.g. local banks, buyers of farm products, etc.

Data are published at the end of the month in a report, *Agricultural Prices: Monthly U.S. Marketing Services*, and annually in *Agricultural Statistics*.

The Parity Ratio

This third calculation, while not strictly an index number, is derived from the above two indexes. It measures the purchasing power of products *sold* by farmers in terms of things they buy as related to the base period 1910–14.

It is obtained by:

$$\text{P.R.} = \frac{\text{Index of prices received by farmers}}{\text{Parity Index}} \times 100.$$

If the result is greater than 100 it signifies that products sold by farmers have a purchasing power which is, on average, higher than in 1910–14. A series of calculations is available from 1910 to date. The Parity Ratio has assumed importance in view of the Agricultural Adjustment Act of 1933, which declared that it was Congress policy that prices paid to farmers should be quoted with the prices they have to pay.

The indexes are regularly used in calculating parity prices for farm products; the percentage of parity which supports prices will be paid.

INDEXES OF PRICES PAID AND RECEIVED BY U.S. FARMERS

(1910–14 = 100)

	Prices paid	Prices received	Parity Ratio
1910	100	100	100
1920	200	240	120
1930	150	140	93
1933	100	10	10
1940	130	100	77
1950	240	240	100
1959	300	250	83
1963	—	—	78

BOARD OF TRADE: ESTIMATES OF CHANGES IN TOTAL RETAIL STOCKS

These statistics are closely related to retail sales and are useful in comparison with wholesale stocks data, provided they are used with care.

The reporting sample is confined to large-scale retailers, of whom about 30% are covered, accounting for about 15% of total retail stocks. The information available is rather limited, but the compilers believe the Index to be of sufficient accuracy to reflect major trend changes.

Independent retailers who are not represented are given an appropriate weighting on the assumption that their stocks are moving in a similar manner to those of the reporting retailers. A substantial sample of department stores is included, as well as some large independent drapers and furniture retailers. The

Co-operative Union collects information by sample and makes the results available to the Board of Trade.

The Index has the same base date as the Wholesale Stocks Index, 31st December 1956 = 100.

ESTIMATES OF CHANGES IN TOTAL RETAIL STOCKS
At cost at end of month (end of 1956 = 100)

1. *At current prices*

Year	Jan.	Feb.	Mar.	Apr.	May	June	July	Aug.	Sept.	Oct.	Nov.	Dec.
1956	96	100	101	102	102	100	97	95	101	109	114	100
1957	100	105	107	109	110	107	104	103	107	117	123	107
1958	105	109	111	112	112	109	106	106	110	119	123	109
1959	108	111	112	114	115	114	111	109	114	123	129	115
1960	113	119	123	124	126	125	120	118	123	131	136	120
1961	119	124	129	131	132	131	126	124	128	136	142	125
1962	124	128	135	137	139	135	132	130	133	144	151	133
1963	130	134	142	142	143	139	135	133	135	147	157	137
19—												

2. *At constant (December 1956) prices to show volume changes*

Year	Jan.	Feb.	Mar.	Apr.	May	June	July	Aug.	Sept.	Oct.	Nov.	Dec.
1956	99	103	103	104	103	101	98	96	102	110	115	100
1957	100	104	106	108	109	106	103	102	106	115	121	105
1958	104	107	109	110	110	107	104	104	108	117	121	107
1959	106	109	110	113	113	113	110	108	112	121	127	113
1960	111	117	122	122	124	123	117	116	120	128	133	117
1961	116	121	125	127	127	126	121	118	122	129	134	118
1962	117	121	127	129	130	125	122	120	123	133	139	122
1963	121	123	131	131	132	129	124	122	124	135	144	126
19—												

For a description see the *Board of Trade Journal* for 19th December 1958.

DOW JONES INDEX OF COMMODITY FUTURES AND SPOT PRICES

This is compiled by Dow Jones & Co. Inc., New York. The Index consists of two sections, one for "spot" and another for "future" prices, both using the base of 1924–6 = 100.

Each item is weighted proportionately to its commercial production value relative to the total commercial value of all the commodities in the Index during the 1927–31 period. To compile the Index the present price of each commodity is multiplied by a factor which is basically the weight divided by its average price in 1924–6. The compilers claim thereby to save one step in the work of calculation.

The twelve items are all important in the U.S. market, and consist of:

	Weight	Multiplier factor
Food		
1. Wheat	19·5	16
2. Maize	8	11
3. Oats	5	13
4. Rye	4	5
5. Sugar	8·5	27
6. Coffee	7	3
7. Cocoa	5	5
8. Cottonseed oil	4·5	4
	61·5	
Natural fibres		
9. Cotton	23	10
10. Wool tops	5·5	4
	28·5	
Rubber		
11. Rubber	6	3
Other		
12. Hides	4	3
Total	100	

The Index is computed in the following stages:

1. The weights are expressed as percentages (*e.g.* rubber 6%).
2. Each of these weights is divided by the base-year price of the commodity. The result is the "factor."
3. The factors are used as multipliers for current prices to be indexed.
4. Add the results to get the current Index.

Example

There are three components to an index:

Commodity	Weight		Base price		Factor
A	30	÷	5c.	=	6
B	20	÷	7c.	=	2·86
C	50	÷	3c.	=	16·67

Then calculations 3 and 4 are performed:

			Current price		Weighted Index
A	6	×	7c.	=	42
B	2·86	×	9c.	=	25·74
C	16·67	×	5c.	=	83·35
			Total Index	=	151·09

The above is the spot index. For the futures index a further set of steps is needed. For instance, early in the year wheat can be bought for December delivery. When December arrives, that futures price becomes spot and disappears. In addition, the interest-charge content varies as delivery approaches—a five-month futures price is not the same as a four-month delivery price. The problem is overcome by the use of two futures quotations for each commodity which are combined to produce on each market day the calculated price that would apply to a delivery exactly five months off. Since the calculation is highly complicated, special tables have been prepared giving the figures arrived at by multiplying the various quotations of each commodity by its factor or multiplier.

The commodity futures index, which originated in 1933, is published once an hour and at the close of commodity markets each day. The spot index, begun in 1950, is published daily. Publication is in *The Wall Street Journal* and receives much additional publicity both in the American press and abroad.

Yearly averages: some comparisons

	Dow Jones (1924–6)	Moody's (Dec. 1931)	Reuter (Sept. 1931)	Financial Times (July 1952)
1932	—	90	125	—
1936	—	177	150	—
1939	—	150	146	—
1944	—	250	214	—
1950	176	418	513	—
1952	183	440	545	96
1955	167	406	494	91
1959	158	385	417	82

"THE ECONOMIST" COMMODITY PRICE INDICATOR

In 1864 William Newmarch first made an attempt to show the relationship between gold and commodity price, and his

Commodity and quotation		Weight
Food		
1. Beef: Argentine chilled hind, Smithfield		4·6
2. Wheat: No. 2 Manitoba ex Fort William	c.i.f. U.K., prompt shipment	14·9
No. 2 American red winter		
3. Maize: No. 2 yellow American	c.i.f. U.K., prompt shipment	4·4
4. Sugar: U.S.T.A. price	c.i.f. U.K., prompt shipment	7·6
5. Coffee: Santos No. 4 New York spot		10
6. Tea: Average price, London tea sales		3·4
7. Cocoa: Ghana, good fermented	c.i.f. Continental ports nearest futures	2·8
8. Copra: Philippines	c.i.f. Continental ports, prompt shipment	2·3
9. Soya beans: American No. 2 Yellow	c.i.f. London, prompt shipment	3·2
10. Groundnut Oil: British West Africa	c.i.f. U.K., prompt shipment	3·7
	Total	56·9
Natural fibres		
11. Cotton: American type contract	Liverpool nearest futures	7·5
12. Jute: L.J.A. firsts	Prompt shipment	0·7
13. Wool: Average previous week's prices Dominion wools 64's and 56's	Clean c.i.f. U.K.	5·6
		13·8
Metals		
14. Copper: London cash		4·9
15. Tin: London cash		0·9
16. Lead: London prompt		0·9
17. Zinc: London prompt		0·6
		7·3
Rubber		
18. Rubber: London, nearest futures		4·8
Crude oil		
19. Crude oil: Venezuelan Tia Juana medium		9·9
Arabian, ex Ras Tanura		7·3
		17·2

calculations were continued to 1911, when a revision appeared which doubled the scope of the index. The opportunity was taken to add new items, including butter, jute, and petroleum; the base date was changed to 1901–5, and alterations were made in relative weights, *e.g.* coal and iron, previously 1, increased to 5 out of 44. The index was calculated by using a weighted arithmetic mean, but another revision in 1928 altered the calculation to weighted geometric mean and the base to 1st January 1929. This index remained in use throughout the second world war, but in 1952 a fourth index appeared, based on July 1949–50 = 100, published monthly in *The Economist*. The index contained 17 commodities: 6 food, 4 fibres, 4 metals, and 3 other raw materials, corresponding to the then relative values of these items in world trade.

In January 1961 the Indicator was completely revised, although the general purpose continues unchanged: it is intended to reflect the general price trend of commodities entering world trade. The range of commodities is still limited, partly owing to the difficulty of obtaining quotations for certain raw materials (*e.g.* timber products). But the number of commodities is now 19 as against 17 previously. Sisal is excluded, but beef, soya beans, and groundnut oil are added; the 19 articles account for about 80% of world trade in primary commodities and are weighted according to their relative shares of world trade in 1958.

In general, U.K. c.i.f. quotations are used except for coffee and crude oil.

In the calculation the current price of each commodity is expressed as a percentage of its average market price in 1958, a particularly suitable year to choose owing to its stability in prices. The total Indicator is a weighted arithmetic mean of the individual price relatives.

The revised Indicator has been re-calculated on its 1958 base from the beginning of 1958. It is intended to use this for some years—until it is obvious that important changes in the trade pattern have again taken place. At 31st December 1963 the data were: All items 113, Fibres 108, Food 124, Metals 123.

"FINANCIAL TIMES" INDEX OF SENSITIVE WORLD COMMODITY PRICES

This commodity index is based on 1st July 1952 = 100 and is calculated by the use of the geometric average of both spot and future prices. It is representative of both sterling and dollar area commodities and is intended to provide a reliable indicator of world commodity price trends *via* a small but representative list of commodities. These were chosen as much for their sensitivity as for their importance in world trade. By "sensitivity" is meant that the prices can fluctuate according to pressures of world supply and demand, without a great amount of artificial price maintenance.

The price used for each item is usually that prevailing at the recognised centre for world trade in that commodity. The items are classified into five categories; the number in each, relative to the total in the Index, is very roughly in proportion to the relative value of each category to the total of world trade. The five categories are: Foods (4 items), Metals (3 items), Fibres (3 items), Edible oil (1 item), Rubber (1 item). The items, in the order we have used for other commodity indexes, are:

Food

1. Wheat	Chicago	Nearest futures
2. Coffee	Santos	No. 2 spot, New York
3. Cocoa	Bahia	Spot
4. Maize	Chicago	Nearest futures

Edible oil

5. Cotton seed oil	London official	Spot	(5 items)

Natural fibres

6. Cotton	New York	Spot	
7. Wool	Wooltops 64's warp	London	
8. Sisal	British East Africa No. 1	London	(3 items)

Metals

9. Copper	London	Spot	
10. Tin	London	Spot	
11. Lead	London	Spot	(3 items)

Rubber

12. Rubber	London official	Spot	(1 item)

This index has much in common with Reuter's and Moody's, although the number of components is different: Reuter's contains 21 items, Moody's 15, and the *Financial Times*, of course, 12. Eight items are common to all three. The *Financial Times* index is the only one of them to include sisal and cottonseed oil. It is published daily in the *Financial Times* and is reported by other newspapers and weeklies.

THE "FINANCIAL TIMES" INDEX OF SENSITIVE WORLD
COMMODITY PRICES
Mid-month only

	1953	1960	1961	1962	1963	19—
Jan.	92	83	77	78	80	
Feb.	91	83	78	77	81	
Mar.	92	82	79	78	81	
Apr.	89	83	80	79	82	
May	88	82	81	78	83	
June	85	82	80	77	83	
July	85	81	79	76	82	
Aug.	85	79	79	75	81	
Sept.	85	78	76	75	82	
Oct.	84	78	77	77	84	
Nov.	86	77	78	78	84	
Dec.	87	76	78	79	84	

MOODIES' SERVICES LTD: DAILY INDEX OF STAPLE COMMODITY PRICES

This index aims at showing the daily overall trend of commodity prices with the highest possible accuracy. It consists of
fifteen primary commodities quoted on U.S. exchanges, weighted
by their relative standing in U.S. production or consumption
during the five-year period prior to 1932. Based on 31st
December 1931 = 100, it uses the arithmetic mean of price
relatives. Prices are domestic spot quotations obtained from
the relevant exchange.

MOODY'S DAILY INDEX OF STAPLE COMMODITY PRICES
Mid-month values (31st December 1931 = 100)

	1962	1963	19—		1962	1963	19—
Jan.	368	375		July	367	370	
Feb.	368	369		Aug.	370	361	
Mar.	369	368		Sept.	368	358	
Apr.	368	374		Oct.	363	372	
May	367	384		Nov.	364	371	
June	371	375		Dec.	371	371	

The method of calculation and the weights employed have
not altered since 1932. There is close affinity between Moody's
and Reuter's in respect of the purpose of the indexes and the
base date (Reuter's being 18th September 1931), although the

number and type of components are rather at variance. Reuter's is British; Moody's is based on U.S. conditions.

Moody's uses only cash spot values (*i.e.* no futures) because not only are futures not available for all items but they are also too sensitive for the purpose of the Index.

	Commodity and quotation	Weight
Food		
1. Hogs	Top price; Chicago	13
2. Wheat	No. 2 soft red winter; Chicago	13
3. Maize	No. 2 yellow; Chicago	4
4. Sugar	Raw 96 degrees; spot, duty paid New York	10
5. Coffee	Santos No. 4; New York	4
6. Cocoa	Spot, New York	2
		46
Natural fibres		
7. Cotton	Middling 1 in.; spot, New York	13
8. Wool	Tops, New York	7
9. Silk	Grade AA, New York	4
		24
Metals		
10. Copper	Electrolytic; delivered Conn Valley	5
11. Lead	Soft Missouri; St Louis	3
12. Silver	Official; Handy & Hardman, New York	3
13. Steel scrap	Heavy melting; average Chicago and Pittsburgh	10
		21
Rubber		
14. Rubber	Ribbed smoked sheets; New York	4
Other		
15. Hides	Packer Ltd native cows; Chicago	5
	Total	100

REUTER'S DAILY INDEX OF UNITED KINGDOM STAPLE COMMODITY PRICES

The main United Kingdom commodity markets deal in international rather than national commodities. This is an integral feature of the Reuter index, whose 21 primary commodities are weighted in proportion to their relative standing in international trade; the aim is that the Index should portray day-to-day changes in world commodity price levels.

The publisher is Comtelburo Ltd of Fleet Street, and full results are supplied in a monthly digest on a subscription basis.

The Index has the base of 18th September 1931 = 100 and the prices of its 21 commodities are selected as being the most accurate of cash or futures—futures, or forward deliveries, being used where speculative trading is likely in any market. A method of splicing is used to prevent any break in continuity when an expiring or inactive futures quotation is replaced by a later one. To some extent the construction of the Index took into account groupings of commodities. For example there is more interchangeability of use and therefore more uniformity of price movements among the grains and oil seeds than among the textile fibres. This is given some recognition in the selection and weighting of commodities.

The calculation uses the geometric average of the price relatives of commodities whose prices are reasonably sensitive. It includes most of the staples traded on organised exchanges, but excludes fixed-price commodities and those with price structures unsuitable for a daily index. The Index is primarily useful for short-period records, but since careful precautions are taken to preserve continuity, it has proved useful for comparisons over fairly long periods of time.

I have placed the 21 items in groups to correspond as nearly as possible with the order used by *The Economist*. They are as at January 1963.

	Commodity and quotation		Weight
Food			
1. Wheat	No. 2 Manitoba	c.i.f. U.K.	17
2. Maize	No. 3 Yellow American	c.i.f. U.K.	5
3. Sugar	Raw (U.K.–T.S.M.A. price)	c.i.f. U.K.	9
4. Cocoa	Accra	c.i.f. U.K.	2
5. Soya beans	American	c.i.f. U.K./N. Continent	2
6. Copra	Straits/Borneo/F.M. Quality	c.i.f. U.K./ Continent settlement price	2
7. Groundnuts	Nigerian	c.i.f. U.K./N. Continent	3
8. Rice	Siam No. 1 100% whole	Spot	6
9. Linseed	No. 1 Canadian	c.i.f. U.K.	4
10. Pepper	White Sarawak	c.i.f. U.K.	1

51

Natural fibres

11. Cotton	American $\frac{15}{16}$ in. spot, L.C.A.	Official "value" price	14
12. Jute	L.J.A. Firsts, Marks	c.i.f. U.K.	2
13. Wool	Bradford 64's B. top	Spot	8
14. Hemp	Manila J.2 grade	c.i.f. U.K.	1
			25

Metals

15. Copper	Daily settlement price		6
16. Tin	Daily settlement price		5
17. Lead	Daily settlement price		2
18. Zinc	Daily settlement price		1
19. Silver		Spot	4
			18

Rubber

20. Rubber	No. 1 R.S.S.	Spot	5
Other			
21. Shellac	1st Future standard one		1
		Total	100

The subscription service gives regular comparative data or commodity prices, including Reuter's, the *Financial Times*, Dow-Jones, and Moody's.

REUTER'S COMMODITY INDEX

Mid-month figures only (18th September 1931 = 100)

	1933	1939	1945	1951	1957	1960	1961	1962	1963	19—
Jan.	114	138	220	590	500	435	408	410	446	
Feb.	113	136	220	612	490	433	413	409	450	
Mar.	113	136	224	620	483	429	412	413	455	
Apr.	114	137	227	624	482	429	420	414	459	
May	122	141	228	620	473	430	424	410	470	
June	130	140	229	621	464	425	424	408	471	
July	133	138	231	601	457	421	418	410	466	
Aug.	125	135	231	598	444	420	420	409	445	
Sept.	124	150	235	593	440	414	413	408	457	
Oct.	119	161	238	593	430	412	413	414	480	
Nov.	118	163	241	593	424	408	410	420	495	
Dec.	117	170	244	595	426	406	413	430	486	

THE SAUERBECK–"STATIST" INDEX OF WHOLESALE PRICES

The Statist, an old-established weekly journal, publishes each month the Sauerbeck Index, which was mentioned in Chapter 12 of Part I. This index measures the average changes in price of 45 articles, grouped into six categories, using as base the average of prices between 1867 and 1877 = 100. Each index number is a simple percentage of the base date average point, for example:

English wheat

s. d.

Average 1867–77   54 6 the average point
In 1914 the price was 35 0 and the Index 35/54·5 = 64
In 1930 the price was 80 7 and the Index   = 148
In 1936 the price was 53 3 and the Index   = 98

This simplicity is maintained in the final Index, which is constructed by using the unweighted arithmetic mean of all 45 descriptions. The components are:

1. Food, vegetable   8 quotations, *e.g.* wheat, rice, potatoes
2. Food, animal   7 quotations, *e.g.* beef, bacon, butter
3. Beverages and sugar   4 quotations, *e.g.* sugar, coffee, tea
4. Minerals   7 quotations, *e.g.* iron, copper, coal
5. Textiles   8 quotations, *e.g.* cotton, silk, jute, wool
6. Sundry materials   11 quotations, *e.g.* hides, seeds, petroleum, indigo, timber

ANNUAL INDEX NUMBERS FOR GROUPS

(1867–77 = 100)

Year	All groups	Vegetable food	Animal food	Sugar, coffee, tea	Minerals	Textiles	Sundry materials
1902–11	74	66	88	49	90	70	74
1912–21	148	136	167	100	166	151	148
1922–31	120	101	150	80	137	128	110
1932–41	97	84	116	49	131	94	91
1942–51	231	201	169	121	300	306	232
1957	376	295	343	298	570	408	338
1960	359	277	356	230	518	416	325
1961	354	274	322	207	524	433	322
1962	359	311	343	213	541	404	344
19—							
19—							

SAUERBECK—"STATIST" INDEX OF WHOLESALE PRICES

1. *Monthly index numbers for selected groups*

Year	Jan.	Feb.	Mar.	Apr.	May	June	July	Aug.	Sept.	Oct.	Nov.	Dec.
					Vegetable food							
1957	313	306	294	289	278	291	303	288	286	293	302	301
1960	289	287	288	289	289	296	279	259	260	261	268	268
1963	314	315	320	336	322	322	294	289	290	299	315	
					Textiles							
1957	428	420	422	436	429	423	415	403	396	392	386	385
1960	395	398	395	402	425	414	401	401	410	446	445	447
1963	418	422	416	413	412	415	412	402	404	419	405	

2. *Greatest and least increases since 1867–77*

	1954	1955	1956	1957	1958	1959	1960	1961	1962	19—	19—
Greatest:											
Italian rice	900	743	636	638	643	618	563	570	702		
Ceylon coffee	700	504	564	505	450	467	400	367	386		
English potatoes	260	320	388	340	543	491	350	372	453		
Straits tin	670	705	750	719	700	748	759	846	854		
Export coal	694	696	843	930	843	700	587	576	685		
Timber	717	762	777	768	729	688	791	812	742		
Jute	495	445	471	549	490	483	701	859	584		
Iron	500	540	603	671	671	671	692	695	725		
Least:											
Java sugar	92	91	101	144	100	82	88	80	95		
Japan silk	160	149	142	148	131	131	145	163	198		
Petroleum	76	73	74	82	71	71	70	64	63		

QUESTIONS AND EXERCISES

1. It has been urged that the geometric mean is to be preferred to the arithmetic mean for the construction of an index of prices. What special property does the geometric mean possess to account for this preference? Illustrate your answer with an example.

What form of average is used by the Ministry of Labour Index of Retail Prices? Suggest reasons for the choice. (*I.P.M. 1956*)

2. Explain the statistical basis of an index number, and discuss the particular problems which arise when constructing an index of wholesale prices. (*I.P.M. 1960*)

3. An important customer says to you, "The Index Number of Retail Prices is derived from basic prices per lb, cwt, bushel, yard. How can an average derived from such a mixture of unit prices be compared with changes in the retail price of the goods you are selling?"

Draft a note to convince him that differences of unit are normally overcome in computing price index numbers, and why, in a hypothetical or real example, you feel that the Index discloses a general trend of prices against which movements in the retail price of your goods may be compared. (*I.M.S.M. 1955*)

4. Give a brief account of the published statistical information available for the United Kingdom concerning: (*a*) retail prices, and (*b*) wholesale prices. (*I.O.T. 1960*)

5. From the following data compute the "all items" index numbers of retail prices, using as the weights: (*a*) those of the U.K. Index of

Retail Prices, and (b) 1955 expenditure of all consumers. Comment on your results.

United Kingdom Index of Retail Prices (17th January 1956 = 100).

Group	Weights	Group index (October 1956)	Personal expenditure (£ million)
Food	350	101·8	4,136
Drink and tobacco	151	104	1,739
Clothing	106	101	1,268
Housing	87	104·5	1,065
Fuel and light	55	102·4	521
Household goods	66	101·3	903
Other goods and services	185	104	3,151
	1000		12,783

(I.O.T. 1957)

6. What original sources should be consulted to obtain statistics of monthly changes in retail sales in Great Britain? Give a brief account of the details provided. *(R.S.A. 1960)*

7. An index of retail prices includes the item "Rent." During the post-war years large numbers of people have been moved from old houses at controlled rents to new local authority houses at greatly increased rents.

Discuss the problem of whether the increase in rent paid should be taken into account in calculating the index. If it were decided to include the increase, how would you compute the monthly changes in "average rent" for the country as a whole? *(I.P.M. 1957)*

8. Discuss the problems involved in constructing an index of the level of living of a country. To what extent do you think it is reasonable to make international comparisons of levels of living?

(University of London 1956)

9. A large number of family budgets have been collected over a year giving for each family, among other details, total family expenditure, expenditure on butter, and complete information on family composition.

For a series of years figures are available for the whole country of total personal income and expenditure, total purchases of butter and margarine and the average prices paid, and an index of retail prices with details about its construction.

Explain how, with these data, you would attempt to estimate the effect on the consumption of butter of a change in its price, stating what other information, if any, you would think desirable.

(University of London 1960)

10. What are the requirements of a good index number of retail prices, and to what extent does the current official index number meet them?

(B.S.I. 1962)

11. Complete the following table of the Index of Retail Prices. Show the effect of the movement in housing prices on the total Index for each year.

Index of Retail Prices (17th January 1956 = 100)

	Weights	1956	1957	1958	1959
Food	350	102·2	104·9	107·1	108·2
Clothing and footwear	106	100·6	102·2	103	102·6
Housing	87				
Tobacco	80	103·5	106·1	107·8	107·9
Alcoholic drink	71	101·3	104·3	105·8	100
Transport and vehicles	68	102·1	110	112·9	114·7
Durable household goods	66	101	101·1	100·5	98·5
Other items	172	102	108·2	113·7	114·6
	1000	102	105·8	109	109·6

(A.C.C.A. 1961)

12. From the details of the components of some of the major raw material price indexes, compile your own with fifteen items, and from a previous issue of the *Financial Times* obtain prices at your base date. At regular intervals calculate the index, having assigned each item with weights representing that class of materials' proportionate share of world trade. How does your index compare with those published by the *Financial Times*, etc., after several months?

13. Give an account of the information collected and published by the Board of Trade on *either* retail *or* hire purchase sales.

(I.O.S. 1962)

14. Give a brief account of the methods of construction and the data employed in *either* the official Index of Industrial Production *or* the official series of index numbers of Wholesale Prices. *(I.P.M. 1962)*

15. Give a brief account of the following aspects of the official Index of Retail Prices:

(*a*) that which it is intended to measure;

(*b*) the section of the population to which it is intended to apply;

(*c*) the form of average which is employed, and the source of the weights;

(*d*) the method of obtaining price quotations in any *one* section of the Index.

(I.P.M. 1962)

16. The weights of the official Index of Retail Prices are obtained from a household expenditure enquiry made by the Ministry of Labour. Explain in some detail how the enquiry was undertaken and what uses the resulting information has. *(I.M.S.M. 1961)*

17. A Swedish bank review recently stated that "One might expect that households with rising income levels were less interested in buying on credit." Describe the statistics available in the United Kingdom on which to argue such a hypothesis.

18. The following three columns have been abstracted from the
Monthly Digest of Statistics:

Food manufacturing industries; price indexes of:

1960	Materials and fuel used (1954 = 100)	Output (1954 = 100)	Food: Index of Retail Prices (17th Jan. 1956 = 100)
January	99·4	107·5	107·8
February	98·2	107	107·4
March	96·4	106·2	106·8
April	96	106·1	106·6
May	96·3	106·4	107·3
June	95·8	106·6	108·9
July	95·7	107·2	108·8
August	95·6	107·4	106·4
September	95·2	107	106·1
October	94·6	106·8	107·6
November	94·9	107·2	107·6
December	95·7	107·5	108·1

Reduce these figures to a comparable basis, and graph them. Write a
brief note commenting on the graph.   (*I.C.W.A. 1961*)

19. Consumers' expenditure on various categories of domestic goods
is given at both current and constant prices in the table. Obtain price
indexes for each category separately, and an overall price index for
these categories. Draw the five series on one graph.

Consumers' expenditure on domestic goods
U.K. 1949–59 (£ million)

Year	Housing		Fuel and light		Household durables		Domestic service	
	Current	1954	Current	1954	Current	1954	Current	1954
1949	756	935	332	432	360	430	103	127
1950	793	954	353	451	424	487	98	119
1951	845	956	388	467	480	485	95	110
1952	904	977	421	462	452	439	95	103
1953	982	1009	447	466	528	517	94	96
1954	1053	1053	486	486	603	603	95	95
1955	1065	1029	522	497	625	617	96	92
1956	1123	1043	590	516	618	572	95	86
1957	1211	1054	610	507	686	629	97	82
1958	1373	1070	676	547	732	679	92	75
1959	1462	1080	675	542	826	780	92	73

(*University of Exeter 1961*)

20. It is maintained that the practical alternative to a base-weighted
(Laspeyres) index is not a currently weighted (Paasche) index but a
chain-based (Laspeyres) index. Comment, with reference to price index
numbers.   (*University of London 1962*)

CHAPTER 14

INVESTMENT PRICE INDEXES

SHARES AND THEIR OWNERSHIP

According to the Radcliffe Report, the value of securities quoted on the London Stock Exchange on 31st March 1959 was as shown in the following table, with 1939 figures for comparison.

Market values (£ million) on	31st March 1959	24th March 1939
British Government and Government guaranteed stocks	14,778	6,598
Other securities at market values		
Corporation stocks, public boards, etc.	661	901
Dominion and foreign government	993	1,427
Company securities: loan capital	1,133	—
Ordinary and preferred capital	18,618	—
Shares of no par value	1,568	555
Preference and preferred capital	1,269	—
Company securities other than no par value	—	9,038
Total	39,020	18,519

Of this £39,000 million, the greater part consisted of gilt-edged securities (those with government backing) and equities ("ordinary" shares whose dividend rate is not fixed but whose holders usually have major rights in meetings, voting, etc.).

Investors select freely between the different classes of security with certain interests in mind: the safety of their capital, the yield on their investment, the availability of the security they want, the probability of dividends being paid, growth prospects, and ease of liquidation if necessary. Some of these can easily be calculated—the yield, for example, is dependent on the price and the current dividend rate. Suppose the investor buys a Rix Manufacturing Company £1 ordinary share, paying 50s. for it, and the latest dividend was 25%. The return he will get (assuming the same dividend in future) will be $20/50 \times 25\%$, in other words the flat yield is 10%. The nominal value of a security (Rix = 20s.) is less important than the market value, just as the fact that a house built in 1939 cost £600 new is of little interest to the present-day purchaser who pays £3000 for it.

Securities are purchased by two types of investor: the private individual, who buys shares for growth or dividend on a small scale; and the institution, which regards investment as a serious part of its operations. Institutions include insurance companies, pension funds, and banks (on this, see the Radcliffe Report). For example, at the end of 1957, of £4000 million of life funds, 68% was invested in securities (29% gilt edged, 17% equities, 15% debentures, and 7% in preference shares); the London clearing banks on 31st December 1958 had 29% of their total deposits invested, mainly in gilt-edged securities. Both these classes of investor have facilities for studying the techniques of investment; the smaller investor (which may be a company, a private individual, or a society) cannot personally employ advisers and often relies on his broker, his bank manager, or some other reliable expert or may follow his own fortunes in the City columns of newspapers and weekly financial journals.

SHARE PRICE INDEXES

Investment information published in daily or weekly journals frequently includes index numbers. Mason and Sachs provide a valuable and comprehensive list of suggestions as to the statistics which should be used in conjunction with investment indexes, including:

1. Rates of interest, long and short term; at home and abroad.

2. Measurement of changes in the flow of money, including notes in issue, advances by commercial banks, provincial clearings, national savings, revenue returns, etc.

3. General economic data on the home and foreign trade situation, including the output of goods and services, wages and employment, the balance of payments, and trends in the foreign exchanges.

4. Information about the expectations of business people on future production and information on recent progress. This will come from reports of new capital issues, the distribution of dividends, bonus issues, and, more sombrely, liquidations and bankruptcies.

To indicate business conditions

Many index numbers have been introduced to serve a specific purpose, but in fact most are of interest to a wide audience.

They are of value as indicators of business conditions, since stock markets are especially sensitive to business conditions, notably in so far as they are likely to affect short-term profitability. These anticipations may be based on commercial evidence or on political or social changes happening or anticipated. Share prices can fluctuate rapidly according to investors' opinions of the future (rational or not), and since these changes will be reflected in most indexes, the user must be prepared to discount some of them.

To measure performance

Index numbers may be used to measure the performance of a portfolio. Published share indicators may serve as a guide to the value of a similar class of shares held by the investor. Although the Actuaries' investment index is no longer published in its original form, an essay by Haycocks and Plymen based on it is still of interest. Investment advisers often devise their own measures of changes, based on published index numbers. One was given by the formula:

$$P_0 = K \times P_c \times D \times R \quad \text{or} \quad R = \frac{P_0}{K \times P_c \times D}$$

where $P_0 =$ the index of ordinary share prices; $P_c =$ the index of $2\frac{1}{2}\%$ Consols; $D =$ the index of dividends being paid; K is a constant (taken here as $=1$); and R is a residual factor which reflects the "confidence" of the ordinary investor in equity prospects relative to the gilt-edged securities. For example, in May 1955 the all-industries share index calculated by the Actuaries was 156·9. The average yield was 5·29%, the dividend index being

$$\frac{156\cdot9 \times 5\cdot29}{100} = 8\cdot3.$$

The Consols index ("Consols" being a term for Government consolidated stock with no date for redemption and $2\frac{1}{2}\%$ coupon) was 84·9.

$$\text{Therefore } R = \frac{156\cdot9}{1 \times 84\cdot9 \times 8\cdot3} = 0\cdot2226.$$

R is explained as being the "index of expectations of preferences *for* or *against* ordinary shares." In general, in times of inflation and full capacity, Consols and other "gilts" are much less in demand than equities. Haycocks and Plymen give a table for the end of 1945 to June 1955, and the figure R ranged from 0·1670 in June 1949, when the prospect of dividend limitation reduced confidence, to a high of 0·2340 in June 1955.

The Companies Act of 1948 enforced greater disclosure of the activities of a company, but even today we cannot claim that stock exchange behaviour is based to a great extent on concrete factual knowledge. The investor with a mixed portfolio must therefore study the swings of the market, and the regular publication of a variety of index numbers is a valuable service to him. The valuation of the portfolio of an institution such as an insurance company is a regular task, and frequently its performance is measured against that of the index.

To be fair, there is no mathematical exactitude in share valuations. A. G. Ellinger studied share values between 1946 and 1950 and hazarded the opinion that the trend of share values no longer follows that of business activity. He quotes an example in the 1949 U.S. recession, in which the Standard & Poor index of ordinary share values *led* the Index of Production. Again, he mentions the growing control of governments over gilt-edged security prices, interfering with the free working of the market.

In an article in 1962 R. Tyssen-Gee studied the values of index portfolios, and commented on each:

1. The *Financial Times* Industrial Ordinary Share Index (begun in July 1935) registered 300 in early 1962, representing a growth of 4·15% per annum compounded annually (showing the *Financial Times* equities to be a better long-term bargain than savings certificates).

2. The *Investors' Chronicle* all-industries index has been calculated since 1923. After 38 years a £100 investment would now be worth £519, which gives a growth similar to the above (4·30%).

3. The Dow Jones (U.S.A.) data show that £100 invested in 1900 would now be worth £1400, a gain of 4·4%, but the advance to the 1928 peak of £550 was halted in the depression, falling to £120. From 1932 the growth has been 4·7%.

4. The Standard & Poor index has improved from 100 to 700 in 36 years, an annual gain exceeding 5·5%.

Trade or political crises affect equity indexes, but the general investment trend for many years has been in favour of well-chosen ordinary shares.

For academic purposes

Index numbers are of use to the economic historian, since several of them date back for a sufficient period of time; in some cases into the early nineteenth century, enabling comparison to be made with the original Consols.

DIFFICULTIES OF CALCULATING SHARE INDEXES

The number of items in any index will depend on the purpose of that index. A sensitive one, such as the *Financial Times* thirty-share index, will not be suited to long-term trend analysis, but may be a valuable day-to-day indicator. In an article by Peter Wilsher in the *Sunday Times* comparisons were made between the *Financial Times*, the *Times*, and the *Daily Mail* index numbers to discover the causes of discrepancies between the results of these share indexes. Wilsher mentions the *Financial Times* index as being frequently quoted—it commands respect, affection, or provokes amusement, but it is seldom ignored, as it has a high record for accuracy. The City believes in it and this, the article points out, has peculiar effects, since brokers (Stock Exchange members who act for the public by buying or selling shares on their behalf) can "talk the Index up," whereas jobbers (members who buy or sell on their own account) can "talk it down again": by following the trend of the Index they can cause it to behave in a certain way.

The *Times* and *Daily Mail* indexes are new and use modern computation methods (as does the *Financial Times*–Actuaries' Index). They cover a far wider selection of stocks and use a different average from the *Financial Times* index.

Sampling

C. Drakatos points out that sampling is the primary constructional problem, since the population is so mixed. The sample taken by the different compilers and the formulae used will explain to a great extent the differences Mr Drakatos discovers when analysing indexes over several years. A stratified sample should be taken, with random sampling of shares within each strata. Again, the greater the number of shares the more representative the sample, provided that not just "high class" or very large companies' shares are chosen. Certain indexes comprise only "market leaders" and are thus of less general use —*The Economist*–Extel Indicator and the *Financial Times* ordinary share index are notable in this respect.

P. Sargent Florence has also taken the *Financial Times* index to task in an interesting essay. Company dividend policies, and therefore market prices, vary so greatly that, for the sample to be in any way representative, a considerable number of shares must be included. Florence considers that the large companies in the *Financial Times* index have not been truly representative even of their kind of company. However, the Index marches on.

Weighting

The compilers of some indexes consider that the components should be left undisturbed for as long as can be, in order not to affect the continuity of the index. This cannot be applied to stock indexes, which must maintain the virtues of comparability yet face the fact that companies of minor size at one date may be of considerable capitalisation ten or twenty years later. Companies may disappear through liquidations, take overs, etc., and must be replaced in the index. One solution to the problem of growing businesses is to weight by "market capitalisation," that is, each company is weighted according to the shares issued at current date. Hyett gives two examples (1st January 1959). First, I.C.I. ordinaries, of which there were 237,000,000 £1 shares at a current price of 37*s*. 9*d*. Therefore the weight was £447 million. Second, Dunhill ordinaries, of which there were 200,000 £1 shares currently priced at 80*s*. so their weight was £0·8 million, giving relative current weights of 447 and 0·8 respectively. If the sample is of sufficient size and is reasonably representative many experts suggest that an elaborate weighting system is not required; weighting will adjust itself automatically as capitalisation changes. Two problems do arise. First, although companies increase their capitalisation as they grow, reduction of capital is less often resorted to, and thus some overweighting might be discovered. Second, some companies have a high capitalisation (weight), but the volume of transactions on the market may be low.

Redeemable shares

H. B. Rose discusses another problem of construction, which is that many indexes mix equities (which are not redeemable in normal circumstances) and dated securities (such as redeemable preference shares). The value of a dated fixed-interest security is determined not only by the demand for that class of security but also by the nearness of the redemption date, when the investor will be repaid, generally at "par" (the nominal value of the security). Thus, if a twenty-year security is included in an index, having ten more years to run, bearing interest of 5% (ignoring taxation) and selling at £95 today, the "flat yield" would be: Interest rate/Market price $\times$ 100 = 5·21%. But in fact the share would appreciate by £5 (from £95 to £100) over the ten years, and (calculated actuarily at compound interest) the "yield to redemption" would be 5·56%. All dated securities include this valuation in their yield, and this affects the index, since the index number is almost bound to rise unless economic events move very strongly downwards. Of course if the price is above par the redemption yield will be below the coupon percentage (*i.e.* the actual percentage on which interest is calculated by the issuer).

Which average?

Much debate has taken place concerning an appropriate average—in practice either the arithmetic or the geometric mean is used, the A.M. often when the portfolio aspect is important, the G.M. when frequent replacement of securities without disturbance is required. G. P. Hyett has other views: it is frequently claimed that the use of the G.M. serves to minimise the effect of extreme high values on the average, but what of the distortion of low values? Hyett makes a further strong point. If the purpose of the index is to show how market influences have affected shares, surely an average which allows such changes cannot be faulty; in other words, why go to great lengths to construct an index of share prices and then prevent it rising or falling!

Another argument concerns the relationship of the various means to each other as seen in the plotted distribution of a time series. The object of an average is to typify a situation. Some commentators say that the G.M., when plotted on a graph, is often much nearer the median and the mode than is the A.M., and should therefore be chosen in preference to the A.M. Hyett retorts that the G.M. will not be nearer to the median or mode in a symmetrical distribution, for the logical reason that the A.M., median, and mode coincide. If the distribution is positively skewed the G.M. *may* be nearer, but with a negatively skewed distribution it cannot be nearer the median and mode. In any case, he continues, if the median and the mode are so significant, why not use them and save calculations! The average selected will therefore depend on the personal preferences of the compiler as much as anything.

SOURCES OF DATA IN GREAT BRITAIN

Official publications

The British stock exchanges (London and 22 associated stock exchanges in Glasgow, Manchester, Leeds, etc.) publish official lists of share prices, but do not compile share indexes.

Newspapers

The *Financial Times* gives regular reports of major indexes. *The Times'* City pages include its own and the Eurosyndicat share indexes. *The Guardian, The Wall Street Journal,* and *The New York Times* also have considerable coverage and, of the more popular press, the *Daily Mail* and *Daily Express* are usefully informative.

The most important Sunday newspapers for City news are the *Sunday Telegraph, Sunday Times* and *The Observer.* They provide investment articles and list share prices.

Journals

Several weekly journals devote space to investment topics, including the *Investors' Chronicle,* which covers every aspect of share investment in a highly readable manner, providing such statistics as those of Standard & Poor, the *Financial Times,* Eurosyndicat, Dow Jones and, naturally, their own compilations. *The Economist* gives important cover to stock exchange matters and publishes several indexes, including its own preparations. *The Statist* gives useful articles and commentaries and includes such index numbers as the *Financial Times,* the *Times, Daily Mail,* Dow Jones, and Standard & Poor's.

There are several learned journals which cover investment in occasional issues, but two are of special interest, *The Investment Analyst* and the *Journal of the Royal Statistical Society.*

Investment services

By subscription, certain institutions provide interested persons with data. Well-known examples are *The Economist* Intelligence Unit, Moodies' statistical services, and the Exchange Telegraph daily service.

Other sources

Stockbrokers, banks, and the press advisory services will all supply investment advice, usually privately. For the qualified reader, perusal of annual reports gives much useful information. Under the Companies Act of 1948 each shareholder on the register of a (public) company must receive a copy of the annual report and accounts; by courtesy of the company, non-members may often be supplied as well, but this is not a right. Not all shareholders appreciate the work which goes into these often bulky publications (see correspondence in *The Times* in March 1962); considerable information can be derived from them. Unfortunately the end of the financial year to which they refer may be some months distant at the time of printing and publication.

CHARTING SHARE PRICE MOVEMENTS

This book cannot delve into analysis of the reasons for changes in indexes—a lengthy and specialised task—but the following summary of interesting features of charts may be of general interest (for a fuller explanation the excellent book *Beginners Please*, by the *Investors' Chronicle*, should be read). Consider Fig. 10. Three movements will be present:

1. A *primary trend*, which may last several years (1955–8 in this imaginary example), during which time the market strengthened although there were many interruptions.

2. The *secondary trend*, weekly or monthly movements which disturb the primary trend somewhat, often because of external causes, such as political or general economic developments.

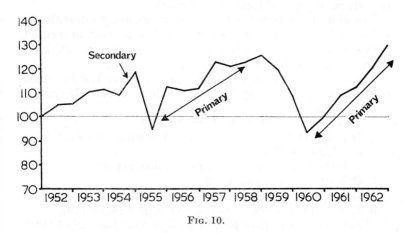

FIG. 10.

3. *Tertiary movements*. Each day the index will move slightly up or down. By themselves such movements are unimportant, but may build up into a considerable movement, leading to a secondary trend. These small movements may not show on published charts, but the investor can plot them for himself from daily share-price reports. In any case, indexes consist of 30–600 shares, and the individual investor has perhaps two or three of these. He will use the published charts as a guide to future movements, and it is suggested that charts of industrial

H

production should be used in conjunction with the share charts. One must beware of projecting trends too far into the future, because equity prices are so vulnerable to external influences. In any case the amateur may project happily with a logarithmic scale and arithmetic data, with disastrous results if he believes his own calculations.

"BANKERS' MAGAZINE" STOCK EXCHANGE SECURITY INDEX

Published monthly by the *Bankers' Magazine*, this index is made up of a fixed portfolio of securities, with the fixed base of 14th December 1956 = 100, the date it is assumed that the securities were bought. The imaginary purchase took place at the then current market prices, £5 million being divided equally between fixed-interest and variable stocks.

The investment is static in the sense that no new capital is invested or withdrawn, but allowance is made for advantageous events, such as bonus issues and conversion offers (*i.e.* offers of new stock in place of time-expired stock).

The aim of the Index is to display at monthly intervals the value of the investment after revaluation at current market prices and to show relative changes in values which have occurred, using the arithmetic mean.

The major categories of security traded on the London stock market are represented by 230 stocks, subdivided into 18 groups.

FIXED RETURN STOCKS

1. British Funds, undated or long, each with a nominal value issued of £2000 million or more (4).
2. British Funds, dated, of similar valuation (6).
3. Other public authorities (5).
4. Industrial debentures, the largest and longest (10).
5. Industrial preference shares, the largest issues (10).
  Value invested in fixed interest stock at base date: £2,500,000.

6. British banks and discount houses (10).
7. Insurance, the largest by market valuation (10).
8. Investment trusts, the largest by value of portfolio (5).
  Value invested in financial stocks: £450,000.

VARIABLE RETURN STOCKS

9. Market leaders with net assets over £50 million or incomes over £10 million in 1954 (25).
10. Large, with net assets of £25–50 million (25).

11. Large–medium, with net assets of £10–25 million or incomes over £5 million (25).

12. Small–medium, with net assets of £5–10 million (25).

13. Smaller, with net assets of £2·6–5 million (25).

Value invested in industrial stocks: £1,250,000.

14. Oil companies (5).

15. Rubber, Malaya, Indonesia, and Ceylon (10).

16. Tea, India and Ceylon (10).

17. Gold and diamonds (10).

18. Base metals and land (10).

Value invested in commodities: £800,000.

TOTAL VALUE OF ALL STOCKS: £5 MILLION

The classification of industrial companies (9–13) is mainly that used in the National Institute of Economic & Social Research publication *A Classified List of Large Companies Engaged in British Industry.*

It will be noticed that many dated fixed-interest stocks are included. There are objections to the use of dated stocks, mainly because of the rise in prices as redemption date draws near, but these objections are outweighed by the fact that most recent issues *have* been of dated securities, and to exclude them would be to bias the sample. The prices are taken from the pages of the *Financial Times* at mid-month dates and ignore accrued interest, dividend, or buying expenses.

"BANKERS' MAGAZINE" INDEX OF STOCK EXCHANGE SECURITIES

New series, 14th December 1956 = 100

Year	Fixed interest		Industrials only		All variable dividend		All securities	
	High	Low	High	Low	High	Low	High	Low
1958	101·9 (Oct.)	94·6 (Jan.)	133·8 (Dec.)	95·3 (Feb.)	123·5 (Dec.)	91·4 (Feb.)	111·8 (Dec.)	93·9 (Feb.)
1959	104·6 (Nov.)	101 (Sept.)	210·1 (Dec.)	141·2 (Jan.)	181·9 (Nov.)	129·2 (Jan.)	143·2 (Nov.)	116·1 (Jan.)
1960	101·6 (Feb.)	93·7 (Dec.)	229·1 (Sept.)	205·8 (May)	191·7 (Jan.)	172·2 (May)	146·3 (Jan.)	134·8 (July)
1961	93·5 (May)	87·2 (Aug.)	265·3 (May)	222·3 (Sept./ Jan.)	219 (May)	182·6 (Oct.)	156·3 (May)	135·7 (Oct.)
1962	104·1 (Oct.)	89·9 (Jan.)	238 (May)	207·2 (July)	205 (May)	181·2 (July)	150 (Dec.)	137·4 (June)
1963	105·7 (Oct.)	99·2 (Mar.)	266·3 (Dec.)	224·9 (Jan.)	223·8 (Dec.)	197·3 (Jan.)	162·3 (Dec.)	149·7 (Jan.)

Each month both value and index figures are given in the *Bankers' Magazine*, together with details of the original investment at the base date. Values are shown by class of security (not individually) and four index numbers are supplied: fixed interest, industrials only, all variable dividend shares, and securities (all classes). Comparative data are given monthly for each of the preceding twelve months and high/low figures of each group for three years (as shown above).

It should be appreciated that the idea of classifying equities by size was novel, and has since been adopted by other compilers (see, for example, the *Times* indexes).

"DAILY MAIL" SHARE PRICE INDEX

Published in the *Daily Mail* and weekly in *The Statist*, the purpose of this recently introduced (1960) share-price index is to provide an overall guide to movements in the prices of industrial shares. No claims are made for it as a forecaster, but it is useful as a record of historical facts. The Index is specially constructed so that the price changes recorded are those due to changes in the market conditions, without disturbing influences from capital structure changes such as rights issues or scrip issues (for which adjustments are made in the base prices to avoid distortion).

The Index is based on 1st January 1959 = 100 and comprises 640 shares (in March 1963), quoted daily in the City columns of the *Daily Mail*, classified into the categories: breweries, catering and food, chemicals, electrical and radio, engineering, entertainment, financial, industrials, motors and aircraft, newspapers, paint and building, paper and printing, shipping, steels, stores and furniture, textiles, tobacco.

The Index is calculated by using a currently weighted arithmetic mean of price relatives, the weights being formed by multiplying the number of shares of each company *currently* issued by the price at which they *were* quoted at the base date:

$$I = \frac{\Sigma n_1 p_0 \left(\dfrac{p_1}{p_0}\right)}{\Sigma n_1 p_0} \quad \text{or} \quad \frac{\Sigma n_1 p_1}{\Sigma n_1 p_0}$$

where n_1 = the number of shares currently issued; p_1 = the current quoted price; and p_0 = base price. The arithmetic mean was chosen because it leads to a simply understood formula which is simply the ratio of the present value of the shares to their value at the base date.

THE "DAILY MAIL" INDEX OF SHARE PRICES

1st January 1959 = 100 (showing mid months only)

	1959	1960	1961	1962	1963	19—
January	100	150	152	154	153	
February	103	147	158	154	156	
March	103	143	166	155	160	
April	111	144	172	157	161	
May	115	143	180	159	162	
June	109	150	167	140	159	
July	110	148	152	142	163	
August	115	155	153	149	165	
September	119	156	151	144	168	
October	137	157	145	147	169	
November	144	156	157	152	171	
December	146	148	153	153	175	
High	153 (31st Dec.)	161 (5th Sept.)	180 (12th May)	161 (27th Apr.)	151 (28th Jan.)	
Low	98 (8th Jan.)	137 (9th May)	145 (16th Oct.)	133 (25th June)	176 (31st Dec.)	

THE "DAILY MAIL" INDEX OF SHARE PRICES

How individual indicators have moved

	Banks	Brew-eries	Cater-ing	Chemi-cals	Elec-tric	Engin-eering	Enter-tain-ment	Misc. in-dustries	Insur-ance	Motors
1962:										
High	211	208	171	135	156	117	211	186	255	176
Low	168	161	139	108	116	94	161	144	189	151
Mid-Nov. 1963	187	185	167	156	168	120	254	187	177	204

	News-papers	Oils	Paints	Papers	Ship-ping	Steels	Stores	Textiles	To-bacco	Trusts
1962:										
High	196	114	184	130	79	155	185	213	114	215
Low	163	81	151	111	55	108	153	169	93	160
Mid-Nov. 1963	211	128	218	138	96	126	203	276	120	187

Capital adjustments are made in response to the following circumstances:

1. Where a rights issue takes place (*i.e.* where each share-holder has the right to subscribe to further shares at a given price, in the proportion of m shares for every n held—sometimes a valuable privilege if the shares are keenly sought after) and an adjustment will be needed:

$$p_0' = \frac{np + mr}{(n + m)p} \times p_0$$

where p_0 = the previous base price; p_0' = the adjusted base price; p = the market price of the shares involved at close of dealings the last day before the day they are quoted "ex rights" and r = price at which rights offer is made, and the offer is m for n held. For example, an original issue of £1 ordinary shares was quoted at 40s. at the base date in 1959. In 1963, when the current price was 60s., a rights offer was made of one share at 40s. for every two held. Therefore

$$p_0' = \frac{3 \times 60s. + 1 \times 40s.}{(3 + 1) \times 60s.} \times 40s.$$

$$= 36s.\ 9d.,\ \text{which is the "new" base price.}$$

2. When the ordinary share capital structure of a company is changed, the general base price adjustment formula is used:

$$p_0' = \frac{mt}{vt} \times \frac{vt - 1}{mt - 1} \times p_0$$

where mt — total market valuation of the ordinary capital immediately following the change; $mt - 1$ = the total market valuation immediately prior to the change; vt = the nominal value of ordinary share capital; and $vt - 1$ = nominal value of ordinary share capital immediately before the scrip.

Where particular categories of ordinary shares carry certain rights (e.g. voting rights) an allowance is made for the value which the market puts on these rights before employing the formulae.

DOW JONES SECURITY AVERAGES

Although these averages are *not* index numbers, they attempt to measure in a general way fluctuations in the security markets and provide a useful continuous basis for historical study. The publishers are Dow Jones & Co. Inc. of New York, who issue *The Wall Street Journal*, although the first averages pre-dated the *Journal* by several years. In 1884 the averages consisted of eleven stocks, nine of which were railways. In 1896 an Industrial Index (separate from the Rail index) appeared in *The Wall Street Journal* and since 1915 has been quoted in dollars per share. For a complete history see the volume by Dice and Eiteman.

The averages attempt to indicate the overall situation in the stock market in terms of the original (dollar) units, and are divided into industrial stocks, railway stocks, utilities, bonds, and a composite average.

1. *The industrial average*, dating back to 1897, was enlarged in 1928 to the present total of thirty stocks, calculated daily.

2. *The railroad average* comprises twenty stocks regarded as representative of all railroads.

3. *The public utility average* since 1929 has contained fifteen stocks.

4. *The 65-stock average* is a simple arithmetic average of industries, rails, and utilities.

5. *The bond average:* bonds are classified into four groups and an average is compiled by calculating the simple arithmetic mean of the closing prices of each group and taking an average of these four prices.

6. *The railroad income bond:* this average commenced in 1947, covering the income bonds of ten important railroad systems (an income bond is equivalent to industrial preference shares in that interest is paid if profits are made).

7. *The municipal bond yield average:* this comprises the yields of state and local municipal bonds, allowance being made for yield to redemption.

Each day the prices of stocks in each group are added and averaged by a "divisor." To illustrate the origin of the divisor, take the example of a group having three stocks. The prices are $5, $10, and $15, therefore the average would be $10.

From time to time stock splits (*e.g.* bonus issues) may be announced, and this would cause a change in the divisor. Suppose the $15 stock is to be split by an issue of two new shares for each existing one (*i.e.* there will be three times as many stocks as before, and they should sell at $5, or one-third of $15). The market, however, takes a favourable view of general business prospects and prices rise, so that the $5 shares close at $6, $10 shares at $11, and the split stock at $6, a total of $23, giving an average of $7·67, that is, less than before. Since all shares have risen, this cannot be accurate, so an adjustment is made using a divisor calculated from the day of the split. This is found by adding the actual current values (five, ten, and five equal twenty dollars) before the price rise and dividing by the previous average, $10, to obtain a divisor of 2, which is used each day until a new split occurs or a substitution of stock takes place.

At the end of the day, if we assume closing prices of $6, $11, $6 the average will be $23/2 = $11·5. In fact, the divisor is variable (in 1960 it was 16·67 in the case of the industrial average).

The averages are reported daily in *The Wall Street Journal* and in many other American dailies and weeklies. They are reproduced briefly in the *Financial Times* and *The Economist* and often quoted in financial articles.

It must be remembered that averages cannot show *relative* changes in the way that an index does; nor are the averages weighted. Calculations are made several times during the business day, at the opening and closing of business and at four intermediate times. Such a formidable quantity of information requires streamlined presentation and Barron's supply a monthly summary and report of all Dow Jones averages, enabling comparisons to be made within the scope of one volume.

Selection of stocks and bonds used in computing the various Dow Jones averages:

30 industrial stocks, e.g. Allied Chemical, Chrysler, General Electric, Procter & Gamble, Swift, Woolworth.

20 railroad stocks, e.g. Erie, Great Northern, Pennsylvania, Union Pacific.

15 utility stocks, e.g. Columbia Gas, Detroit Edison, Peoples Gas.

10 higher-grade rail bonds, e.g. Atchison Topeka & Santa Fé general, New York Central first, Virginia & Truckee.

10 second-grade rails, e.g. Chicago Great Western, Lehigh Valley, Wabash.

"THE ECONOMIST"–EXTEL ORDINARY SHARE INDICATOR

The aim of this index is to provide an up-to-date, sensitive measure of share-price changes of interest to investors rather than to statisticians. For this purpose the index is frequently revised in terms of the constituents, which are 50 in number.

The shares involved are British industrial equities (not divided into groups), including oil and shipping shares; a requirement for inclusion is that the security be actively dealt in by substantial investors. It is based on 1953 = 100. In that year an average was taken of the mid-monthly closing prices of the chosen shares for each month of the year.

The index number for each stock is calculated and the final

index is the arithmetic average of all the components, adjustments having been made to preserve continuity despite the replacement of one share by another from time to time. It is calculated twice daily, at noon and at the official close of Stock Exchange business, put out on the Extel news services and published weekly in *The Economist*.

Since the index is an investment indicator, continuity can be regarded as less important than "modernity" and chaining is an annual procedure. The unweighted arithmetic mean of price relatives is rebased at the end of each calendar year and linked back to the original 1953 base before the final average is taken. The rebasing is necessary because not all securities fluctuate equally rapidly. The current prices will form the base for the following year (see *The Economist*, 27th October 1956 and 1st June 1963).

For example:

(*a*)

Stock	Original base	Price relative	Price at 15th Dec. 19— (year 1)	Price relative
Alpha	15*s*.	100	20*s*.	133·3
Beta	30*s*.	100	35*s*.	116·7
Gamma	60*s*.	100	90*s*.	150·3
All stocks	—	100	—	133·3 = index

(*b*)

Stock	New base at year 1	Price relative	Price at 15th Dec. 19— (year 2)	Price relative
Alpha	20*s*.	100	25*s*.	125
Beta	35*s*.	100	28*s*.	80
Gamma	90*s*.	100	80*s*.	88·9
All stocks	—	100	—	98 = index

(*c*) 98 is the unadjusted indicator, which is now linked with the original base by means of a conversion factor 133·3/100 and the final adjusted indicator is: $98 \times 133\cdot3/100 = 130\cdot6$.

"THE ECONOMIST"–EXTEL INDICATOR (1953 = 100)

	1960	1961	1962	1963	19—
January	372	363	364	350	
February	360	375	357	354	
March	357	398	357	361	
April	351	414	355	360	
May	348	427	356	368	
June	359	402	315	363	
July	354	374	313	370	
August	366	369	337	378	
September	375	363	326	385	
October	377	343	330	390	
November	369	369	345	400	
December	357	356	349	406	
Year: High	381·7	472·2	364	408	
	(Sept.)	(May)	(Jan.)	(Nov.)	
Low	335·6	342·7	310	344	
	(May)	(Oct.)	(June)	(Jan.)	

"ELECTRONICS WEEKLY" SHARE PRICE INDEX

In September 1960 appeared the first issue of the specialised paper *Electronics Weekly*. As has every subsequent issue, it included a share price index intended to measure changes in the prices of quoted ordinary shares on the London Stock Exchange. All major electronics companies (about 70 in number) are represented, with the exception of Philips Lamp. This omission was decided upon in view of the size and international character of the company.

The base date is 4th June 1960 = 100, from which date prices of all the stocks included are used to compile the Index by arithmetic mean. Weighting is based on the percentage of the company's business which is in the electronics field. Since many of the companies have substantial interests outside the scope of electronics, downwards adjustments were accordingly made in the base weights where necessary, and this, it is felt, results in a truer measure of the size of the electronics industry. These movements can be taken to reflect very closely changes in the stock-market capitalisation of the ordinary shares of the industry.

The Index is printed each week, but for reasons of space I have averaged the weeks and give below monthly averages (which possibly therefore smooth out the fluctuations somewhat). As might be expected, an electronic computer is used in the calculation.

"ELECTRONICS WEEKLY" SHARE PRICE INDEX

Recalculated on a monthly basis (4th June 1960 = 100)

	1960	1961	1962	1963	19—
January	—	98	122	121	
February	—	102	124	122	
March	—	110	122	127	
April	—	118	127	130	
May	—	121	127	131	
June	99	113	111	131	
July	98	105	109	135	
August	102	106	111	141	
September	106	106	112	142	
October	102	104	112	149	
November	97	105	117	149	
December	93	117	122	155	

By December 1963 the Index reached 158, but this, of course, concealed larger rises by individual company shares, *e.g.* Advance Components exceeded 500.

Some seventy shares are represented in the Index; the full list is printed in each issue of the newspaper. They include several large companies, such as Automatic Telephone & Electric, Decca Record, Westinghouse, and some less known to the general public, such as Brayhead Ltd. It is an interesting attempt to create a specialised sectional index designed for a technical audience.

The N.C.R. Financial Computing Centre performs the calculations for this index and, acting on information received when adjustments to company situations take place, the Centre will amend the Index. For example, if a scrip issue is made more shares are in existence and the price per share will fall, but adjustment via the computer can easily be made.

If m shares are given for n held, the base price alters as follows:

$$\frac{n}{m + n} \times p = p'$$

THE EUROSYNDICAT INVESTMENT RESEARCH BUREAU

The Eurosyndicat index is published by the Eurosyndicat Investment Research Bureau in Brussels and is calculated in collaboration with technicians of the Institut National de Statistique et d'Etudes Economiques at Paris. The Bureau was founded by several Continental banks, in Belgium, Germany, France, Italy, and the Netherlands. The aim of the Bureau is to conduct investment research on behalf of companies and other business interests, including the provision of reports and statistics.

The Eurosyndicat index has been designed to furnish investors in Europe with data of company performance in countries of the European Economic Community. Already several national stock exchanges have welcomed Common Market "blue chips" (shares of leading companies) and certain investment funds specialise in such shares.

About 100 shares are represented, selected according to their market capitalisation on 31st December 1958, the day before the Treaty of Rome came into force. The coverage is considerable, because these shares account for over 60% of the total capitalisation of the Common Market exchanges, and selection is on the basis of relative importance of groups of shares over all the stock exchanges. This grouping is under eleven headings, namely:

	Original Index	Revision 1962
1. Banks, finance, and insurance	(11)	14
2. Steel and metals	(22)	19
3. Coal mining and mines	(3)	1
4. Building and materials	(2)	4
5. Chemicals	(13)	13
6. Gas, electricity, and telephone	(17)	8
7. Motors and engineering	(6)	8
8. Electrical and electronics	(5)	8
9. Oil	(11)	6
10. Textiles	(5)	6
11. Foodstuffs, paper, and retail trade	(5)	13

These include many international concerns, such as Unilever, Philips, Shell, Esso, and Michelin. Sub-category indexes will also be published by regrouping the shares of groups 1, 2, 5, 6, 8, and 9.

The formula is expressed as:

$$\frac{\Sigma(n_1 c_1)}{\Sigma(n_1 c_0)} \times 100$$

which is the Paasche formula, where n represents the number of shares of each company, and c the prices of the various shares. For reasons of comparison share prices are converted into a value unit equivalent to the West German mark. If other countries' exchange rates swing against German currency an adjustment will be made. The Paasche formula is regarded with favour because it allows for basic changes in the sample at each date to be taken into account, in other words the weighting is variable.

Adjustments are made when a significant change in capital structure occurs which may influence share prices, such as cash subscriptions (*e.g.* rights issues) or bonus issues.

The Index is therefore composed of a wide span of shares, 100 in total, based on 3rd December 1958 = 100, calculated as an arithmetic average weighted by market capitalisation; revised as mentioned above and in any event at regular intervals.

It is published weekly in the financial press, compiled on the basis of the prices each Tuesday; monthly and quarterly supplementary information is also given (such as sector indexes, charts).

At the time of its appearance several financial papers commented; an interesting article is that in the *Investors' Chronicle* of 17th February 1961, which gave a generally favourable welcome to the new index. It pointed out certain interesting facts based on consideration of the geographical and "economic activity" breakdown of the hundred shares. Geographically, the share capitalisations correspond closely with the geographical proportions—the largest discrepancy was the Netherlands, with 21·7% of the Index but only 17·9% of the capitalisation. Even this, however, does not seem to be serious. From the viewpoint of economic activity there is a satisfactory relationship between representation in the Index and market capitalisation; the largest discrepancies are oil shares (18·5% in terms of capital, but 28% weight) and banks, finance, and insurance (13·4% capital, 7·6% weight). The Index is published in *The Times*, the *Investors' Chronicle*, *The Economist*, and other journals.

EUROSYNDICAT SHARE INDEX

31st December 1958 = 100

End of quarters	General index	Banks, finance, and insurance	Gas, electrical, and telephone	Steel and metals	Electrical and electronics	Oil	Chemical, rubber, and paper
1960 Mar.	140	140	131	161	178	92	160
June	168	160	155	193	252	86	204
Sept.	178	181	179	193	245	82	225
Dec.	168	163	169	183	242	74	218
1961 Mar.	182	175	174	192	267	89	238
June	182	186	184	192	247	76	241
Sept.	166	172	169	170	234	68	216
Dec.	167	180	159	168	247	78	205
1962 Mar.	167	180	149	163	251	86	209
June	134	131	121	136	194	79	165
Sept.	136	131	119	133	195	86	169
Dec.	145	149	131	139	197	93	173
1963 Mar.	137	137	126	128	188	98	158
June	147	154	145	128	200	98	167
Sept.	146	148	144	133	193	97	164
Dec.	143	145	142	124	182	100	163
19— Mar.							
June							
Sept.							
Dec.							

"FINANCIAL TIMES" SHARE PRICE INDEXES

This series, published for many years by the *Financial Times* newspaper, has received much praise and a fair measure of criticism. The Index (called in its early days the *Financial News* Index) was originated by the late Hargreaves Parkinson and described in his book *Ordinary Shares*. It was designed to provide a guide to changes in stock exchange prices in an up-to-date manner, especially since the Stock Exchange itself does not construct such index numbers.

Several groups of index numbers were published daily from 1935 onwards, but some have now been abandoned in favour of the new *Financial Times*–Actuaries' share indexes. Two that are being retained are:

The "Financial Times" Industrial Ordinary Share Index

Based on 1st July 1935 = 100, this comprises 30 securities, whose prices (unit weighted) are averaged by geometric mean. The middle closing prices (that is, the mean between the buying and selling price for each security at the close of reported business) are taken each day and the logarithms of those prices are used to calculate the G.M. It is calculated three times daily, at prices ruling at 12 noon, 2.45 p.m., and at the close of the market. The early prices are available in news agency tape machines within twenty minutes and are published in the *Financial Times*. The later price is available about 6 p.m.

It is a highly volatile index, consisting as it does of so few shares, but all of which are dealt in frequently on the stock market. They represent the top "slice" of British industry and trade, and account for nearly 30% of the market valuation of the new *Financial Times*–Actuaries' 500-share Index. However, the *Financial Times* Index is intended purely as a price index, whereas the *Financial Times*–Actuaries' is designed also to measure the performance of a portfolio. Provision is made so that changes in market prices due to capital changes do not affect the index number.

The industries represented are: brewing and distilling (Distillers Company, Watney Mann), building (Associated Portland Cement, London Brick), stores (House of Fraser, Woolworth), electrical (E.M.I., G.E.C.), rubber (Dunlop), chemicals (I.C.I.), metallurgy (Murex), steel (United Steel), food (Spillers, Tate & Lyle), paper (Bowaters), shipbuilding (Swan Hunter), motors and aircraft (B.M.C., Hawker Siddeley, Leyland, Rolls-Royce), shipping (P. & O. Deferred), machine tools (Herbert), engineering (Guest Keen & Nettlefold, Tube Investments, Vickers, Turner & Newall), textiles (Courtaulds, Lancashire Cotton, Coats, Patons & Baldwins), and tobacco (Imperial Tobacco). This list may be altered in content from time to time.

"FINANCIAL TIMES" INDUSTRIAL ORDINARY SHARE INDEX

1st July 1935 = 100 (mid-month shown)

Year	Jan.	Feb.	Mar.	Apr.	May	June	July	Aug.	Sept.	Oct.	Nov.	Dec.
1960	330	326	316	315	310	321	314	330	332	326	313	302
1961	312	319	338	349	366	337	306	311	308	285	306	294
1962	306	303	299	298	300	262	261	284	276	276	291	288
1963	288	294	304	314	310	312	314	319	321	338	343	348
19—												

Highs and Lows

	1960	1961	1962	1963	19—
High	343	366	310	348	
Low	293	284	252	288	

The "Financial Times" Gold Mine Index

This consists of 30 securities based on 12th September 1955 = 100, calculated by the same method as the Industrial Ordinary Share Index. This index is sensitive not only to economic events in the industry but to political crises as well. Many of the securities relate to mining activities in South Africa.

"FINANCIAL TIMES"–ACTUARIES' SHARE INDEXES

In November 1962 a new series of share indexes was introduced to replace the Actuaries' Investment Index and some of the *Financial Times* indexes. It was agreed that the Institute of Actuaries and the Faculty of Actuaries should design the indexes; the *Financial Times* would supply the data, provide for calculation by computer, and publish the result. The original Actuaries' Indexes (with 200 shares) were designed for investment analysis, but appeared too infrequently (monthly) to be of full value. The *Financial Times* indexes were regarded as too narrowly based and the new *Financial Times*–Actuaries' complements the continuing Industrial Index.

The Indexes are compiled jointly by the *Financial Times*, the Institute of Actuaries in London, and the Faculty of Actuaries in Edinburgh, each of which has a professional interest in investment analysis. An investigation into all United Kingdom companies whose shares are in the Daily Official List showed that the "top" 650 companies (those with a market capitalisation in excess of £4 million each) composed about 90% of the value in capital terms of all companies whose capital exceeded £1 million at market valuation. From the results of this investigation a selection was made of components. The object of the Indexes is to demonstrate how the investor in equities is faring.

Fifty price indexes are calculated, based on the prices of 690 securities (including 635 equities and 25 fixed-interest stocks):

1. *The 500-share Index*

(a) Capital goods: 196 securities, including aircraft, building materials, contracting and construction, electricals, non-electrical engineering, machine tools, shipbuilding, and steel.

(b) Consumer durables: 58 securities, including electronics and radio, household goods, motors, and rubbers.

(c) Consumer non-durables: 195 securities, including breweries, entertainment, food, newspapers and publishing, paper, stores, textiles, and tobacco.

(*d*) Other groups: 51 shares of chemical, oil, and shipping companies.

2. *The All-share Index*

This consists of 594 securities (including all the above groups) plus

(*e*) Financial group: 94 shares in banks, discount houses, hire purchase, insurance, investment trusts, merchant bankers, and property.

3. *Commodity shares*

Forty-three securities, including rubbers, teas, coppers, lead–zinc, and tins.

4. *Fixed interest*

Consisting of a 20-year Government stock, the $2\frac{1}{2}\%$ Consols, redeemable debentures, and 35 preference stocks.

The Indexes are all based on 10th April 1962 = 100, the date being chosen as of special significance because it saw the beginning of the short-term capital-gains tax. At this date the market valuation of the 594 stocks was in excess of £18,000 million, or 60% of the value of all quoted equities in the sections concerned, providing a comprehensive and representative set of indexes. Daily indexes can speedily be calculated by using the services of the Financial Computing Centre of the National Cash Register Company (*see* p. 343).

Whereas the *Financial Times* Index is calculated by geometric average, the new Indexes are weighted arithmetic averages of price relatives, the weights used being the initial market capitalisation, subsequently modified to maintain the continuity when capital and constituent changes occur. The Indexes thus consist of a number of chain-linked series, each link occurring at the point of time of a capital change. This system facilitates replacement of companies when it is necessary, because the index value before the alteration is readily linked with suitable factors incorporating the new constituents correctly weighted. Replacements will be made to keep each index up-to-date as economic and business conditions alter, ensuring that the Indexes will always provide a fair sample of the United Kingdom share market.

The compilers feel that in comparison with the *Financial Times* index the new ones have much that is new to offer. The historian will be satisfied that they epitomise the day-to-day movements and the long-term changes in prices and yields of the whole United Kingdom equity market. The Indexes can also be taken to reflect the performances of model portfolios, comprising as they do many groups and sub-sections.

The formulae (using *Financial Times*–Actuaries' symbols) are as follows:

(*a*) Until the first capital change, equity price indexes are calculated as follows—

$$I_t = \frac{\Sigma \left(\text{Market value at base date} \times \dfrac{\text{Price at time } t}{\text{Price at base date}} \right)}{\Sigma \text{ Market value at base date}} \times 100.$$

(*b*) After a capital change (for example a rights issue) a chain index procedure is used, the first link being the movement in the index (by the formula above) from base date to the time the first capital change occurs.

After a change at time S the formula for the *next link* of the index at time t (which is later than S) until the next change is:

$$\text{Link } t = \frac{\Sigma \left(\text{Market value at time } S \times \dfrac{\text{Price at } t}{\text{Price at } S} \right)}{\Sigma \text{ Market value at } S} \times 100$$

and the index, I_t, is the result of this calculation multiplied by the factor I_t which produced the index immediately before the capital change.

With this formula the market value at time S allows for the changes in capital and price that have already occurred.

For interest, the computer formula is also given. It is derived as follows. The index at time t equals the market capitalisation at time $t(\Sigma N_t P_t)$ divided by the market capitalisation at the base date $(\Sigma N_o P_o)$ as adjusted for any capital changes happening between the base date at time t multiplied by factors of the form:

$$\sum \frac{n_s p_s + v_s}{\Sigma n_s p_s}$$

where N_o = number of shares in issue at base date; P_o = price of shares at the base date; N_t = number of shares in issue at time t; P_t = price of shares at time t; n_s = number of shares immediately before a change occurring at time S; p_s = price of shares immediately before a change occurring at time S; v_s = value of shares involved in the capital change at time S

(positive, *e.g.* a new issue of shares, or negative, *e.g.* a return of capital or a take-over).

The formulae employed for the fixed-interest indexes are as follow:

1. *Investment trust preference shares*

$$\text{Price Index at time } t = 100 \times \frac{1}{15} \sum \frac{\text{Price at time } t}{\text{Price at base date}}$$

2. *Commercial and industrial preference shares*

$$I_t = 100 \times \frac{1}{20} \sum \frac{\text{Price } t}{\text{Price at base date}}$$

3. *Redeemable debentures*

The fifteen constituents are divided into three groups of five, according to redemption date. For each group

$$\frac{\text{Price at } t}{\text{Price at base date}}$$

gives the factors I_1, I_2, I_3, which are combined to give:

$$I_t = 100 \times \frac{1}{2}\left(\frac{1460 - t}{1825} \times I_1 + I_2 + \frac{365 + t}{1825} \times I_3\right)$$

where $t =$ number of days from 31st December 1961.

4. *20-year Government stocks*

At base date the price of a 20-year stock 4% coupon, redemption yield 6·24%, would be 74·58 and the Index at time t:

$$\frac{\text{Price at time } t}{74·58} \times 100.$$

"FINANCIAL TIMES"—ACTUARIES' SHARE INDEXES
Mid-month (10th April 1962 = 100)

	1962 June	1963 Jan.	Feb.	Mar.	Apr.	May	June	July	Aug.	Sept.	Oct.	Nov.	Dec.
Capital goods (196)	87	96	98	100	101	102	100	101	104	106	111	114	115
Consumer durables (58)	84	92	95	98	100	100	96	98	101	102	107	107	110
Consumer, non-durables (195)	89	94	95	97	97	99	98	99	102	104	106	107	109
Chemicals (14)	85	100	100	102	102	106	105	106	110	116	114	118	122
Oil (3)	93	131	131	137	141	138	138	145	147	149	145	149	156
Shipping (11)	92	116	123	118	119	136	131	133	146	143	161	164	160
Unclassified (23)	91	98	105	106	110	110	109	113	114	115	115	118	121
500-share Index	88	98	99	102	103	104	102	105	107	110	112	114	116

"FINANCIAL TIMES"—ACTUARIES' SHARE INDEXES

Mid-month (10th April 1962 = 100)

	1962 June	1963 Jan.	Feb.	Mar.	Apr.	May	June	July	Aug.	Sept.	Oct.	Nov.	Dec.
Financial (94)	88	84	84	85	84	83	81	81	84	82	81	82	82
All-share Index (594)	88	95	96	98	98	99	97	99	102	103	104	106	108
Commodities:													
Rubbers (10)	86	100	93	95	98	92	99	98	100	91	92	95	95
Teas (10)	97	93	96	95	96	97	99	99	96	99	99	101	109
Copper (6)	100	104	113	118	112	123	121	116	118	118	113	118	118
Lead–zinc (6)	94	115	112	125	131	142	145	145	155	161	166	167	183
Tins (11)	73	81	78	75	85	87	89	83	82	81	81	88	92
Fixed Interest													
20-year Government stock (6)	100	112	109	108	109	112	113	115	115	115	115	110	109
Redeemable debentures and loans (15)	100	109	109	108	108	109	110	111	112	113	113	112	109
Preference:													
Investment trusts (15)	101	108	107	105	107	109	109	109	111	114	114	108	105
Commercial and industrial (20)	97	110	109	106	107	110	112	114	113	114	115	111	107

"INVESTORS' CHRONICLE" MONTHLY SECURITIES INDEXES

Are published by the *Investors' Chronicle* at monthly intervals in the first issue of the month. The object is to show change in the market values of 200 securities, which are placed into groups and sub-groups:

1. *Gilt-edged securities* (19), which are sub-grouped into British funds, Dominion securities, and United Kingdom corporations. For example, the "British funds" sub-group consists of: conversion $3\frac{1}{2}$% 1961, funding 4% 1960–90, Consols $2\frac{1}{2}$%, funding 3% 1959–69, savings 3% 1965–75.

2. *Industrial fixed interest* (14), including both debentures and preference shares.

3. *Banks, insurance, trusts, and property* (23).

4. *Industrials* (96), covering a wide range of companies in manufacturing, retailing, building, etc.

5. *Gold mining* (10).

6. *Commodities* (38), covering copper, lead, zinc, oil, rubber, tea, and tin mining.

Each month a price relative is calculated for each security in the sub-group (*e.g.* British funds) and an average is found of the sub-group total, which is then incorporated into the group along with other sub-groups' averages; the average-price relative for the group is then calculated.

The all-securities index is obtained by averaging the 33 sectional indexes and *not* by averaging the six groups. In all the above the arithmetic mean is used, weighting being performed *via* the number of securities in each group.

For most indexes the base date is 31st December 1923 = 100, but this does not apply where new indexes are taken into the list of securities. This is done either at the level of the old indexes which are being replaced or at the equivalent level of the general Industrial index.

Other adjustments are required occasionally, such as the replacement of a fixed-interest security which has become "short-dated" by a comparable longer-dated stock. Again, price adjustments of shares occur when a scrip issue or bonus issue has been made. Finally, mergers may cause companies to disappear from the Stock Exchange, in which case the base of the substituted security is related to the market price of that which is disappearing at the date of its demise.

All changes which take place are reported in the next issue of the *Investors' Chronicle*. For example, in the edition of 2nd June 1961 it was reported that the Plastics section was being eliminated, a section on Steel Shares was re-introduced and a new Property index put in. The aim of all changes is to render the Indexes more responsive and representative. All take-overs are noted and amendments made: for example, in the issue mentioned, Odhams shares were replaced by those of the *News of the World*.

The Indexes are published in one table each month together with a commentary describing the major features of the previous month. Two charts accompany the table, plotted on semi-logarithmic scale, one displaying the progress of industrials and gilt-edged securities since the commencement of the Indexes, the other showing the *Investors' Chronicle* Commodity Share Index and that of gold shares together with a series of U.S. commodity prices by the U.S. Bureau of Labour. A third chart shows Standard & Poor's U.S. Stock Price indexes (rails and industrials) from 1926 onwards to provide a useful comparison, since the bases are reasonably similar.

"INVESTORS' CHRONICLE" MONTHLY SECURITY INDEXES

End of month figures (31st December 1923 = 100)

Group	1946 Dec.	1960 Mar.	1960 June	1960 Sept.	1960 Dec.	1961 Dec.	1962 Mar.	1962 June	1962 Sept.	1962 Dec.	1963 Mar.	1963 June	1963 Sept.	1963 Dec.
1. Gilt edged (19)	137	90	88	87	86	84	85	86	93	94	92	95	96	94
2. Industrial fixed interest (14)	157	94	91	89	88	81	83	84	88	87	88	92	94	92
3. Banks	154	243	218	249	257	338	354	319	322	330	307	287	289	291
Insurance	216	365	360	428	395	510	483	473	457	453	471	453	438	433
Investment trusts (17 in all)	56	326	311	325	311	395	378	340	343	368	383	396	417	433
4. Industrials (96)	187	468	451	473	480	527	510	465	482	501	539	558	598	650
5. Gold mines (10)	130	70	60	65	73	58	55	64	69	71	76	72	73	71
6. Commodities and land (44)	134	384	361	345	322	294	300	287	311	333	359	383	408	429
7. All securities (200)	164	369	354	366	365	400	391	362	375	390	412	426	453	483

Investors' Chronicle: *a selection of changes*

	British Funds (Gilts)	Industrial Fixed interest	Investment Trusts	Industrials Index	Oil	Tea
Dec. 1946	138	157	56	187	258	83
Dec. 1962	88	87	368	501	938	77

MOODIES' SERVICES LTD SECURITY INDEXES

Several share indexes are published by Moodies' Services Ltd of London (who are correspondents of Moody's Investors' Service of New York) and appear in *Moodies' Review* and Moodies' Security Indexes and Charts Service, available to subscribers. In addition, the Share Price Index is used (with a recalculated base) by the London & Cambridge Economic Service.

The service concentrates on equities, with the aim of providing the investor with yardsticks against which he can measure his own investment portfolio. Equities cover a very large number of types of business and the service assembles them into sections from which the investor can select to suit his own requirements.

Charts are drawn both yearly and monthly, covering prices, earnings, and dividends of equities: the yearly chart compares over many years the relationship between the price of shares and the earnings available for equity holders; the monthly charts show current trends of dividends paid compared with earnings available for those dividends. The individual indexes are as follow.

Equity Share Price Index

The aim is to provide a complete picture of equities, using sixty securities (excluding plantations and mines, and banks), following two studies into market capitalisation and the number of investors, in 1948 and 1949.

Classification of companies selected: (a) *by size*

Total market capitalisation (%)	Size of company	Number of companies represented in Index
14	£100 million and over	6
39	£10–under £100 million	24
38	£1–under £10 million	24
9	Less than £1 million	6

Classification of companies selected: (b) *by activity*

Activity	Percentage of companies	Number of companies represented in Index
Brewing	9%	6
Commerce and industry	60	36
Financial trusts	5	3
Insurance	6	3
Iron, steel, coal	8	5
Oil	10	6
Shipping	2	1
		—
		60

The six giant companies in (*a*) were self-selecting. The remainder were chosen at random on the basis of a stratified sample—using a Stock Exchange List and a pack of cards—so that the Index should represent both the differing sizes and different occupations of companies. Moodies believe that the result is representative of the equity portfolios of some 1 million investors.

Prices are taken on Fridays and averaged by the geometric mean, on a base of 1947 = 100. The results are in turn averaged to provide the monthly data as published to subscribers.

MOODIES' EQUITY PRICE INDEX

Averages (1947 = 100)

Begun in 1919						High	Low				High	Low
1925	58	1937	78	1949	86			1961	260	294	238
1926	60	1938	64	1950	85			1962	244	256	226
1927	65	1939	59	1951	99			1963	278	301	255
1928	74	1940	52	1952	82			19—			
1929	73	1941	58	1953	88						
1930	60	1942	66	1954	117						
1931	46	1943	79	1955	138						
1932	46	1944	86	1956	126						
1933	55	1945	90	1957	136						
1934	63	1946	97	1958	139	168	120				
1935	69	1947	100	1959	199	254	165				
1936	79	1948	93	1960	252	265	240				

Highest each 5 years: 78 (1929); 65 (1930 and 1934); 85 (1937); 91 (1944); 108 (1947); 106 (1951); 254 (1959).

Lowest each 5 years: 55 (1925); 39 (1932); 54 (1939); 44 (1940); 80 (1949); 76 (1952); 117 (1956).

Yearly Index of Company Earnings

With a coverage of 150 companies, this index uses the arithmetic average of the percentage earnings of those companies, mines and plantations excluded, and is based on 1947 = 100. Dates refer to the year in respect of which the profits were made and dividends paid.

MOODIES' INDEX OF YEARLY EARNINGS AND DIVIDENDS ON EQUITIES

	1926	1927	1928	1929	1930	1931	1932	1933	1934	1935
Earnings	59	72	69	66	55	41	36	41	49	56
Dividends	34	39	41	39	33	27	24	26	31	35

	1936	1937	1938	1939	1940	1941	1942	1943	1944	1945
Earnings	66	67	59	64	56	58	58	67	66	73
Dividends	40	41	38	32	32	33	33	35	35	38

	1946	1947	1948	1949	1950	1951	1952	1953	1954	1955
Earnings	89	100	121	130	159	172	145	160	208	225
Dividends	44	45	46	47	54	56	56	66	78	83

	1956	1957	1958	1959	1960	1961	1962	19—	19—	19—
Earnings	214	212	209	253	262	244	233			
Dividends	86	89	96	112	126	125	129			

Monthly Index of Company Earnings

A very interesting index is constructed from the earnings of 150 industrial companies selected on the basis of: (a) the spread of their financial year ends throughout the year, so as to obtain a year-over coverage; (b) the speed with which the accounts are published; (c) the activities of the company. The method used is to enter the latest earnings figures for each company under the month of publication and to repeat them for the following eleven months. The geometric mean of each month's figures therefore represents the latest known earnings published during that month of the 150 companies. The Monthly Index changes each month according to changes in the earnings of individual companies reported that month.

The earnings of each company are taken as representing the sixth month of its financial year; about four months usually elapse between year end and publication of the results, and consequently the data refer to a date about ten months earlier than that in which they appear. The "earnings" are based on the profits available for equity shareholders, which are not usually the same as *total* profits—indeed total profits might rise even though the sums available for equity holders' dividends have fallen, and vice versa. It is none the less believed that were an index of total profits compiled, the trend would be similar to that shown by this index.

Consols Index

The index of undated Government stock is based on 1947 = 100, using price movements of $2\frac{1}{2}\%$ Consols.

MOODIES' OLD CONSOLS PRICE INDEX

						High	Low *
1925	62·3	1939	74	1953	67·4		
1926	60·7	1940	80·9	1954	73·1		
1927	60·5	1941	88·1	1955	65·3		
1928	61·8	1942	91	1956	57·7		
1929	59·9	1943	88·8	1957	54·8		
1930	61·6	1944	87·7	1958	55	57·4 (Dec.)	51·9 (Jan.)
1931	62·7	1945	94·3	1959	56·8	57·9 (Jan.)	54·7 (Dec.)
1932	73·5	1946	106·3	1960	50·5	53·3 (Jan.)	48·5 (July/Dec.)
1933	81·4	1947	100	1961	44·1	47·5 (Jan.)	41·3 (Aug.)
1934	89·3	1948	86	1962	45·8	48·8	41·9
1935	95·2	1949	83·5	1963	49·1	50·9	46·5
1936	93·6	1950	77·7	19—			
1937	84·1	1951	72·7				
1938	81·7	1952	64·7				

* These are the highest and lowest monthly averages.

Dividend Declaration Index

Since the dividend policy of companies is influenced by more than events within the company, it is interesting to follow the changes in dividends. Each month a tally of all declarations by industrial companies is made and calculations are produced of the percentages which show an increase, decrease, or no change. These three are then combined to form an index by the process of weighting every increase two points for each percentage rise; one point is given for every company dividend unchanged; and none for any percentage decrease.

As an example of how the Index is arrived at, let us assume that there are 400 dividend declarations:

$$200 \text{ are unchanged, } i.e. \ 50\% \quad \text{weighted} \times 1 = \quad 50$$
$$150 \text{ are increased, } i.e. \ 37\tfrac{1}{2}\% \quad \text{weighted} \times 2 = \quad 75$$
$$50 \text{ are decreased, } i.e. \ 12\tfrac{1}{2}\% \quad \text{weighted} \times 0 = \quad —$$

$$\text{Index} = 125$$

It will be seen that the more increases outnumber the decreases the further the Index rises (and vice versa). When increases and decreases are evenly balanced the Index returns to zero.

MOODIES' DIVIDEND DECLARATION INDEX

1959	120	111	117	125	124	128	129	130	131	130	134	141
1960	146	155	152	155	151	148	148	135	127	140	138	128
1961	131	136	141	136	136	131	127	107	110	107	104	105
1962	102	98	104	115	111	112	114	112	108	113	107	113
1963	120	118	115	123	120	120	122	120	128	125	126	141

Confidence Index

This Index (1947 = 100) is similar in principle to a "deflating" index, in that it tries to isolate "confidence" from share-price changes. There are three factors which (say Moodies) influence the prices of equities: the current dividend rates, long-term rates of interest, and the confidence of the market in the future. The formula is:

$$\frac{\text{Equity Index} \times 100 \times 100}{\text{Dividend Index} \times \text{Consols Index}}$$

The resultant index represents the important factors of economic and political events. Moodies emphasise, however, that all three indexes should be watched before reaching conclusions as to investment policy.

MOODIES' CONFIDENCE INDEX

						High and low monthly averages	
1925	105·7	1939	94·6	1953	102·3		
1926	108·4	1940	81·6	1954	108·5		
1927	122·9	1941	83·7	1955	124		
1928	131·5	1942	94·1	1956	123·7		
1929	124·1	1943	111·7	1957	132		
1930	101·8	1944	119	1958	127·2	147 (Dec.)	117 (Apr.)
1931	90·4	1945	115·3	1959	165·8	202 (Dec.)	146 (Jan.)
1932	90·5	1946	106·5	1960	204·3	213 (Jan.)	196 (May)
1933	106·7	1947	100	1961	227·8	246 (May)	210 (Jan.)
1934	110·2	1948	102·7	1962	208·1	223 (May)	194 (Sept.)
1935	102·9	1949	97·2	1963	215·1	231 (Dec.)	208 (June)
1936	108	1950	102·3	19—			
1937	106·4	1951	116·8				
1938	90	1952	102				

COMTELBURO–REUTER'S DAILY INDEXES

A series of indexes covering stock exchange prices, and others covering commodities, are produced by Comtel–Reuter's—in England, Comtelburo Ltd.

The purpose of the share indexes is to provide an accurate daily measurement of the direction and relative size of appreciation or depreciation of marketed securities.

Five indexes are regularly produced, covering South African uranium, gold mining (developers), gold mining (Kaffirs), industries, and gilt-edged securities.

1. *Reuter's Daily Index of London Stock Exchange quotations for South African uranium-producing shares*

This index is calculated by using an unweighted geometric average of a representative selection of shares, based on 1st July 1953 = 100. There are six shares in the Index, all African.

2. *South African gold-mining (developer) shares*

This uses an unweighted geometric average of a representative selection of shares quoted in London. A "developer" is a mine which has not yet (or has only just) reached the stage of paying a dividend. The Index comprises eleven shares, all South African, and is based on 21st September 1955 = 100.

3. *South African gold-mining shares (Kaffirs)*

With a base of 31st December 1934 = 100, this uses an unweighted geometric average of a representative selection of twelve quoted South African gold shares representing both old and new producers and some holding companies.

With all the above securities care is taken to avoid a break in continuity when shares go "ex-div" (*i.e.* when they are quoted at a price which excludes the right to the dividend which will shortly be due) or when some shares are dropped and others inserted as replacements. Adjustments are made to quotations to take account of accrued dividends.

4. *London Stock Exchange Daily Industrial Share Index*

This index measures the prices of a representative selection of United Kingdom industrial and commercial equities with the object of providing a prompt measure of day-to-day changes. It is based on 31st December 1934 = 100 and consists of 25 stocks classified into eight groups: three basic industries, three aircraft and motors, three electrical engineering, two construction materials, two textiles, five stores and food, two brewing and distilling, and five general companies.

5. *Reuter's Daily Index of London Stock Exchange quotations for Gilt-edged Securities*

The index is based on the par values of seven securities, six of which are dated.

The Index is compiled by deduction of any accrued interest from the gross price of the stocks, and dividing the total net value by the number of stocks (seven) to give a simple arithmetic mean shown to one decimal point.

Reuter's indexes are published daily in commercial news media distributed throughout the world by agents and Comtelburo reporters, and are to be found in many newspapers.

STANDARD & POOR'S INDEX OF STOCK PRICES

Published by Standard & Poor's Corporation of New York, the aim of this Index is to measure the behaviour of stock prices for the information of the investing public, security analysts, brokers, and economists.

Since 1957 the Index has been expanded to cover 500 stocks, although the same method of calculating it has been used since 1926. It consists of 500 common stocks (ordinary shares) distributed in the proportion of 425 industrials, 25 railroads, and 50 utilities, covering 90% of the value of common shares quoted on the New York Stock Exchange. Several indexes and associated statistics are compiled from the 93 groups: (a) Industrial Composite Index, (b) Railroads, (c) Utilities, (d) 500 Composite Index; also (e) bank stocks (New York City and outside New York City), (f) investment companies, (g) fire insurance and casualty insurance. There are, in addition, four supplementary group series: (h) capital goods companies, (i) consumer goods, (j) high grade common stocks, (k) low priced common stocks.

Each index is calculated on the aggregate market value of the common stocks of all the companies in the sample, and the formula used is:

$$\frac{\Sigma p_1 q_0}{\Sigma p_0 q_0} \times 10$$

or base weighted aggregative, with the average value for the base period 1941–3 = 10. This basis of 10 is unusual. It was selected so that the resulting index numbers should be close to the true average price of all stocks listed on the New York Stock Exchange (i.e. roughly interchangeable into dollars and cents). The formula gives two major advantages, flexibility, so that rights issues, etc., can be allowed for; and a high degree of continuity.

The indexes are weighted by multiplying each stock by the number of shares outstanding (i.e. issued), displaying the aggregate current value of the investment in the 500 issues by all stockholders. This is then related to the 1941–3 average of aggregate values, which is accorded the value of 10 and has the effect of gearing the Index close to the *actual* average of stock prices, as explained above (thus a change of a dollar in the actual average market value will mean about a one point change—not six or seven points, as in other indexes or averages).

The four main groups are calculated hourly, with a closing and a high/low index for the day. In addition, monthly, weekly, daily, and hourly indexes are identical and interchangeable. For maximum utility, companion calculations are made of share earnings, dividends, dividend yields, and price-earnings ratios.

The Indexes receive world-wide distribution daily over almost all English language syndicated presses, but are fully reported only in Standard & Poor's publications.

STANDARD & POOR'S FOUR MAIN INDEXES

Mid-month data (1941–3 = 10)

Year	Jan.	Feb.	Mar.	Apr.	May	June	July	Aug.	Sept.	Oct.	Nov.	Dec.
1. 425 industrials												
1959	59	58	60	61	62	61	64	62	61	61	61	63
1960	62	59	59	60	59	61	60	60	59	57	59	60
1961	63	66	67	70	71	70	68	72	72	72	75	77
1962	72	74	75	72	68	58	59	61	62	59	63	66
1963	67	69	69	72	73	74	72	75	77	76	77	79
19—												
2. 25 rails												
1959	36	35	36	36	36	36	37	35	34	34	33	34
1960	34	33	31	31	30	31	30	31	29	28	29	29
1961	32	32	32	32	34	33	32	33	33	35	35	33
1962	34	34	33	32	31	28	28	28	28	27	30	32
1963	34	35	35	36	39	39	39	39	39	38	39	41
19—												
3. 50 utilities												
1959	44	44	45	45	44	42	44	45	43	44	44	44
1960	45	44	44	46	46	48	48	49	49	48	48	50
1961	53	55	56	59	60	59	60	61	62	64	68	67
1962	62	64	65	64	60	54	55	57	57	56	58	60
1963	63	64	63	65	66	65	64	67	67	66	65	66
19—												
4. Government bonds												
1959	90	90	90	89	89	88	88	88	85	86	87	85
1960	84	86	88	87	88	90	90	92	92	90	90	91
1961	90	91	92	91	92	90	90	88	88	89	89	88
1962	88	88	89	90	90	90	89	89	90	90	90	90
1963	90	89	89	89	89	89	88	89	88	88	87	87
19—												

"THE STATIST" EQUITY PREFERENCE INDICATOR

This interesting Index is based on the daily average in December 1962 of the yield in Consols $2\frac{1}{2}\%$, as a percentage of the yield on the *Financial Times*–Actuaries' 500-share Index. The average yield on Consols in December 1962 was $5 \cdot 506\%$;

the average yield on the *Financial Times*–Actuaries' index was 4·666. The base, 5·506 × 100/4·666, is therefore 120·15. Each day the current Consols yield is divided by the *Financial Times* Actuaries' yield and the result is divided by 120·15 to obtain the current indicator. When the indicator (multiplied by 100) is below 100, the implication is that investors have a lower preference for equities in relation to fixed-interest stocks than they had in December 1962. When the indicator is above 100 a higher preference for equities in relation to fixed-interest stocks is indicated. The calculation is simply a way of measuring the gap between the pure rate of interest (the yield on Consols) and relating this to the gap which existed at an earlier date.

Although the system outlined above is not new (Moodies dates back to 1926), the *Statist* indicator has the advantage of being related to a recent period. See *The Statist*, 8th February 1963.

"THE STATIST" EQUITY PREFERENCE INDICATOR

Mid-months (December 1962 = 100)

Year	Jan.	Feb.	Mar.	Apr.	May	June	July	Aug.	Sept.	Oct.	Nov.	Dec.
1963 19—	—	106·3	108·1	105·7	102·3	100·5	100·7	101·7	104·2	106·1	113	115

"THE TIMES" DAILY INDEXES OF STOCK EXCHANGE SECURITY PRICES

These are compiled by *The Times*, with the intention of establishing standards against which an investor can measure his own portfolio performance.

The Indexes were first published on 26th April 1960, having been prepared with the assistance and advice of Professor M. G. Kendall of the London School of Economics, who advised on the technical problems of construction and calculation.

The twelve Indexes are published daily in *The Times* and are each calculated by the method of weighted arithmetic mean, on the price changes of all stocks and shares included in that index. The price relative formula is:

$$I = \frac{\Sigma w \frac{p_1}{p_0}}{\Sigma w}$$

and like most similar indexes it therefore uses a fixed base date —in this case 2nd June 1964 = 100 for the base prices (p_0) but the weights are on market capitalisation of 31st March 1964, the end of the Stock Exchange financial year.

Since the indexes are published daily a large number of calculations must be performed, and for this purpose use is made of the NCR Electronics financial computer centre.

Each index is fully weighted according to the various sizes of the companies. Each share is weighted in proportion to the market value of the *total amount* of that share or stock in issue at the date mentioned above. As an example let us postulate I.C.I. ordinary stock £483,874,000 and Babcock & Wilcox £21,866,000. Thus in the Industrial Ordinary Share Index I.C.I. counts for 22 times as much as Babcock & Wilcox, and a change in the price of I.C.I. stock will therefore have a proportionally larger effect on the Index.

In common with most indexes of their type, *The Times* indexes are adjusted when events make it necessary. The prices used are the daily closing Stock Exchange price lists, as found in the City columns of *The Times*. Occasionally prices change, owing not to normal trade fluctuations but to some alteration in capitalisation such as rights issues, the capitalisation of reserves (scrip issue), etc.

In the case of a scrip issue (such as an issue of one for three) the new market price *per share* will fall to 75% (more or less) of its original value. The weight will remain unchanged (since *total* capitalisation is unaltered), but p_0 will be reduced in proportion to the issue.

When a rights issue is made for cash the compilers assume that the rights are sold at the first opportunity and the proceeds invested in the same security: weights are not altered in magnitude. Other bonus issues are similarly treated. The general rule is that the Index is adjusted whenever an event occurs which causes the market to quote a security at a lower price when it is "ex" some privilege. If a company is taken over it will frequently be found that the shares are taken by another company in the Index, and will thus in effect continue *via* the Index.

There are twelve Indexes, A to L, of which A comprises $B + C$; D is a selection of industrial shares from lists B and C; E is a selection of consumer-goods shares from B and C.

Index A: The Times *Industrial Share Index*

This consists of 150 ordinary shares of large and small industrial companies. A selection is: (from list B) Beecham,

Bowater, British Oxygen, Debenham's, Dunlop, Butlin's, Guinness, English Electric, I.C.I., Imperial Tobacco, Marks & Spencer "A," Woolworth; (from list *C*) Aspro-Nicholas, A.T.V. "A," Babcock & Wilcox, Bristol Aeroplane, John Brown, Cerebos, Coast Lines, E.M.I., Gestetner, J. Lyons "A," Qualcast.

Index B: large industrial companies

This comprises 50 companies whose ordinary share capital was valued at Stock Exchange prices at over £60 million on the relevant dates. A selection is given above; others include Distillers Company, Tube Investments, Shell Transport & Trading.

Index C: smaller industrial companies

There are 100 in all, whose capital was less than £60 million each. A selection is given under *A* above. Others include Fisons, Montague Burton, Calico Printers, Furness Withy, Schweppes.

Index D: capital goods shares

A selection from *B* and *C* lists of 43 companies producing mainly or wholly capital goods, the list includes Associated Portland Cement, Guest Keen & Nettlefold, Colvilles, Reyrolle, and some mentioned in *A* list above.

Index E: consumer goods shares

This consists of 43 companies, including Pye, B.D.H., Fine Spinners & Doublers, Cerebos, and British Match, Coats, Patons & Baldwins.

Index F: Store shares

Twelve stores, including Debenham's, Marks & Spencer "A," and G.U.S. "A."

Index G: Financial shares

This covers the 25 largest finance companies, *e.g.* Lloyds Bank, Royal Insurance, Mercantile Investment Trust.

Index H: Combined Equity Index

This covers the 50 largest industrial companies and the 25 largest finance companies.

Index I: Commodity Share Index

Thirty companies, including Bancroft Mines, Burmah Oil, Jokai Tea, London Tin Corporation, London Asiatic Rubber, and Ultramar.

I

Index J : Gold mining shares

This covers 25 companies, such as Ashanti Goldfields, Doorfontein, and Union Corporation.

Index K : Industrial Debenture Index

Twenty debentures, including Distillers Company $5\frac{1}{2}\%$, and Rolls-Royce 4% 1974–84.

Index L : Preference Share Index

Twenty preference shares of industrial companies, *e.g.* B.M.C. 5% preference shares.

The *B* list is very roughly comparable to the *Financial Times* Index, although the items included and the method of calculation differ. The subdivision into groups can be very useful, both for following the separate fortunes of capital and consumer goods industries and for comparing the progress of large and smaller companies. This is brought out in broad terms in the graphs. The compilers hope that the new indexes answer most of the day-to-day questions which the economist, the businessman, and the investor need to ask. A revision was made in 1964 after five years because of radical changes in certain financial affairs, *e.g.* new take-over bids.

HOW "THE TIMES" INDEXES HAVE MOVED

Daily Indexes, shown here quarterly or end-of-month only as in *The Times*
Pre-1964 classification (2nd June 1959 = 100)

Date	Industrial Share Index (150)	Large companies (50)	Smaller companies (100)	Capital goods (43)	Consumer goods (43)	Commodity shares (30)	Gold-mining shares (25)	Industrial preference and debentures (40)
				1959				
2nd June	100	100	100	100	100	100	100	100
30th Dec.	136	134	143	146	137	119	111	104
				1960				
31st Mar.	130	128	135	138	130	107	85	103
30th June	128	127	134	134	135	107	81	97
30th Sept.	134	133	138	134	141	95	87	96
31st Dec.	131	131	132	124	137	103	91	94
				1961				
31st Mar.	147	146	148	144	152	116	78	92
30th June	138	140	133	130	143	121	68	89
30th Sept.	129	131	121	118	136	120	68	87
31st Dec.	132	134	125	115	151	124	78	88

Date	Industrial Share Index (150)	Large companies (50)	Smaller companies (100)	Capital goods (43)	Consumer goods (43)	Commodity shares (30)	Goldmining shares (25)	Industrial preference and debentures (40)
				1962				
Jan.	130	130	127	116	147	117	74	89
Feb.	129	131	124	116	147	114	75	89
Mar.	127	128	122	110	144	116	74	89
Apr.	134	134	132	115	156	116	74	90
May	123	123	120	103	140	105	84	89
June	120	121	115	100	137	100	87	88
July	117	118	112	98	129	105	89	90
Aug.	123	123	120	108	134	106	94	94
Sept.	121	123	116	104	132	104	95	97
Oct.	123	124	118	104	133	104	92	99
Nov.	131	132	125	112	142	112	93	97
Dec.	128	130	124	109	138	116	91	98
				1963				
Jan.	131	132	125	108	140	123	95	98
Feb.	136	137	132	112	148	120	99	97
Mar.	137	138	132	115	148	122	103	96
Apr.	138	139	133	118	145	125	98	97
May	139	140	134	117	148	129	97	99
June	137	139	132	114	146	133	97	100
July	139	140	136	115	150	127	100	101
Aug.	145	147	140	120	158	133	102	102
Sept.	146	147	143	120	160	134	100	102
Oct.	152	152	152	132	164	133	96	102
Nov.	154	154	153	130	166	130	98	99
Dec.	156	156	156	132	170	144	96	97

SECURITIES AND EXCHANGE COMMISSION STOCK PRICE INDEXES

These are compiled by the Division of Trading and Exchanges of the Securities and Exchange Commission, Washington. The Index of Common Stock Prices on the New York Stock Exchange was revised in 1960 and first published in its present form in October of that year, using the base of 1957–9 = 100, linked to 1939. The Index comprises 300 common stocks (equities) in five major categories (italicised in the table below).

Before the items were chosen a selection was made of the groups of industries which were of major importance to Stock Exchange traders, and 32 groups were recorded. In each industry the most active stocks were selected for the Index and they are subject to annual revision so that substitution can be made where necessary.

Such stock is weighted by the number of issued shares, and the last reported selling price each week-end for each stock is multiplied by this weight to obtain the current market value. The stocks are added together by groups and percentages extracted, leading finally to a composite index. It is based on the Paasche formula with modifications,

$$I = \frac{\Sigma p_1 q_1}{(\Sigma p_0 q_0) + (\Sigma p_0 q_a)} \times 100$$

q relating to the number of shares issued and q_a referring to the additional quantity of shares issued after a change in capitalisation. Thus $(p_0 q_a)$ is the amount of the additional investment in the company, evaluated at the average price level in the base period, q_0 and q_1 being the number of shares outstanding at base and current periods.

The base period is 1957–9, and prices are related to the average weekly closing prices during those years, chosen to comply with American Government policy of using a standard base date where feasible.

Current data appeared in the American financial press and the S.E.C. *Statistical Bulletin* each month but were discontinued in May 1964.

The stocks in the Index at February 1962 were:

	Number of stocks
1. *Manufacturing*	
Durable goods, including industrial machinery, iron, steel, non-ferrous metals, and electronic equipment	108
Non-durable goods, including food, drink, drugs, tobacco, and industrial chemicals	85
2. *Transport*, rail (14) and air (4)	18
3. *Utilities:* telecommunications, electric and gas supplies	34
4. *Trade, finance, and services:* retailing (21), radio and cinema (7), finance and services (17)	45
5. *Mining*	10
Total	300

S.E.C. STOCK PRICE INDEXES
Select data annual averages (1957–9 = 100)

19–	39	40	41	42	43	44	45	46	47	48	49	50	51
Composite	27	25	23	20	27	29	35	40	35	36	34	41	50
Durables	22	21	18	16	21	23	29	31	26	27	26	34	39
Non-durables	20	19	18	16	21	22	26	31	29	30	30	37	47
Transport	34	34	33	31	42	48	64	68	50	53	46	54	67
Utilities	55	55	49	39	50	55	62	67	59	55	54	60	62
Trade, etc.	29	27	24	21	30	34	44	60	48	46	47	54	61
Mining	29	21	21	18	24	27	34	37	34	39	38	42	60

19–	52	53	54	55	56	57	58	59	60	61	62	63	64
Composite	52	52	62	82	93	89	93	117	114	134	127	142	
Durables	42	43	55	79	92	88	90	121	117	129	116	129	
Non-durables	50	50	60	80	95	93	94	113	105	124	119	137	
Transport	75	74	78	108	111	93	91	116	99	106	98	123	
Utilities	65	67	75	85	86	86	96	118	129	168	167	181	
Trade, etc.	60	61	69	87	90	82	95	122	127	160	155	161	
Mining	81	70	78	92	105	107	98	85	74	93	98	97	

QUESTIONS AND EXERCISES

1. Discuss the problems encountered in constructing an index number of share prices and suggest methods by which those problems could be solved. *(University of London 1960)*

2. Ten ordinary shares, selected from a wider group of high-grade shares, showed price movements after the general election of 1959:

1959 share prices in s.

Share	7th Oct.	31st Dec.	Share	7th Oct.	31st Dec.
Bowater	59	76	P. & O.	$39\frac{1}{2}$	51
British Motor*	18	24	Shell*	142	$158\frac{1}{2}$
Debenhams†	$37\frac{1}{2}$	$44\frac{1}{2}$	Tate & Lyle†	47	61
English Electric	45	53	United Steel	43	83
Lancs. Cotton	56	$67\frac{1}{2}$	Vickers	28	$39\frac{1}{2}$

Shares marked * have twice the sales, and those marked † have half the sales of shares not marked.

Obtain an index of these share prices at 31st December with 7th October = 100: (a) without weights, and (b) with weights, according to sales as indicated. To what extent would you regard your index numbers as representative of the general movement of high-grade share prices? *(University of London 1960)*

3. Describe any *one* index number of ordinary share prices and discuss its usefulness as an indicator of changes in economic activity. *(I.O.S. 1962)*

4. Indicate what primary sources you would consult to derive current information relating to the following. Outline briefly the extent and nature of the published information.

  (a) Changes in the distribution of personal income.
  (b) Fluctuations in the level of ordinary share prices.
  (c) Monthly changes in the cost of living.
(I.O.S. 1959)

5. Re-calculate Question 2 with similar data before and after the General Election of 1964.

CHAPTER 15

INDEXES OF PRODUCTION

PRODUCTION indexes can be revealing indicators of economic progress or stagnation. Many measures of national productivity are available and, although none can claim to be completely successful, regular reference to the best of them will reveal trends and changes. An article in *Lloyds Bank Review* of January 1963 by Sir Robert Hall noted that national production per head of the population in Great Britain had changed over the centuries at very different rates. Before 1745 there was an annual output rise of 0·3% per head. In 1800 the rise was 0·9%, and in 1950 it was 2–2·5%. Agriculture declined in importance from the largest industry to one which now contributes less than 5% of the national income. It was replaced by mining, manufacturing, and building, which are now declining in relation to the growing distribution and service industries. The percentage composition of gross domestic production in the United Kingdom during the period 1950–60 was made up in the following proportions: agriculture 5·1, mining 3·3, manufacturing 36·8, construction 5·7, utilities 2·4, transport 8·6, and services 38·1.

The article includes a valuable table taken from the 1961 World Economic Survey of the United Nations, showing growth rates per annum for countries and industries during 1950–60. As a country's standard of development increases there is a tendency for its rate of increase of production to fall. For example, Japan showed outstanding rates of growth—18% per annum in manufacturing and 14% in textiles. By contrast, the United Kingdom showed 3·5% and −1%. One of the major growth industries, chemicals, increased at the rate of 18% in Japan and 6% in the United Kingdom.

Productivity measurements need careful interpretation, and it is frequently found that index numbers cannot help, since the underlying factors influencing production have become part of the index. Changes in labour, including output per man or man hour, the state of the economy at various dates, the efficiency of management, and methods of production are some of these factors.

Production can be measured in terms of money (Volume × Unit price), which, after due allowance is made for changes in money values, can be simple to compile; or in terms of man-hours and output, care being taken that changes in capital equipment per man are allowed for.

Several kinds of production index are feasible, including:

1. *Unadjusted indexes*, a simple index of unit of production × a factor such as man-hours, men employed, or machinery used. The practical difficulties are great when attempting to obtain statistics such as man-hours. The United Nations Statistics Office paper series M, number 4, suggests that the Standard Industrial Classification be used as the basis on which to organise production indexes, and this is frequently done.

2. *Seasonally corrected indexes*. Output fluctuates in a regular fashion owing to such recurring features as holidays in the summer and climatic variations. These can be allowed for, and several production series are so adjusted.

For a short discussion of this type of index, see Blyth, *Use of Economic Statistics*, pp. 97 ff. For details of the Central Statistical Office, see Marris, chapter 2. For criticisms see Paul Chambers' presidential address to the Royal Statistical Society, 1964.

CENTRAL STATISTICAL OFFICE INDEX OF INDUSTRIAL PRODUCTION

The importance of measuring productivity has already been discussed, and the Index of Industrial Production is the most important index designed to help in this. It is a "combined operation," being compiled by the Central Statistical Office in conjunction with the Statistics Divisions of the Board of Trade, the Ministry of Works, the Ministry of Power, the Ministry of Agriculture, the Ministry of Supply, the Admiralty, and other departments, as well as companies and trade associations.

Its aim is to reflect changes in the volume of industrial production in the United Kingdom, and as such it is an important indicator of the current economic situation, finding use in Government departments to help determine economic policy. It is also widely used by nationalised industry and by private companies, both to indicate general movements in industrial production and to show movements in particular industries. The Index is so straightforward that it is especially suitable as a layman's guide to growth.

There are two main "official" indicators of the movement of output, namely Estimates of the Gross Domestic Product (G.D.P.) and the Index of Industrial Production. The former measures *all* goods and services, and is published in the Quarterly and Annual National Income and Expenditure Accounts. The Index of Industrial Production measures *industrial* activity, which composes about half the G.D.P.—the other half is published in estimates of service activities annually.

Between 1948 and 1959 the gross domestic product expanded by nearly one-third. Industrial production increased to a larger extent, but erratically—services have increased less, therefore, but more steadily.

A full description of the Index is given in *The Index of Production: Method of Compilation* (Studies in Official Statistics, No. 7, H.M.S.O.), but in 1962 a revision was made which is intended to bring about improvements and additions to the series used. Reference should therefore be made to *Economic Trends*, No. 101, March 1962 (C.S.O.), which dealt with these changes in detail, but the description of the Index in *Official Statistics*, No. 7, remains unchanged. A further essay appeared in *Treasury Bulletin for Industry*, No. 161, March 1963, and a critical comment appeared early in April 1963 in *The Times*.

The base date

The new one is based on 1958 = 100, relying on the Census of Production of that year.

Average and weighting

The Index is fundamentally a ratio of quantities valued at last-year prices. Re-weighting is done if necessary after the results of the next Census of Production. The calculation uses a weighted arithmetic mean of quantity relatives, computed according to Laspeyres' formula. The weights are in proportion to the value of the work done in each industry, as shown by the latest Census of Production. It is measured by net output (before deducting depreciation), net output being equal to the selling value at factor cost of services, finished goods, and partly finished goods in the base year, less any costs incurred in their production which are payable to other industries. It therefore excludes work done outside the industry, such as advertising and insurance.

Production series

The new Index covers 880 items. Both capital and consumer goods produced by private or public bodies are included, whether for home, export, or military use. The series excludes agriculture, forestry, fisheries, distribution, transport, finance, and all other public and private services. The coverage is about 90% of the output of all industries.

Choice of the items

In general, figures of industrial *output* are used, since they are most readily available and are usually reliable. Other measures are work in progress, labour employed, and man-hours worked.

The following figures show the spread of items, but it should be noted that they were compiled for the 1954 Index. However, I assume that differences are small in the new one. Of the 880 items:

% of weights

48·1 are measured by Output: quantity delivered or produced.
35·6 are measured by Output: value of deliveries and sales.

Total: 83·7% measured by output.

13·7 are measured by Input: quality of major materials received.
2·6 are measured by Input: number of persons employed.

Total: 16·3% measured by input.

Value is preferred to quantity where the industry produces a great variety of items, and this is equally true of the engineering and construction industries. Where value *is* used, a deflated value series has been incorporated to try to eliminate the effects of price changes.

Input items are mainly used in Orders III, IX, XV, and XVI, for example, rubber and paper articles. Input is preferable where raw materials are highly significant.

Input of labour, where used, is adjusted for holidays and usually derives from the number of persons on the payrolls at the month end.

Calculation and adjustments

Changes in qualities of goods are incorporated into the Index; allowance is made in the original series for number of days in the month, but seasonal adjustments are not made until totals are reached. In 1961 a more detailed method of seasonal adjustment was made possible by the use of an electronic computer, aiming at smoother de-seasonalised series. The method used is basically the conventional ratio-to-moving-average method, but with refinements giving an improved trend. Most series cover calendar months, or weekly averages of four- or five-week periods.

All possible steps are taken to avoid delays in assembly and compilation. At present the Index is compiled about six to seven weeks after the end of the month, and even then revision in the total index may prove necessary later on.

Publication is widespread, being reported in most daily papers and often used in radio commentaries. The main sources are the *Board of Trade Journal, Monthly Digest of Statistics, Economic Trends,* and the *Annual Abstract of Statistics.* The student is recommended to read *The Provisional Index of Industrial Production,* by C. H. Feinstein, in *L.C.E.S. Bulletin* No. 47 (*Times Review,* September 1963).

The industries covered

For the complete list, weights and units, see *Economic Trends,* No. 101, March 1962. A selection follows, including in each case the estimated net output of the order in 1958. An asterisk (*) means that the item has 50% or more of the weights for the order. Note that most orders are incomplete as I give them.

S.I.C. Order Number		Weight	£ million
II	*Mining and quarrying*	71·73	700
	Coal mining	*	
	Stone and slate quarrying and mining		
III	*Food, drink, and tobacco*	85·98	850
	13 items, including all common foods and drinks, *e.g.* brewing and malting, sugar, and biscuits		
IV	*Chemicals and allied industries*	67·83	670
	15 items, including paints, dyestuffs, soaps, and polishes		
V	*Metal manufacture*	68·47	680
	Iron and steel (general)*		
	(*e.g.* pig iron, wrought iron, and finished steel)		
	Light metals, etc.		
VI	*Engineering and electrical goods*	166·88	1650
	32 classifications covering a very wide range, such as office machinery, photographic equipment, electrical machinery, insulated wires and cables		
VII	*Shipbuilding and marine engineering*	21·78	215
	Including both naval and merchant marine		

S.I.C. Order Number		Weight	£ million
VIII	*Vehicles*	79·08	780
	6 minimum list headings, the largest of which are the motor-vehicle sections		
IX	*Metal goods not elsewhere specified*	42·13	415
	7 headings, including bolts, nuts, etc., cans, cutlery, tools, etc.		
X	*Textiles*	58·25	575
	14 headings, covering natural and man-made fibres, jute, rope, lace, carpets, and textile finishing		
XI	*Leather, leather goods, and fur*	4·07	40
XII	*Clothing and footwear*	29·51	290
	All made-up clothing, boots and shoes, hats		
XIII	*Bricks, pottery, glass, cement, etc.*	28·08	280
	including abrasives and refractory goods		
XIV	*Timber, furniture, etc.*	19·95	200
	Seven headings, including hard and soft woods, bedding, sawmilling		
XV	*Paper, printing, and publishing*	54·66	540
	Five headings, including boxes, book-binding, etc.		
XVI	*Other manufacturing industries*	21·58	210
	Rubber, lino, toys, plastics, etc.		
XVII	*Construction*	125·95	1240
	Both for Great Britain and Northern Ireland		
XVIII	*Gas, electricity, and water*	54·07	530
	of which electricity* (60%)		

Sub-indexes

As part of the compilation process, the Government compiles sub-indexes, which then are incorporated into the Index. A selection of the more important sub-indexes follows.

Order VII: Shipbuilding, repairing, and marine engineering (M.L.H. 370)

This mainly measures work in progress on ships of over 100 tons gross. The Index measures the proportion of work done to the length of time it will take in all: it is multiplied by the gross tonnage of the ship and weighted by the relative value per ton of that type of ship. The total for all ships is then divided by the number of workers in the industry who are building merchant ships, and is expressed as an index.

Order VI: Munitions (M.L.H. 342)

A separate index in this order includes over 100 items of specialised defence equipment not elsewhere included.

Order VIII: Aircraft (M.L.H. 385)

This is an index of both defence and civilian items, covering 100 separately weighted series of quantities produced, and six of value produced or exported.

Order XI: Leather tanning and dressing (M.L.H. 431)

An index is based on 67 separately weighted series of quantities produced.

Order XII: Made-up clothing (M.L.H. 441–5, 449)

About 600 firms (50% of all concerned) report to the Board of Trade. These are manufacturers whose main business is production in tailoring, dress-making, overall, shirt, and underwear manufacture; the Index does not reflect the total sales of any particular type of garment. It is published monthly in the *Board of Trade Journal* with other textile statistics. Data are subject to wide seasonal fluctuations and need careful interpretation.

Order XVII: Construction (M.L.H. 500)

The Ministry of Works collects data quarterly and produces three separately weighted series of the value of work done, based on the number of workers engaged. The estimates are adjusted by indexes of building costs based on wages and cost of materials to obtain a measure of the quantity of output.

	% weight
1. *New work, not housing:* shops, offices, churches, industrial buildings, power stations, schools	29
2. *New work on housing,* public and private	31
3. *Repair and maintenance work*	40

Order VI: Engineering and electrical goods

In 1958 the estimated net output of the whole order was valued at £1650 million, with weighting of 16·7% of the whole Index. An index covering many of the minimum list headings of the order appears as a sub-index to the Index of Industrial Production and is published monthly in the form of Table 2 of two engineering index tables, covering volume of production, exports, and orders in hand, described below.

Returns are made of total deliveries and orders on hand from all except very small firms. It is not a measure of the final output of the industry because of variations in work in progress and stocks of finished goods and in the proportion of materials purchased (at constant prices) to output.

The section "Volume of Exports" is compiled from the Trade and Navigation Accounts, and shows changes in one section of the industry's final deliveries. It is not a measure of production for exports, nor does it record *when* goods are actually exported.

The section "Orders on Hand" represents *changes* in the total value at constant prices of orders held by firms in Order VI and is intended to aid illustrations of the pressure of changes on demand. Care must be taken not to misinterpret changes, since a rise or fall can be assigned to a multitude of causes, many requiring special knowledge of a sector of the industry. The two engineering index tables are entitled "Orders, Deliveries, Production and Exports in the Engineering Industries" and published monthly in the *Board of Trade Journal*. The two tables are:

1. *Engineering Industries: volume of orders and deliveries (not part of Index of Industrial Production)*

The table covers engineering and electrical goods (Order VI), locomotives and railway equipment, heavy commercial vehicles and wheeled tractors, using constant (average 1958) prices and covers both home sales and exports, in separate sections. It was introduced in 1960 (see *Board of Trade Journal*, 22nd July 1960) to show changes in demand and the extent to which the demand is being met. Sharp changes in orders received may not necessarily lead to sharp changes in levels of production, since order books may lengthen or shorten. Most companies supply data on orders on hand and deliveries net of cancellations. The series is expressed as index numbers which relate net new orders and deliveries each month to the monthly average rate at which deliveries were made in the base year. Orders on hand at the end of the month are related to base date orders on hand.

INDEX OF INDUSTRIAL PRODUCTION (average 1958 = 100)

S.I.C. order	Total all industries Seasonally adjusted (II–XVIII)	Mining and quarrying (II)	Total mfg. industries Seasonally adjusted (III–XVI)	Food, drink, and tobacco (III)	Chemical and allied industries (IV)	Metal manufacturing (V)	Engineering and electrical goods (VI)	Shipbuilding and marine engineering (VII)	Vehicles (VIII)	Metal goods not elsewhere specified (IX)	Textiles (X)	Leather, leather goods, and fur (XI)	Clothing and footwear (XII)	Bricks, pottery, glass, cement, etc. (XIII)	Timber, furniture, etc. (XIV)	Paper, printing, and publishing (XV)	Other mfg. industries (XVI)	Construction (XVII)	Gas, electricity, and water (XVIII)
1958	100	100	100	100	100	100	100	100	100	100	100	100	100	100	100	100	100	100	100
1959	105.2	97.4	106	103.6	110.7	104.5	105.4	93.6	100.3	99.8	105.6	103.3	111.5	106.9	111.9	107	108.2	105.6	102.6
1960	112.5	93.9	114.5	106.7	122.5	121.7	113.7	84.8	117.6	112.2	110.4	101.6	119.6	119	114.8	119.4	120.1	111.1	110.5
1961	113.9	92.6	114.7	110.2	124.4	114.5	121.2	85.7	109.3	104.7	106.6	102.4	121.9	124	115.1	119.7	115.9	119.6	115.6
1962	115	95	115.2	112	129	108	123	87	111	101	104	97	118	126	111	122	118	121	125
1963	118.9	95	119.8	115	138	113	126	77	120	108	109	99	120	130	113	128	126	121	133
19—																			

2. *Engineering and Electrical Goods Industries (Order VI): volume of production, exports and orders on hand*

This covers production (mechanical and electrical engineering) exports (based on 1954 = 100) and orders on hand, classified into "For export" and "For home market." Only the Volume of Production section of this table is incorporated into the Index of Industrial Production.

The Index of Industrial Production is given opposite (in a yearly form), but from time to time the individual classifications are made known in more detail. For example, in the *Board of Trade Journal* for 10th May 1963 the chemical industry is given (for 1962). This comprises part of Order IV including dyes, fertilisers, explosives, plastics, paints, varnishes, soaps, and detergents. These analyses are useful, since the classifications given in the main Index are wide and may mask conflicting movements. Thus the index for plastics materials reached 167 for 1962 and pharmaceuticals 142, but soaps and detergents only 108.

MINISTRY OF AGRICULTURE INDEX OF AGRICULTURAL NET OUTPUT IN THE UNITED KINGDOM

A completely new Index has been devised to replace the prewar (1936) one used until 1960, which employed weights relative to 1945–6 that are now out of date. The new Index has been re-defined, and it now measures changes in value added by industry to all goods and services it purchases, whether from abroad or from other industries. It is *separate* from the price indexes and does not replace them.

The Agriculture sector includes landlords, farmers, and farm workers, and the Index measures the value added by them during the processing of goods and the using of services bought from outside the industry. Agricultural merchants, distributors, contractors, feed processors, and veterinary surgeons are outside the scope of the sector.

Farm "output" includes plants and livestock, and is measured at the farm gate or the nearest sale point (*e.g.* auction market). Forestry and studs are excluded. The amount of "value added" is measured as the difference between the output of end products (*i.e.* those sold by farmers or used in their households) and the input of materials, products, and services from other industries, as adjusted for changes in work in progress. The period covered is the whole year.

Inputs consist of some 400 items: feedingstuffs 97, seeds 87, livestock 23, machinery 136, fertilisers 11, other inputs 44; *total* 398.

Outputs consist of: farm crops (wheat, barley, oats, potatoes, sugar-beet, and other) 28, livestock (cattle and calves, sheep, lambs, pigs, poultry) 20, livestock products (eggs for human consumption, milk and milk products, wool clip, other) 15, horticulture (vegetables in the open, under glass, top fruit, soft fruit, and flowers) 110, sundries 25, stock changes (growing crops, livestock) 52, miscellaneous grants and subsidies 21; *total* 271 categories.

To calculate the Index, the quantity of each individual item of output and input of any year is multiplied by (or weighted by) the price in the base period. The total net value in the base period provides the divisor for converting annual totals into index numbers. The base used is the average of prices ruling in 1954–5, 1955–6, and 1956–7 (these were the first three years of decontrol). Price weights are given gross, including the element of Government subsidy. The choice of items is flexible to allow for some differences in product quality and for differences in end use, *e.g.* apples of different qualities in the former case; and apples for domestic, culinary, or industrial use or milk for drink or manufacture in the latter case. Seasonal availability is also an important factor allowed for in the calculations.

For references see *Economic Trends*, March 1960; the White paper "Annual Review and Determination of Guarantees" 1960 (Cmd. 970) and annually; *Treasury Bulletin for Industry*, No. 129, April 1960.

NATIONAL INCOME AND EXPENDITURE OF THE UNITED KINGDOM

The problems of measuring the national income have fascinated both economists and statisticians for generations, although regular Governmental publication of estimates commenced as recently as 1940. Each year the Central Statistical Office issues a Blue book on National Income and Expenditure, which is a valuable attempt to do the impossible—measure changes in real national product, whose very definitions are blurred. For example, is administration part of the gross national product? Are the armed forces' munitions capital in a social or industrial sense? For a full discussion on these problems, the reader should consult C. A. Blyth, R. Marris, C.S.O. *National Income Statistics: Sources and Methods*; Carter and Roy, E. Devons, and M. G.

Kendall. In addition, regular reading of the bank reviews will reveal up-to-date essays on these topics.

The bulk of statistics published in the Blue book on income and expenditure are in "real" terms, but a description of the indexes found therein will be useful. The Blue book is produced by the C.S.O. in collaboration with other Government departments, and contains estimates of the national product, income and expenditure for several years, grouped into sections. It appears annually, and quarterly estimates are available in the *Monthly Digest of Statistics* and *Economic Trends.*

Ten headings are given (1962). Each is given below, with details only where index numbers are involved.

1. *Summary tables*

An overall picture of the gross national product is given in the dozen tables 1–12, all in monetary terms.

2. *Output and expenditure at constant prices*

Of three tables under this head, two are indexes.

(*a*) Table 13 describes the national income at constant (1958) prices in £, but also gives indexes of gross national product and gross domestic product (G.N.P. includes overseas net incomes) with 1958 = 100. Part of it follows.

United Kingdom Gross National and Domestic Products
(1958 = 100)

	1951	1952	1953	1954	1955	1956
Gross Domestic Product at factor cost	86·3	86·4	89·9	93·4	96·4	98·7
Gross National Product at factor cost	86·6	86·3	89·7	93·3	95·9	98·3
Net National Product at factor cost	87·3	86·7	90·2	93·8	96·3	98·9

	1957	1958	1959	1960	1961	1962
Gross Domestic Product at factor cost	100·3	100	103·2	107·7	111·3	111
Gross National Product at factor cost	100	100	103·1	107·4	110·9	111
Net National Product at factor cost	100·4	100	102·9	107·3	110·6	110·3

(b) Table 14 consists of index numbers of output at 1958 factor cost, divided into industries and services under major group headings. The G.D.P. consists of the total of goods and services arising within the economy of a country measured by either: (i) expenditure at constant prices, or (ii) by products. The sum of the net products of all industries is the G.D.P. Each individual industry's net product is the value of its total output minus its input from other home industries and from imports.

Table 14 uses a wide range of indicators, including indexes. For details, see C.S.O. *National Income Statistics*, Chapter III and Appendix IV, and *Economic Trends* of August 1960.

In the Blue book all years from 1951 to date are given, but a selection is given here.

Index of output at 1958 factor cost (1958 = 100)

	1951	1954	1958	1960	1961	1962	1963	19—
Agriculture, forestry, fish	90	95	100	110	112	114	119	
Mining and quarrying	104	106	100	94	93	95	95	
Manufactures								
Food, drink, tobacco	85	91	100	107	110	112	115	
Chemicals, etc.	73	87	100	122	124	129	138	
Metals	92	99	100	122	114	108	113	
Engineering, etc.	80	89	100	112	113	115	119	
Textiles, leather, clothing	108	110	100	113	111	109	112	
Other	87	95	100	118	118	120	125	
Total manufactures	86	94	100	114	115	115	120	
Construction	83	95	100	111	120	121	121	
Gas, electricity, and water	72	84	100	110	116	125	133	
Transport and communications	93	97	100	109	112	113	116	
Distribution	83	91	100	109	112	112	117	
Insurance, banking, and finance	81	89	100	118	120	122	128	
Ownership of dwellings	90	93	100	104	106	108	110	
Professional and scientific services	80	86	100	106	109	112	116	
Miscellaneous services	90	93	100	109	111	115	118	
Public administration and defence	108	110	100	97	97	99	99	
Gross domestic product	87	94	100	110	112	113	117	

(c) Table 15 relates to index numbers of costs and prices, with 1958 = 100. The first part of the table derives from statistics used in previous tables; the second part consists of currently weighted average-value indexes. Some years have again been omitted in the following table.

Index numbers of costs and prices (1958 = 100)

	1951	1954	1958	1960	1961	1962	1963	19—
			Indexes of costs					
Home costs per unit of output:								
Income from employment per unit of output [1]	73	82	100	104	109	115	115	
Gross profits and other trade income per unit of output [2]	74	89	100	108	106	109	113	
Total [3]	73	84	100	103	107	111	112	
Imports of goods and services [4]	112	99	100	100	100	100	103	
			Indexes of prices [4]					
Consumer goods and services	79	87	100	101	104	108	109	
Fixed assets	77	86	100	100	102	105	107	
Goods and services sold on the home market	78	85	100	102	105	109	111	
Export goods and services	93	91	100	101	101	104	104	
Final output [5]	80	86	100	102	105	108	110	

[1] Derives as the product of: $\dfrac{\text{Estimates of income from employment}}{\text{Estimates of G.D.P. at 1958 factor costs}}$ expressing the result as a percentage of the same quotient for 1958.

[2] In a similar manner: $\dfrac{\text{Estimates of G.D.P. and other trading income}}{\text{Estimates of G.D.P. at 1958 factor cost}}$ allowing for stock appreciation.

[3] In a similar manner: $\dfrac{\text{Estimates of G.D.P. at current factor cost}}{\text{Estimates of G.D.P. at 1958 factor costs}}$

[4] Each price index is the result of dividing an estimated total for the year in question at current prices by a corresponding total revalued at 1958 prices.

[5] Goods and services (home and imports) available for private and public consumption investment and export, valued at market prices.

3. *Industrial input and output*

These two tables (16 and 17) measure G.D.P. by industry and type of income, *e.g.* Mining and quarrying: wages, salaries, employers' contributions.

4. *The personal sector*

Seven tables (18–24) deal with consumer spending, taxes, subsidies, and distribution of incomes both before and after taxation; categories of personal income, *e.g.* wages, pensions; and the capital account of the personal sector, including hire-purchase debt, insurance, etc.

Table 20 is an index table, derived from Table 19, which measures consumers' spending at 1958 prices in sterling, partly from the Retail and Wholesale Price Indexes and partly from special indicators. The group classification is identical with the Retail Price Index. The actual table contains 33 sub-groups, which are not all given below.

Consumers' expenditure: index numbers of prices (1958 = 100)

	1951	1954	1958	1960	1961	1962	19—	19—
Food	73	87	100	101	102	106		
Alcoholic drink	92	94	100	93	97	103		
Tobacco	89	90	100	105	111	118		
Housing	69	78	100	109	114	120		
Fuel and light	65	78	100	101	104	108		
Clothing	95	95	100	101	103	106		
Durable goods	90	91	100	97	98	98		
Other household goods	90	90	100	102	104	107		
Books, papers, magazines	67	73	100	103	113	120		
Vehicle running costs	84	93	100	102	105	108		
All other goods	95	90	100	97	101	103		
Travel	72	82	100	108	114	120		
Communications	62	70	100	99	101	107		
Cinemas	69	81	100	107	110	118		
Other services	77	85	100	105	108	113		
Total consumer expenditure	79	87	100	101	104	108		

5. Companies

Five tables (25–9) cover the appropriation accounts and profits of companies.

6. Public corporations

Five tables (30–4) deal with the operations, capital, and appropriation accounts of public corporations, *e.g.* transport, housing, etc.

7. Central government

Four tables (35–8) deal with revenue and capital accounts showing the source of funds (*e.g.* taxes on income, customs duties, etc.) and expenditure (on goods, services, grants, interest). The capital account shows receipts from, for example, sales of securities, and the increase in capital formation (factories, General Post Office, Civil Defence).

8. Local authorities

Two tables (39–40) on current and capital accounts.

9. Combined public authorities

Six tables (41–6) link local and central authorities, since their spending and methods of collecting revenue are similar and designed for the same end, *e.g.* education, the fire service, police.

10. Capital formation

Fifteen tables (47–61) give important information about the creation of capital by industry, by type of asset, and by sector (public or private) and about the financing of investments by companies, persons, and governments.

References are given above. Regular publications include the Central Statistical Office's *National Income and Expenditure*, published by H.M.S.O. annually; the annual White paper on National Income, published before the budget; quarterly estimates in the *Monthly Digest of Statistics*, and regular articles in *Economic Trends*.

Information comes from a variety of official records, including Inland Revenue returns, the various Board of Trade censuses, Government accounts; and use is made of industrial records.

THE LONDON & CAMBRIDGE ECONOMIC SERVICE QUARTERLY INDEX OF REAL PRODUCT

The L.C.E.S. assembles much material from a variety of sources and presents this with interpretations in its *Bulletin*. The Service (University of Cambridge Department of Applied Economics) calculates one independent series, the Real Product Index, whose aim is to show seasonally adjusted changes in each quarter in the gross domestic product at constant factor cost. When the Index was introduced the L.C.E.S. considered that the lack of coherent, up-to-date information was an obstacle to understanding the current economic position. It attempted to overcome this by two analyses:

1. A seasonally adjusted quarterly series for the main categories of consumer spending at constant prices.

2. An index of production covering services as well as industrial production, relatively up-to-date and seasonally adjusted. National income data will be often as much as a year old when published, and the L.C.E.S. attempt to overcome this.

The Index is intended for the use of economists, statisticians, businessmen, and others interested in short-term fluctuations in the economy. The items are all components of the gross domestic product and based on 1958 = 100, weighted in terms of the contribution of each section to the G.D.P. in 1958.

For the first description, see the *Bulletin* No. 17, in the March 1956 issue of *The Times Review of Industry*: "Production and Consumption—some new quarterly series," by A. A. Adams.

Each issue of the *Bulletin* is quarterly in *The Times Review of Industry and Technology*.

BOARD OF TRADE INDEX OF THE VOLUME OF TOTAL ORDERS AND DELIVERIES IN THE TEXTILE AND CLOTHING INDUSTRIES

These industries are regarded as reasonably sharp indicators of the state of trade, but it should be noted that they are subject to considerable seasonality in demand. There is not necessarily a strong correlation between orders on hand and deliveries, since sharp changes in orders may indicate a lengthening or shortening of order books or levels of stocks and need not be followed at once by a similar change in production.

INDEX OF VOLUME OF TOTAL ORDERS AND DELIVERIES IN THE TEXTILE AND CLOTHING INDUSTRIES

At constant (average 1958) prices

Year	Quarter	Orders on hand (end of period) April 1959 = 100	Net new orders * Average 1959 delivery = 100	Deliveries * Average 1959 delivery = 100
1959	1			
	2	107	105	100
	3	119	108	96
	4	135	122	107
1960	1			
	2	137	103	101
	3	130	89	95
	4	136	112	107
1961	1	129	95	103
	2	124	94	99
	3	107	77	94
	4	104	97	99
1962	1	98	91	96
	2	99	90	91
	3	92	83	89
	4	100	103	97
1963	1	100	96	95
	2	104	96	92
	3	101	89	92
	4	118	119	102

* Adjusted for differences in length or month but not for holidays or other seasonal variations.

The industries are to a high degree sensitive to fashion, on the one hand, and to prices of raw materials, on the other. This is reflected in order books, which usually cover deliveries of two to five months—much shorter than most engineering firms'. However, they do resemble engineering in the habit of firms' working to specific orders from customers (although some output is made for stock).

The industries are wool, hosiery, and other knitted goods; made-up clothing; and the spinning, weaving, and merchant converting sections of the cotton and man-made fibre industries.

The Index measures the volume of deliveries, prices being held constant at the average of 1958. The bases are: orders on hand (end of period)—April 1959 = 100; net new orders—average 1959 delivered = 100; deliveries—average 1959 delivered = 100. Deliveries have been adjusted to allow for differences in the length of calendar months but not for holidays or for other seasonal variations.

Data are not available before April 1959. The Index was introduced in mid-1960 and appears monthly in the *Board of Trade Journal* with a short commentary. It differs in concept from the textile sections of the Index of Industrial Production. See the *Board of Trade Journal* for 22nd July 1960.

"NEW YORK TIMES" WEEKLY INDEX OF BUSINESS ACTIVITY

The aim of the Index is to show fluctuations of business volume without dollar-value distortions, by the use of production and distribution data. That is to say, measurements are made only in actual physical volume of production, *not* in prices.

There are five major components: freight-car loadings, steel-mill activity, electric power output, paperboard output, and lumber production. They are chosen for their importance as barometers of the state of the American economy. Each component gives two kinds of information: (*a*) news about each major industry, and (*b*) news about its customers. Each one has its own base, and a compromise 100 = the estimated "normal" is used as a base for the whole Index. The individual norms are: 48,000 miscellaneous car loadings a day (average 1928–37); 72,000 other car loadings (average 1928–37); 69% of steel ingot capacity (average 1919–39); for electric power production a straight-line rising trend with a weekly increase of 186,000 kWh in the daily average; 20,240 tons of paperboard a day (average 1933–9); 35,660 thousand ft of lumber a day (average 1933–9).

Each week the production data are divided by the number of working days in that particular week. This figure is then divided by the seasonal variation, each being seasonally adjusted except steel (a long-term trend is applied to steel and electric power, the data for these being divided by the long-term trend figures to obtain a growth element). The figure thus obtained is multiplied by an assigned weight to give the weekly Index figure.

The weights for the components of the combined Index are as follow:

	Effective weights	Adjusted weights
Miscellaneous car loadings	22	0·21
Other car loadings	12	0·13
Steel ingot production	25	0·10
Electricity production (power)	17	0·38
Paperboard production	12	0·10
Lumber production	12	0·08

The adjusted weights are obtained from the effective weights by dividing the sum of the individual weighted items by the range of each index of the periods from 1934 to 1939. The purpose of this is to give assigned weights their due value, undistorted by varying cyclical amplitudes of the various components.

The weekly figures appear on different days each week, and on Sunday are combined into the weekly index (plus a chart). The component indexes are multiplied by an adjusted weight as given above. The result is added and the total is multiplied by 1·024, which is an adjusting factor introduced when automobiles and cotton mills were dropped. A few figures from two years follow:

New York Times *Index of Business Activity monthly averages*

	Miscellaneous car loadings	Other car loadings	Steel	Electric power	Paperboard	Lumber	Monthly average
			1950				
Jan.	136	68	145	181	202	90	152
Mar.	121	90	120	184	198	105	150
May	120	95	155	188	220	106	158
July	123	97	150	191	180	100	158
Sept.	122	98	153	194	208	111	162
Nov.	135	94	158	197	229	118	168

	Miscellaneous car loadings	Other car loadings	Steel	Electric power	Paperboard	Lumber	Monthly average
			1959				
Jan.	120	61	151	315	260	120	209
Mar.	115	68	190	317	304	117	218
May	118	78	191	318	329	111	222
July	106	70	160	328	260	108	208
Sept.	90	55	24	305	300	109	192
Nov.	120	70	*	307	328	127	210

* From 26 (7th November) to 183 (28th November). Why?

"STEEL" INDUSTRIAL PRODUCTION INDEX

The American magazine *Steel* published in Cleveland, Ohio, issues each week an index designed to chart the weekly progress of United States industry, with special emphasis on metal working, mining, refining, smelting, and fabrication of metals into components or end-products. Based on 1957–9 = 100, it consists of four elements: (*a*) output of electricity; (*b*) production of ingot steel; (*c*) production of automobiles and trucks; (*d*) railway loading of revenue freight cars.

Each week the latest Index reading is made up from preliminary data or estimates and revised for the final figure the following week. The preliminary figure in the Monday-morning issue is for the week ended Saturday nine days earlier. The four elements comprise:

1. *Electricity output (weight 32):* the weekly average (using Edison Electricity Institute of New York data) for the base was 5,289,500,000 kWh.

2. *Steel (weight 35):* derived from estimates of the members of the American Iron & Steel Institute, New York. At the base date the weekly average was 1,606,500 net tons.

3. *Automobile and truck production (weight 11):* obtained from an agency in Detroit, Ward's Automotive Reports, which are based on production schedules each week. The weekly output at base date was 104,325 units.

4. *Freight car loading (weight 22):* data are obtained through the Association of American Railroads. The base figure was 786,486 cars.

FEDERAL RESERVE SYSTEM REVISED INDUSTRIAL PRODUCTION INDEX

The Board of Governors of the Federal Reserve System, Washington, U.S.A., publishes two major series, an Industrial

Production Index, and Department Store Sales and Stocks, both on seasonally adjusted and on unadjusted bases.

Index of U.S. industrial production

The Production Index was originally presented in 1927 and is periodically revised. It contains a wide coverage of industries and since, in general, industrial production tends to be subject to wider fluctuations than the economy as a whole it serves as a rapid indicator of changes which may soon affect all economic activity.

The Federal Reserve Board does not compile its own basic industrial statistics but makes use of a wide variety of series compiled by both Government and private sources relating especially but not exclusively to physical output.

The Index measures the physical volume of output of manufacturing, mining, and utilities, covering one-third of the national income, but is not a measure of *total* economic activity (that is provided by estimates of the gross national product). It is now based on 1957 = 100 (previously 1947–9 = 100).

The 1927 Index comprised 60 series of 35 industries with 1923–5 = 100. Frequent revisions included one in 1953, when the base was shifted to 1947–9 and a thorough rearrangement made. Annual series, as well as the original monthly series, were begun too. These have a much wider coverage (about 1400 compared with 175 in the monthly series). Most components come from U.S. Government agencies, while the rest come from trade associations and their publications. The S.I.C. is mainly used for classification.

In 1959 a thorough revision was made, many new features being added and comparative data brought up to date. Coverage has been broadened to include Utilities to facilitate comparison of the U.S. Index with other countries'. The changes may be summarised as follows:

1. Expanded coverage (as above).

2. New market groupings—the present 207 series are now newly grouped into broad market categories: Consumer Goods, Equipment, Materials. Cyclical and growth changes shown by these separate groupings are useful in analysing general economic developments on a monthly basis. By aiding comparisons between the production of materials and finished products, and between output of finished products and final sales or expenditure data, the market groupings contribute to an analysis of strategic fluctuations in industrial

output and inventories. The total and summary groupings are as follows:

	Weights (%)
(a) By industry	
(i) Total industrial production	100
(ii) Manufacturing: total	86·49
durable	49·66
non-durable	36·83
(iii) Mining	86·49
(iv) Utilities	4·96
(b) By market	
(i) Total final products and materials	100
(ii) Consumer goods	31·13
(iii) Equipment, including defence	15·62
(iv) Materials	53·25

3. More up to date through various surveys such as the annual census surveys, 1954 Census of Manufactures, etc.

4. A number of new monthly series developed.

5. A new base year adopted.

6. The latest S.I.C. adopted.

7. Better seasonal adjustment. For this purpose an electronic computer proved invaluable.

The Index is calculated by the following process:

1. The data of the individual industry or product are converted to a percentage of the average monthly output of that industry or product in the base period.

2. Weighting is then incorporated.

3. The items are combined to form indexes for the various published classifications.

4. These are combined to produce an overall index.

The Federal Reserve System publishes monthly index figures in each issue of the *Business Indexes Release.* As from January 1960 the *Federal Reserve Bulletin* gives the total Index, major industry and market groupings both seasonally adjusted and unadjusted, but does not supply most individual series.

For references see: *Federal Reserve Bulletin* Reprint 1451, "Revised Industrial Production Index"; F.R.S. *Industrial Production, 1959 Revision; The American Statistician,* Vol. 14, No. 1, 1960. *Federal Reserve Bulletin* "Selected Economic Indicators," December 1954.

INDEX OF TOTAL U.S. INDUSTRIAL PRODUCTION FROM 1919

1919	25	1929	38	1939	38	1949	64	1959	106
1920	26	1930	32	1940	44	1950	74	1960	109
1921	20	1931	26	1941	56	1951	81	1961	110
1922	25	1932	21	1942	69	1952	84	1962	118
1923	30	1933	24	1943	82	1953	91	1963	124
1924	28	1934	26	1944	81	1954	86	19—	
1925	31	1935	31	1945	70	1955	96		
1926	33	1936	36	1946	59	1956	99		
1927	33	1937	40	1947	65	1957	100		
1928	35	1938	31	1948	68	1958	94		

Comparison with the Index's British counterpart

The table below compares the British and United States indexes of Industrial Production and shows the relative importance of the major groupings.

THE UNITED KINGDOM AND U.S.A. INDUSTRIAL PRODUCTION INDEXES COMPARED

S.I.C.	Industry	U.K. (1958 = 100)		U.S.A. (1957 = 100)	
II	Mining and quarrying	72		86	
	Of which Coal mining		64		13
	Oil and natural gas		1		58
III	Food, drink, and tobacco	86		106	
	Of which Food		55		83
	Drink		22		15
	Tobacco		9		8
IV	Chemicals and allied	78		109	
	Including rubber, plastics, and petroleum products		37		
V	Metal manufacture	110		131	
IX	Of which iron and steel				62
VI	Engineering and electrical	167		150	
VII VIII	Transport equipment	63		110	
X	Textiles	58		28	
XI	Leather, etc.	4		11	
XII	Clothing and footwear	30		34	
XIII	Bricks, pottery, glass	28		29	
XIV	Timber, etc., furniture	20		32	
XV	Printing and publishing, paper	55		79	
XVI XVII	Other manufacturing Building	138		29	
XIII	Utilities	54		49	
	Totals	963		983	

QUESTIONS AND EXERCISES

1. For the purpose of an index of production, how would you measure changes in the production of: (*a*) a brewery; (*b*) a brass foundry; (*c*) the trades concerned with the construction and maintenance of dwelling-houses?   (*I.P.M. 1959*)

2. From the following data relating to the I.I.P., calculate for each of the years 1955–8 the following: (*a*) a combined "Textiles" and "Clothing and Footwear" index, and (*b*) an index for the residual industries.

| | | Average 1954 = 100 | | | |
Groups	Weights	1955	1956	1957	1958
Textiles	77	98	96	97	87
Clothing and footwear	33	104	106	105	101
All industries	1000	105	106	107	106

(I.M.S.M. 1960)

3. Describe the Index of Industrial Production. What are the main differences you expect to find between movements in this index and variations in the gross national product?   (*I.O.S.*)

4. Give an account of the current method of constructing *one* of the following official index numbers: (*a*) Index of Industrial Production; (*b*) Index of Wholesale prices (commodities only); (*c*) Index of Wage Rates.   (*I.O.S. 1960*)

5. Explain how an "Index of General Business Conditions in Great Britain" can be constructed. State what you would include as a necessity and where you would get the data.   (*R.S.A. 1958*)

6.

	Index of production (all industries)	Electricity supply generated for public use (monthly avs.) million kWh	Total in civil employment (June) (000's)	Value of exports (monthly avs.) (£ million)
1954	100	6075	22,604	220·5
1955	105	6679	22,933	239·3
1956	106	7263	23,149	261·5
1957	107	7581	23,245	274·2
1958	107	8209	23,080	264·3

Show these figures in a graph so as to bring out their relative movements.   (*I.M.T.A. 1959*)

7. "The British Index of Industrial Production fails in its purpose: it does not measure either the changing output of firms grouped into industries, or the movement in production of particular types of commodity." Discuss.   (*University of London 1961*)

8. Discuss the problem of obtaining index numbers of the volume of capital used in manufacturing industry. (*University of London 1961*)

9. Discuss the main problems met in designing and compiling an index of industrial production.   (*University of London 1957*)

10. Describe how you would make adjustments for the contributions of small firms in calculating an index number of the physical volume of production based on the census of production material.

(*University of Manchester 1955*)

11. The "Index of Industrial Production" table in the *Monthly Digest of Statistics* shows an index of production for all industries plus the same index "seasonally adjusted." Explain briefly the principles upon which the index is calculated and how the seasonal adjustment is made. Why is there a seasonally adjusted index as well as the original index?

(*University of Bristol 1960*)

12.   *Index of Industrial Production (average 1954 = 100)*

Industry	Weight	Percentage increase in production 1960
1. Food	53	+13
2. Drink and tobacco	28	+26
3. Textiles	77	− 5
4. Clothing and footwear	33	+20
5. Bricks, cement, etc.	19	+ 8
6. China and earthenware	4	+ 3
7. Glass	7	+35
8. Timber, furniture, etc.	22	+ 3
9. Paper, printing, and publishing	53	+33
10. Manufacturing industries	22	+34
Total	318	

(*a*) Calculate the Index of Industrial Production for the above groups combined for 1960.

(*b*) There are 22 groups in the complete Index, with total weights of 1000. If the complete Index for 1960 was 120·3, what was the Index for that year for the remaining twelve groups?

(*c*) Explain what the "weights" in the above table represent, and how they are derived.   (*Queen's University of Belfast 1962*)

13. (*a*) What information published in the *Monthly Digest of Statistics* would you use to measure changes in productivity in any one industry?

(*b*) How would you use the information?

(*c*) Indicate any weakness inherent in your method.

(*I.C.W.A. 1962*)

14. Calculate and interpret the correlation coefficient between the changes in output and productivity given in the table below:

Index numbers of output and productivity in manufacturing for 1954
(1948 = 100)

	Output	Productivity
Bricks, china, glass	127	121
Chemicals	138	139
Metals	121	118
Engineering	110	119
Vehicles	143	122
Other metal goods	112	112
Precision instruments	126	134
Textiles	111	105
Leather	98	110
Clothing	113	112
Food	111	101
Drink and tobacco	101	101
Wood and coke	128	127
Paper and printing	127	107
Other manufacturing	126	124

(University of Liverpool 1961)

CHAPTER 16

STATISTICS OF LABOUR

A CONSIDERABLE volume of statistics is compiled about labour. In Britain the majority come from the Ministry of Labour, which has a statutory duty to assemble and publish them. In the following pages the index numbers are briefly described. Here are the principal ones and the main facts about them.

MINISTRY OF LABOUR: GENERAL LABOUR STATISTICS

Labour statistics were first compiled by the Board of Trade in the 1880s and became the responsibility of the Statistics Department of the Ministry of Labour in 1917. This office continues to produce them comprehensively, including figures for the number insured in employment, estimates of the total working population, figures for unemployment, wages and hours of work, data on retail prices, trade-union disputes, and membership of the unions.

The available series of wage data are:

1. *The Index of Weekly Rates of Wages:* this measures, monthly, the movement of full time or standard weekly time rates for all industries.

2. *Details of average weekly earnings:* this shows earnings for certain industries and is produced twice a year, in April and October. The data are affected by the number of hours worked (including overtime and short time) and by absenteeism.

3. *Annual estimates of the national wage bill:* these appear in the Blue book on national income.

4. *Hourly Rates of Wages Index:* this is derived from the Weekly Rates Index and published monthly. It corrects the weekly rates according to changes taking place in the length of the normal working week (for which there is an index).

5. *Seasonally adjusted quarterly estimates of wages and salaries:* the seasonal variations such as Christmas are eliminated as far as possible.

6. *Index of Average Salaries:* this extends wage statistics to salaried workers.

7. *Index of Average Earnings.*

Wage rates and normal hours of work

Efficient recording began in 1909 with the first Trade Boards Act covering four specific trades (later increased to eight). This was superseded by the 1945–8 Wages Councils Acts; today other authority includes the 1948 Agricultural Wages Act (1949 in Scotland). Now all the Wages Councils Acts are consolidated in the Wages Councils Act of 1959. Hourly rate statistics date from 1920.

Indexes of wage-rates and hourly rates are the only indicators of very recent changes in the incomes of industrial wage-earners. They measure only a part (though the main part) of the changes which take place. The Hourly Rate Index has indicated changes in the incomes of wage-earners more accurately than Weekly Rate Index.

They are a reasonably satisfactory means of measuring the *real incomes* of wage-earners. Hourly rate movements can be compared with output per man, which will give a rough idea of changes in "unit labour costs." The following figures indicate the way the rates have moved in the last decade or so in Great Britain: they show the percentage changes.

	1947–51	1951–5	1955–9
Hours of work	These have changed little during the period		
Weekly rates	+26	+22	+19
Hourly rates	+29	+22	+20
Weekly earnings	+36	+33	+22
National wages bill	+37	+32	

Early in the 1947–51 period the week was shortened by almost 2%; in 1951–5 it was almost unchanged, and by the end of 1955–9 it fell $\frac{1}{2}$%.

The divergence between the hourly rate and increase in earnings has been caused by upgradings, wage increases in excess of those negotiated, increased productivity, and changes in the combination and distribution of the labour force.

The earnings figures cover about two-thirds of manual workers, excluding agriculture, coal, railway, shipping, docks, distribution, catering, and entertainment.

Ministry of Labour Index of Weekly Rates of Wages

The aim of the Index is to measure changes in the incomes of industrial wage-earners, thus giving a guide to real incomes. It measures the average movement from month to month in

K

the level of full-time weekly rates of wages in the principal industries and services in the United Kingdom on a base of 31st January 1956 = 100 (in the previous series June 1947 = 100). No account is taken of changes in working hours, nor of the earnings of piece-workers and others paid by results, nor of the introduction of new machinery (the reader might now refer to the *Guardian* Index).

Eighty industries and services are represented (previously there were 75), covering the S.I.C. except order XXI (Insurance, banking, and finance). The weights as at February 1959 were:

S.I.C. order	Industry group	Index of weekly wages	Index of normal weekly hours
I	Agriculture, forestry, and fisheries	399	524
II	Mining and quarrying	758	536
III	Food, drink, and tobacco	425	485
IV	Chemical industries	258	241
V–IX	Metal manufacture, engineering and electrical goods, shipbuilding and marine engineering, vehicles, metal goods not elsewhere specified	2,733	2,332
X	Textiles	487	589
XI	Leather and fur	38	44
XII	Clothing and footwear	237	341
XIII	Bricks and similar materials	224	207
XIV	Timber, furniture, etc.	184	178
XV	Paper, printing, and publishing	307	290
XVI	Other manufacturing industries	155	153
XVII	Construction	979	864
XVIII	Gas, electricity, and water	205	186
XIX	Transport and communications	951	869
XX	Distribution trades	798	1,030
XXII	Professional and scientific services	98	124
XXIII	Miscellaneous services	471	660
XXIV	Public administration and defence	294	347
	Total weights	10,000*	10,000
	Total of manufacturing industries only (orders III–XVI)	5,047	4,860

* Do not add up owing to rounding.

The rates used

Many rates or systems of payment are found in industry. The Index takes the minimum or standard rates for manual workers, including shop assistants but excluding clerical, technical, and administrative workers.

1. *Time workers.* The Index is regarded as reliable, although wages do vary above or below standard. For boys and youths, the mean of rates at 16, 17, 18, 19, and 20 years is taken, for girls the mean of 16 and 17 years.

2. *Shift workers.* Account is taken of differential rates paid at the various times.

3. *Piece-workers.* In industries where both piece- and time-rates are common, account is taken of both. Piece-work wages are commonly made up of two elements:

(*a*) Earnings derived from basic piece-rates (or, on occasion, basic times). Sometimes this is determined by collectively agreed piece price lists applicable to a whole industry or section (*e.g.* cotton), but is more often by piece price lists for individual firms (*e.g.* engineering).

(*b*) Additions to the basic rates in the form either of a percentage or a flat-rate money amount paid in addition to piece-work earnings. As a rule this is determined by collective agreement.

4. *District rates.* Where wages vary from one district to another the Index takes this into account. The district rates are combined in proportion to the numbers of workers employed in the selected districts at the base date.

Weighting

Weights were obtained principally from the Earnings and Hours Enquiry in October 1955 and from estimated numbers of manual workers in each industry.

These weights are used in separate industries which are combined for the purpose of producing index numbers for "all industries and services" and for "manufacturing industries only." The weights are approximately in proportion to the aggregate weekly wages bill in each of the selected industries. Thus the Index at any time represents the net change in the weekly wages bill had it been affected only by changes in wage-rates and not by any other factors.

The Index is published each month. The first series came out in 1880, and the 1956-based Index was the eighth. It appears under "Wages and Hours of Work" in company with other indexes and a commentary. It is regarded as sufficiently reliable to provide a measure of the average movement of wage-rates for men, and juveniles separately.

INDEX OF WEEKLY RATES OF WAGES

(31st January 1956 = 100)

1. *All industries and services (yearly data only shown)*

Monthly average	Men	Women	Juveniles	All workers
1956	105	104	106	105
1957	110	110	111	110
1958	114	114	116	114
1959	117	117	120	117
1960	120	121	123	120
1961	125	125	130	125
1962	129	130	136	130
1963	134	136	141	134
19—				

2. *Industry groups, all workers (a selection from the eighteen given)*

	1959	1960	1961	1962	1963	19—
Agriculture, forestry, and fisheries	117	120	127	132	138	
Chemicals, etc.	112	115	118	124	131	
Textiles	112	116	121	124	128	
Construction	120	122	125	133	138	
Professional	119	123	129	134	140	

Index of Hourly Rates of Wages

This Index takes account of changes in the normal working week. The *Weekly* Index does not reflect changes in actual earnings, which may be due to such factors as alterations in working hours or in earnings of piece-workers and other payment-by-result workers because of variations in output or the introduction of new machines. Thus the *Weekly* Index shows no movement when the normal weekly hours of work are altered without any corresponding change in weekly rates of pay.

The Index can be calculated, showing, every month, changes ˅al weekly hours of work. It uses the following formula:

ᵀourly Wage-rates =

$$\frac{\text{Index of Weekly Wage-rates}}{\text{Index of Number of Normal Weekly Hours}} \times 100.$$

INDEX OF HOURLY RATES OF WAGES

All industries and services (yearly data only shown)
31st January 1956 = 100

	Men	Women	Juveniles	All workers
1956	105	104	106	105
1957	110	110	111	110
1958	114	114	116	114
1959	117	118	119	117
1960	122	123	126	123
1961	130	131	136	130
1962	136	137	143	136
1963	141	143	148	141
19—				

Index of Average Salaries

Manual workers' wage indexes have been compiled for some years, but recently there has been a demand, which is now being met, for similar statistics relating to rates of salaries and changes in the earnings of salaried employees.

The Ministry relies on two sources of information. First, since 1955 non-manufacturing industries have submitted data voluntarily. These include local and central government, nationalised industries, the National Health Service, education (teachers), banking, and insurance.

The second source relates to administrative, technical, and clerical workers in manufacturing and other industries. In 1959 the Ministry took over from the Board of Trade the responsibility of collecting information on the earnings of these workers, under the authority of the 1947 Statistics of Trade Act.

In 1961 the available information covered 2,165,000 male and 1,500,000 female workers of a total of 7,000,000 salaried workers in the United Kingdom.

Each year the Ministry publishes a table in respect of all industries supplying information. This shows average money earnings and an index (from 1959 onwards) of salaried employees. The tables relate to the October of the previous year, and are based on October 1959 = 100.

In time this index will provide a useful measure of comparison between "salaried" and "weekly" workers, although the fact of its appearing annually naturally means that it cannot be a rapid indicator of changes in earnings.

NUMBERS OF SALARIED EMPLOYEES COVERED BY RETURNS

Average earnings and indexes of changes in average earnings
(October 1959 = 100)

October	Males			Females		
	Number of employees covered by returns	Average earnings monthly and weekly paid on a weekly basis	Index of change in average earnings	Number of employees covered by returns	Average earnings monthly and weekly paid on a weekly basis	Index of change in average earnings

Manufacturing industries

		£ s. d.			£ s. d.	
1959	1,059,200	18 6 2	100	527,900	7 10 0	100
1960	1,073,400	19 7 0	105·7	541,700	7 16 7	104·4
1961	1,105,200	20 7 1	111·2	550,600	8 5 4	110·2
1962	1,117,100	21 5 7	116·2	551,400	8 12 11	115·3
1963	1,141,700	22 5 9	121·7	554,600	8 19 9	119·8
19—						

Other productive industries (including mines, quarries, gas, electricity, water, and construction)

1959	218,600	16 17 3	100	74,700	8 5 10	100
1960	219,800	18 7 0	108·8	76,500	8 19 3	108·1
1961	225,400	19 2 9	113·5	77,900	9 6 7	112·5
1962	227,400	20 2 2	119·3	79,300	9 14 10	117·5
1963	233,400	21 4 7	125·9	80,900	10 3 4	122·6
19—						

Public administrative and certain other services (N.H.S., B.T.C., air, education, banks, and insurance)

1959	796,600	17 19 3	100	812,300	11 3 7	100
1960	810,200	18 19 4	105·6	834,000	11 15 4	105·3
1961	834,200	19 17 3	110·6	871,800	12 6 5	110·2
1962	855,200	21 4 4	118·1	898,700	13 2 11	117·6
1963	891,600	22 9 9	125·2	927,000	13 18 1	124·4
19—						

All services and industries covered

1959	2,074,000	18 0 6	100	1,414,800	9 13 1	100
1960	2,103,000	19 2 0	106	1,452,200	10 3 0	105·1
1961	2,165,000	20 0 9	111·2	1,500,300	10 13 6	110·6
1962	2,199,000	21 2 8	117·2	1,529,400	11 6 11	117·5
1963	2,266,700	22 5 1	123·5	1,562,500	11 19 4	123·9
19—						

Index of Average Earnings

An enquiry was initiated in November 1962 by the Ministry in response to a desire for regular information about total wages and salary earnings in industry. Each month 8000 firms with 6½ million workers (half the labour force of the industries concerned) report, and the resultant information supplements the six-monthly Manual and annual Salaried Worker Enquiries. It enables trends to be studied without long time-lags.

The enquiry form has been kept simple—a "shuttle" form is sent back and forth for several months to avoid the need to fill in repetitious details—and the number of firms involved kept small: all those employing 500 or more, but a sample of those employing fewer. Publication can be within six weeks of the month concerned.

The remuneration shown is gross, including overtime payments, bonuses, gifts, commission, etc., before tax or other deductions at source. It has been shown that, as regards weekly paid employees, there is little difference between the wages of salaried and manual workers and therefore the fact that employers have not been asked to provide both sets of information is considered insignificant. Geographical analyses have not been made, one reason being that some large concerns operate on a nation-wide basis, and derived data would not (in

INDEX OF AVERAGE EARNINGS IN GREAT BRITAIN
(January 1963 = 100)

Industry group	February 1963		All employees
	Employees paid each week	Employees paid monthly	
Manufacturing:			
Food, drink, and tobacco	100·2	98·3	99·9
Chemicals and allied metal	99·4	113	104·1
Engineering and electrical goods	100·4	103·2	102·5
Shipbuilding and repairing	99·8	104·6	100
Marine engineering	99·6	101·7	99·7
Vehicles	101·8	101·8	101·8
Metal goods not elsewhere specified	101·3	105·9	101·9
Textiles	100·9	102·1	101·1
Leather, leather goods, and fur	100·8	99·5	100·6
Clothing and footwear	100·8	102·9	101
Bricks, pottery, glass, and cement	102·4	101·3	102·2
Timber, furniture	103·3	93·8	102·3
Paper and paper products	99·6	102·7	100·1
Printing and publishing	101·2	101·7	101·3
Other manufacturing	101	101·5	101·2
Total	101	102·9	101·3
Other industries and services:			
Agriculture	98·4		98·4
Mining and quarrying	102·6	100·3	102·5
Construction	105	99	104·4
Gas, electricity, and water	99	100·4	99·3
Transport and communication	99·7	101·4	99·9
Miscellaneous	100·8	95·9	100·1
All industries and services	101·3	102	101·4

See the *Ministry of Labour Gazette*, March 1964.

many areas) show any geographical differences. Fluctuations from month to month may be due to the payment of large annual or half-yearly bonuses or to seasonal changes in average hours worked. At present it is not possible to assess the extent of these fluctuations.

From the *Ministry of Labour Gazette* of April 1963 data are provided monthly (the average of the twelve-monthly indexes for 1963 = 100) and in the fashion shown in the table given above.

Index of Normal Weekly Hours Worked by Operatives in Industry

The classification and coverage of industries and services is made to correspond with those for indexes of wages, and in the table of weights given earlier. Hours and wages weightings are both tabulated. The index has 31st January 1956 = 100 as the base, and data can be linked back to 1920.

The aim of the Index, which appears in the *Ministry of Labour Gazette,* is to measure the average movement from month to month in the level of normal weekly hours of work in the main industries and services, on similar lines to the official Index of Wage Rates. The hours are those corresponding to the rates payable in the Wages index, as laid down in voluntary collective agreements, in arbitration awards, or in wage regulation orders under the Wages Councils Acts or Agricultural Wages Act. In general, the normal weekly hours for day workers are exclusive of meal times, although shift workers' hours usually include an allowance for meals.

INDEX OF NORMAL WEEKLY HOURS

(31st January 1956 = 100)
All industries and services

Monthly average	Men	Women	Juveniles	All workers
1957	99·9	99·9	99·9	99·9
1958	99·7	99·6	99·8	99·7
1959	99·6	99·5	99·8	99·6
1960	97·9	98·3	98·1	98
1961	96	95·8	95·9	95·9
1962	95·1	95·1	95·1	95·1
1963	95·0	95·0	95·0	95·0
19—				

Index of Total Weekly Hours Worked by Operatives in Industry

This series, from which the next one of average hours is derived, is based on average 1962 = 100. Total weekly hours worked are calculated by multiplying a figure of the estimated number of operatives at work in a specified week each month by an estimate for the same week of the average number of hours worked by operatives. In the calculation, account is taken of overtime and short-time working, sickness, holidays, and of women part-time operatives' hours.

Revisions are liable to be made from time to time. For example, the details were revised back to July 1961 following information derived from the mid-1962 count of National Insurance cards and from May 1962 onwards through information obtained by the enquiry into the hours of manual workers.

The index of total hours worked provides for the first time a regular and frequent measure of changes in total hours worked by operatives in manufacturing industry which can be used for comparisons with the Index of Industrial Production.

From May 1961 both this and the following index are calculated for one week in each month, and the new base has been chosen as the twelve-monthly average for 1962 = 100 (see the *Ministry of Labour Gazette*, October 1963).

INDEX OF TOTAL WEEKLY HOURS WORKED

(Average 1962 = 100)

Year	All manu- facturing industry	Engineer- ing, electric goods, metal goods	Vehicles	Textiles, leather, clothing	Food, drink, and tobacco	Other manu- factures
1956	104·6	98·6	106·9	119	100·1	103·6
1957	103·9	98·6	104·6	117·7	99·5	103·1
1958	100·4	96·5	101·6	108·3	100·1	99·6
1959	100·9	96·3	104·9	108·6	99·1	100·5
1960	103·9	99·4	107·9	110·1	100·1	104·9
1961	102·9	101·9	102·9	104·7	100·1	103·7
1962	100	100	100	100	100	100
1963	98·2	97·5	99·2	98·2	98·2	98·8
19—						

Index of Average Hours Worked by Operatives in Industry

The data for average weekly hours worked by full-time operatives are estimated in the course of the calculations of the total weekly hours worked in the preceding table.

INDEX OF AVERAGE HOURS WORKED PER PERSON

(Average 1962 = 100)

Year	All manu- facturing industry	Engineer- ing, electrical, metal goods	Vehicles	Textiles, leather, clothing	Food, drink, and tobacco	Other manu- factures
1956	103·7	103·7	104·1	104·3	102·8	103·8
1957	103·6	103·5	104·5	104·5	102·7	103·7
1958	102·5	102·4	103·2	103	102·5	102·5
1959	103·3	102·8	104·9	104·5	102	103·2
1960	102·4	101·7	101·7	104·8	101·7	102·5
1961	101	101·3	100·6	101·1	100·4	101·1
1962	100	100	100	100	100	100
1963	99·8	99·6	100·2	100·5	99·8	100
19—						

"THE GUARDIAN" INDEX OF WAGES

The aim of the *Guardian* wage-rate indexes is to enlarge the detail of industrial wage information to help in the analysis of wage movements and to spotlight relative movements of wage-rates and wage earnings in the post-war period. Having the basic material available enables indexes to be calculated by other groupings, *e.g.* by degree of skill, by region, or by institutional form of wage fixing. Background details are given in the article "An Index of Wage-rates by Industries," by E. Devons and R. Ogley, in *The Manchester School* of May 1958.

1948 was chosen as the base year, since detailed statistics were available and at that time several significant indexes were based on 1948, most notably the Index of Industrial Production. The indexes are weighted in terms of the size of wage bills in the base year.

Two publications of the Ministry of Labour are used: the annual *Time Rates of Wages and Hours of Work*, which supplies wages rates as at 1st April for that year, and the monthly *M.L.G.* table "Principal Changes in Rates of Wages" of the previous month.

The rates shown are a summary of those agreed by collective-bargaining procedures and statutory wage fixing. Statutory rates account overall for $22\frac{1}{2}\%$ of the total weight; for women it is 46%, for men 18%. Such rates are common in agriculture, clothing, food, drink and tobacco, and miscellaneous service industries. To a lesser extent they affect textiles, leather manufacture, cork, paper and printing, and public administration.

Other rates in the *Ministry of Labour Gazette* are not incorporated into the Index, which is, however, quite comprehensive except for the exclusion of juveniles. Piece-rates and bonus payments do not come into the Index. An implicit assumption is that collectively agreed rates apply to all workers in the relevant industry, but it is impossible to say if this *is* so; again, the rates used are the minimum agreed, and so do not allow for excess payments which employers may make. Allowances in kind (such as cheap coal or meals provided with the job) are included.

Weighting by wage bill is derived from information available from the 1948 Census of Production. The Index is base weighted, with the intention of converting in due course to a current-year weighted index.

An article in *The Guardian* for 27th October 1961 by E. Devons and J. R. Crossley introduced an extended series of indexes. The original (continuing) one measured changes in *weekly* wage-rates (1948 = 100), but if and when the length of the working week changes the weekly wage and hourly wage indexes would obviously diverge. Since 1959 standard hours have changed considerably, and therefore new supplementary indexes show changes in wage-rates per hour, through the calculation:

$$\frac{\text{Weekly Wage Rate Index}}{\text{Index of Standard Hours per week}} \times 100.$$

Since data are lacking, both indexes are based on minimum rates, and do not measure *actual* wages.

Thus from October 1961 *The Guardian* publishes each month four indexes:

1. *The* Guardian *Wage Index*

Showing wages weekly classified by major industries and services, for men and women. Twenty-three headings include Vehicles, Mining and Quarrying, Gas, Electricity and Water, Clothing, Professional Services, and Textiles. Within each heading are more detailed groups, for example "Textiles" contains twelve groups, including Jute, Cotton Spinning, and Carpets. The monthly tables should be consulted in *The Guardian*, but for interest I show herewith a run of annual averages for a few selected groups.

Selected Index of Wage Rates (weekly)

(average 1948 = 100) annual averages

	Weight (out of) 1000)	1949	1950	1951	1952	1953	1954	1955	1956
				Men					
Agriculture	56	104	105	112	122	128	133	140	151
Coal mining	88	100	101	112	124	128	134	144	158
Cotton spinning	4	104	106	119	123	126	131	137	141
				Women					
Agriculture	29	104	106	113	123	128	133	140	151
Cotton spinning	26	103	106	118	122	126	130	136	141
Dressmaking	18	109	109	116	121	130	139	146	158

	Weight (out of 1000)	1957	1958	1959	1960	1961 Dec.	1962 Dec.	1963 June	19—
				Men					
Agriculture	56	159	168	174	178	189	203	205	
Coal mining	88	167	170	175	177	187	194	202	
Cotton spinning	4	147	151	151	162	169	174	174	
				Women					
Agriculture	29	159	168	174	178	189	194	205	
Cotton spinning	26	146	151	150	160	163	168	168	
Dressmaking	18	174	185	194	197	198	212	212	

2. *Index of Hourly Wage-rates*

Showing 23 broad groups on the 1948 = 100 base, using the same major industrial classification as (1) above.

3. *Index of Hourly Earnings*
4. *Index of Weekly Earnings*

The latter pair are issued every six months, following the Ministry of Labour's half-yearly survey of earnings and hours worked in industry.

The first two indexes appear monthly in *The Guardian*, in each issue of the N.I.E.S.R. *Economic Review*, and in each *Manchester School* May issue. See also *The Manchester School*, May 1958, May 1959, September 1959, January 1960, May 1960; *The Guardian*, 27th October 1961.

The calculations are made by Professor Ely Devons and J. R. Crossley of the London School of Economics with the help of the computer staff of L.S.E.

MANAGEMENT SELECTION LTD: INDEX OF TRENDS IN THE DEMAND FOR EXECUTIVES IN GREAT BRITAIN

Management Selection Ltd is a professional organisation which serves important companies in the role of management employment adviser and selector. A consultancy service has operated since 1955 and M.S.L. has developed a high standard of advertising for executives, which is considered a reliable guide to the supply and demand position.

Between October 1958 and September 1959 an analysis was prepared of advertisements for positions carrying a salary of not less than £1000, as placed in six national publications: *The Times, Daily Telegraph, The Guardian, The Observer, The Sunday Times,* and *The Economist.* The analysis covered positions from "assistant to," at £1000, to managing director at £10,000 or over; despite this considerable range, the analysis is believed to be a useful indicator of trends in demand. However, it does not show (say) how many scientists were given employment, nor was the pattern of managerial employment distinct.

All advertisements are divided into six categories (academic appointments are excluded) and an index compiled, on the base of average 1959 = 100. Published every quarter, beginning in the autumn of 1959, the Index and a commentary are distributed privately as a service to clients in industry and commerce. The six categories comprise:

1. *General management:* chairmen, managing directors, general managers, group managers and their assistants and deputies.

2. *Finance and accounting:* specialists, including financial directors, office managers, and company secretaries.

3. *Sales:* includes selling, exports, marketing, market research, advertising, distribution, and service.

4. *Research and development:* includes design.

5. *Production:* managers, production engineers, works engineers, quality control, work study, site managers in building, civil, and chemical engineering.

6. *Others:* purchasing, personnel, consultants, surveyors, and medical officers.

In March 1963 the scope of the Index was widened. The report was retitled *Management Matters* and now includes articles on which M.S.L. are qualified to write with authority, including one on "Demand for Executives." This latter is a commentary on advertised appointments and, since I have not obtained figures for groups, I append the table showing the actual appointments advertised.

Executive appointments advertised

Category	1959	1960	1961	1962	1963
General management	631	723	978	1,123	1,148
Accounting	1,908	1,983	2,014	2,733	2,846
Sales	4,279	3,961	3,340	3,606	4,904
Research and development	6,928	7,238	4,947	4,139	5,498
Production	5,390	5,663	4,339	5,639	6,802
Others	2,196	2,543	2,749	4,334	4,475
Totals	21,332	22,111	18,367	21,574	25,673

M.S.L. INDEX IN GRAPH FORM
(Average 1959 = 100)

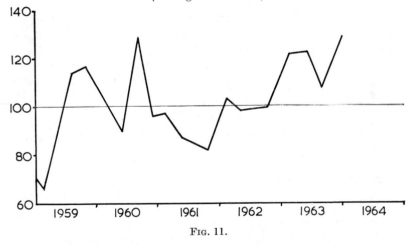

FIG. 11.

SLIDING SCALES: WAGES AND INDEX NUMBERS

One function of trade unions is to provide workers with collective power so that they can face their employers on equal terms and negotiate improvements in wages, hours, and other benefits. This method is usually welcomed by both sides, since time is saved, and experts may be engaged to draw up agreements. Unions may claim better conditions when profits have risen, when other firms have raised wages or when they feel that living costs have risen against them. Employers and workers in several industries have made agreements which are designed to eliminate casual encounters, by making wage revisions automatic according to "sliding scales." The system is roughly approximate to the method used in the early nineteenth century to limit the import of corn into Britain. As home prices increased more imports were permitted. Wages may be linked to a cost-of-living index.

The argument is as follows: wages and the cost of living are closely connected, since changes in the prices of goods in the shops (food, clothing, household equipment) and services (bus fares, cinema seats, hair-sets) affect the worker and his family directly. Wages should therefore rise (or fall) as the cost of living rises or falls; if the cost of living can be measured we have a simple basis for automatic collective agreement. The measure selected is the Index of Retail Prices.

When an agreement is reached, changes in wages thus follow changes in the Index as published. The general idea of sliding scales is not of recent origin, as was evidenced in an interesting article in *Manchester School*. It explains how in the 1870s one major coal-field adopted a scale which linked changes in wage-rates to variations in the selling price of specified grades of coal. This method was not unique: it was used in many English coal-fields, in Lanarkshire and in the anthracite mines of the U.S.A. in the late nineteenth century. Some agreements based on the prosperity of the industry lingered until early in the second world war and in coal mining until 1944. Such arrangements work well when the market has reasonable stability or when a fairly standard product is involved such as iron and steel, coal and coke—some employers favoured them, since they related wage changes directly with industry's ability to pay. In recent years raw-material controls have nearly all collapsed, and most sliding-scale systems are linked to retail price changes.

The end of the first world war saw the first of the cost-of-living arrangements using the base 1914 = 100 for the Index. By 1922 three million workers were affected in several elaborate systems. Because of resistance to wage reductions, and poor business generally, the inter-war years saw a fall in the number of agreements, and by 1939 only one and a half million workers were involved. In wartime more industries were covered— coal, iron and steel, tobacco, and pottery, and by 1947 two and a half millions were involved in spite of abandonment by some industries. This maintenance of numbers was mainly due to the expansion of particular industries. An estimated two million workers were linked in 1951, the larger proportion in building, boot and shoe manufacture, civil engineering, furniture manufacture, glass processing, hosiery, iron and steel, lock, latch and key manufacture, printing, textile bleaching, dyeing and finishing, and the wire and rope industry; and these agreements were responsible for over 7% of the total net weekly increase in wage-rates in that year.

To illustrate the scope of the agreements, the following are the sub-industries in Metal Manufacturing (S.I.C., Order V): Pig iron manufacture (blast furnaces) (main areas of Great Britain), Iron puddling (Midlands and west Scotland), Steel melting, rolling, etc. (main areas of Great Britain), Galvanising (England and Wales), Tinplate (South Wales and Monmouth-shire), Tube manufacture (Landore and Newport).

Provisions

In recent years price levels have been rising steadily and at times rapidly. Agreements ensure automatic revision of wages and avoid frequent negotiations so long as the Index basis is accepted. Of course, the unions are not precluded from claiming changes in their conditions on other grounds if they see fit.

The provisions vary and are embodied in formal contracts, but these usually include:

1. The change of index needed to affect the wage-rate. For example the wire and rope industry agreement provides a 5s. per week adjustment for each movement of three points in the Index—say from 113 to 116. Other contracts may call for revisions when the Index passes certain fixed points, such as 114, 116, any intermediate stages being ignored.

2. The length of time between one change and the next: for example the lock and key making industry's agreement provides for a review each January based on changes in the Index for the previous year. Others call for immediate changes once the Index has moved the agreed number of points (often three or four).

3. The type of change and the amount—often a flat-rate amount for all and sometimes, in addition, a flat amount for time-workers and a percentage for piece-workers. Thus in hosiery the operatives receive a halfpenny on each shilling of the basic wage for each three points' change at a half-yearly review.

Although the proportion of the total working population covered is small (about 1 in 12), the contracts do display confidence in the Ministry of Labour Index. It seems unlikely that the scheme will extend greatly in the near future, and Dr Norman Hunt considers it doubtful whether such a system is to be desired because by linking wages to the Index of Retail Prices the problems of spirals of inflation or deflation may be intensified.

Sliding scales can hardly provide a direct incentive to greater effort by workers (manual workers are those mainly included), since changes in wages do not depend on their own exertions. Again, skilled workers complain that one effect of the adoption of sliding scales has been to reduce the differential between the earnings of skilled and unskilled workers. Most wage adjustments involve flat-rate changes, which as wages rise cause a reduction in the percentage differential.

Many workers, however, may be comforted to know that some adjustment will be made as the Index rises. Whether a corresponding elation would be felt if the Index fell has been a matter of conjecture for some years. Perhaps the Index will one day begin a steady decline, and then we shall see!

The new (1962) Index of Retail Prices was published together with the 1956-based Index until the end of 1962, and this allowed industries with sliding scales based on the Index to revise their agreements. A *Times* leader of 17th March 1962 said, "present day conditions make most sliding scales of doubtful value . . . nowadays unions in every sliding scale industry make

Aggregate net increase in U.K. basic weekly wage rates, 1962

Method	Increases in weekly rates of wages	
	Aggregate amount net increase (£000)	Percentage of total
Direct negotiation	£1561	29·9
Joint industrial councils and other voluntary agreements	1485	28·4
Wages councils and other statutory wages boards	1210	23·1
Arbitration	486	9·3
Sliding scales based on the Index of Retail Prices	485	9·3
Total	£5227	100

regular claims for additional increases and usually get something. There is still some case for sliding scales as a cushion against substantial inflationary price movement in long-term agreements, as for instance they have been used in printing and in the boot and shoe industry, but there are possible alternatives, such as provision for the re-opening of an agreement, if the Index rises above a certain point."

The above table from the *Ministry of Labour Gazette* for January 1963 shows the aggregate amount of net increase in basic full-time weekly rates of wages in 1962, to illustrate the various methods.

In the United States

An interesting example of the geographical use of index numbers is afforded by the following case. The United Nations employ staff all over the world and find it necessary to make estimates of the relation between the purchasing power of salaries paid to officials in New York and those in other places, so that emoluments, grade for grade, may be the same for all duty stations. During the last ten years the United Nations have been computing what may be termed "cost of living relatives" applicable to international officials.

These figures are severely restricted in their applications. They measure the approximate relation between the price levels in two places, through a "basket" of goods and services of the kind bought by international officials. Therefore subjective influences on location (such as pleasantness of climate, availability of cultural activities, political atmosphere, etc.) are not included. It must be remembered that the officials are generally serving overseas (*i.e.* are not nationals) and therefore their purchasing is not typical.

Prices of about 120 items are obtained at intervals all over the world (similar items basically for each city). Prices are obtained by United Nations price surveys or through specialist private organisations; and the aim is to measure local living costs with those in New York as a basic criterion. The prices include:

Food: commodities in the medium price range (by local standards).

Housing: this item presents great difficulties, but specifications are as explanatory as can be, *i.e.* number of rooms, whether rented, the kind of area, shortage of houses, etc.

Clothing: New York prices are for ready-made clothing, but prices abroad may include tailored and imported. The prices are collected from three to five retail outlets which are stores patronised by officials in the medium income range.

Miscellaneous: includes household operations, furnishings, medical, personal care, recreation, and transport.

Large consumer durables such as cars are not included, nor is money spent on holidays, gifts, etc.

It was decided to use the Fisher formula, where price relatives are weighted according to expenditure patterns derived from data obtained from U.N. staff in New York City on the one hand and, on the other, in the city concerned. The formula used is

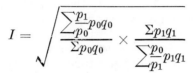

$$I = \sqrt{\frac{\sum \frac{p_1}{p_0} p_0 q_0}{\sum p_0 q_0} \times \frac{\sum p_1 q_1}{\sum \frac{p_0}{p_1} p_1 q_1}}$$

where p_1 and q_1 are prices and quantities in the city under consideration, and p_0 and q_0 prices and quantities in New York City.

Information comes from staff who have been resident in the area for at least six months. The questionnaires are in three sections:

1. Estimated monthly or annual expenditure on all groups and sub-groups, clothing and miscellaneous.

2. Itemised list of all food expenses for a period of two weeks.

3. Housing and domestic service.

Each family is reckoned to have a United States income of $7000 net of taxes. In some cities the local official cost of living index can be used; in others U.N. statistical staff calculate it. In New York City the Consumer Price Index is used. Let us consider an example.

For London the latest survey was November 1955. After taking a complete selection of retail prices, weights were assigned and comparison made by the formula, with the following results:

November 1955 (New York = 100)

Food	87
Housing	90
Clothing	67
Miscellaneous	85
	—
Total	84 (*excluding housing* 83)

The exchange rate was taken as $2.80 = £1. From November 1955 to November 1958 the cost of living in London increased by 9%, with the exchange rate stable. Therefore, with the London and New York rates changed, the London index in November 1958 becomes 85.

As a comparison, Rio de Janeiro in October 1955 was 66. This became 105 in April 1957, but exchange rates were not the same. Two others: New Delhi, December 1957, 85; Bangkok, September 1957, 130.

In France

French law in 1950 and 1952 established a national guaranteed minimum wage, to be revised whenever the monthly cost of living in Paris changed by more than 2% (*Salaire horaire minimum inter-professional garanti*).

Movements of a Retail Price Index of 179 articles were based on the spending habits of a Parisian bachelor employed in the lowest-grade wage-earning occupation. When the Index over two months rose above that level wages increased by the average of the two increases. Collective bargaining above that was freely permitted. This, however, came to be regarded as the pivot of the wage structure, and many collective agreements were linked with it.

But in 1954 the Government legislated that any increase in the *Salaire* should not entail a further upward movement in the whole wage structure. Today only about 5% of all workers are paid at minimum rates and are affected by the *Salaire*. Since 1959 it has been illegal for wages other than those under it to be linked to any index.

An article in *The Times* of 6th February 1961 discussed another interesting application of sliding scales. The past financial history of France has encouraged the issue of bonds with "inflation hedge" clauses—usually providing that interest payable and redemption values are linked to a yardstick measuring changes in the value of money (a price index). There are over a hundred of them at present, many linked to specific prices (*e.g.* coal, electricity) and some linked to the increase in profits or sales of the issuing companies. This gives the bonds an element of the equity share.

Let us take as an example Electricité de France bonds 1952–3. Interest paid is equal to 100 × the average price of 1 kWh in the year preceding payment, with a guaranteed minimum of 7·20 *fr.* The redemption price (1967–77) is 2000 times the average price of a kWh in the year preceding redemption, with a guaranteed minimum of 160 *fr.* (interest and redemption pay-

ments are free of French taxes). Another interesting issue is
that of the S.N.C.F. 100 *fr.* bonds of 1953, which give an interest
of 90 × the cost per kilometre of second-class rail travel at the
time of payment, or the holders may elect to receive a voucher
granting free travel for 100 km (see *The Theory of Wage Determination,* ed. John T. Dunlop, Macmillan, 1957).

In Norway

For a discussion, see *Labour Relations in Norway,* by H.
Dorfman, Oslo, 1957. In the depression of 1923 the Board of
Arbitration, which enforced compulsory arbitration where
necessary, expired but one provision remained, that of linking
wages with the cost-of-living index. This is now a common
provision, but it caused a major strike in 1923.

A typical clause (the metal workers' contract) provides that
if the official index shows a rise or fall of six points on either
15th March or 15th September the unions or the employers can
ask for a wage adjustment.

Trades Union Congress: cost-of-living sliding scales

Iron and steel trades: addition of 1*s.* 3*d.* a shift for each point
by which the Index of Retail Prices, when multiplied by 1·534,
exceeds 90. (This calculation links the 1947-based index with
the current Index.) Review is monthly; changes take place
from the first Sunday in each month following that in which
the index number is published in the *Ministry of Labour Gazette.*

Wire and wire rope industries: adjustment of 5*s.* per week
for each movement of three points in the Index of Retail Prices.
The adjustment takes effect as from the first full pay week in
the month following the official announcement in the *Ministry
of Labour Gazette.*

Lock, latch, and key making: a 1% increase or decrease in the
basic time rate for each rise or fall of one point in the Index of
Retail Prices. There is an annual review: adjustments take
place in January, based on figures published in the previous
year from January to December.

Hosiery manufacture: addition of ½*d.* to each shilling in basic
wages for each movement of three points in the Index of Retail
Prices. There is a half-yearly review for January to June and
July to December; any alterations in bonus to become effective
on the first pay days in September and March.

Textile bleaching, dyeing, and finishing: adjustment of 1*s.* 5*d.*
a week for men and of 1*s.* per week for women for each movement of one point in the Index of Retail Prices. There is a
quarterly review for the quarters ending November, February,

May, and August; adjustments become effective on the second Friday or equivalent payday in January, April, July, and October.

Boot and shoe manufacture: adjustment of rates is usually based on a three-point movement in the retail price Index (although the present rate is based on a four-point range, 108–111 inclusive): men's rates rise or fall by 5s. a week for each three-point movement and women's rates in general do likewise. Adjustments take place on the first payday of the second month after announcement of the Index figure in the *Ministry of Labour Gazette.*

Glass processing: wage-rates are altered according to a table given in the National Joint Council agreement: an increase or decrease of $\frac{1}{2}d$. an hour usually accompanies a movement of one point in the Index of Retail Prices. Changes in rates take effect in February and August in accordance with movements of the average of the Index for periods in July to December and January to June.

Furniture manufacture: an adjustment, for men, of $\frac{1}{2}d$. an hour for each movement of one point in three out of four movements of one point in the Index of Retail Prices (*e.g.* $1\frac{1}{2}d$. for four-point movements). The women's allowance is 75% of the men's. There is a quarterly review, based on the Index figures published during November, February, May, and August; adjustments take place as from the first full pay weeks in January, April, July, and October.

Building: adjustment of $\frac{1}{2}d$. an hour for each two-point movement in the Index of Retail Prices. There is an annual review in January, based on the average Index figure for the past twelve months. Adjustments take effect in February.

The above notes were prepared in November 1960, but see an article in *The Times* of 1st July 1963.

For further reference the student should consult the following publications: Ministry of Labour, *Method of Construction and Calculation of the Index of Retail Prices* (H.M.S.O., 1959). Ministry of Labour, *Industrial Relations Handbook* (H.M.S.O.). Morris and Williams, "The South Wales Sliding Scale 1876–9: an Experiment in Industrial Relations" (*Manchester School,* May 1960). Sir Godfrey Ince, *The Ministry of Labour & National Service* (Allen & Unwin, 1960). Norman C. Hunt, *Methods of Wage Payments in British Industry* (Pitman, 1951). B. C. Roberts, *National Wages policy in War and Peace* (Allen & Unwin, 1958).

QUESTIONS AND EXERCISES

1. Explain how the Index of Weekly Wage Rates is compiled. Explain carefully what it does and what it does not measure.

2. The Managing Director (who has no statistical knowledge) has asked you for a report on the movements of prices and wages in this country as background data to a pending wage claim. What figures would you submit? Prepare a brief statement explaining the source of your data and the basis of the figures you have supplied.
(*I.O.S. 1960*)

3. Give a brief survey of the official statistics published in the United Kingdom about *either* production *or* wages. (*I.P.M. 1958*)

4. Describe *either* the Ministry of Labour Index of Wage Rates *or* the Board of Trade Indexes of Wholesale Prices. (*I.P.M. 1959*)

5. Explain how you would construct an Index of Real Wages.
(*I.P.M. 1959*)

6. Index numbers of wage-rates by industry have recently been published. Discuss the possibility of constructing other significant divisions of an overall index, mentioning some of the difficulties which would be encountered. (*University of Manchester 1959*)

7. Describe and comment on the official statistics currently published as measures of hourly earnings in different industries.
(*University of Liverpool 1959*)

8. What statistics would you use to show the changes in prices and wages during the last ten years: (*a*) for wage negotiations in a particular industry, and (*b*) for a study of real wages in the country as a whole?
(*University of Liverpool 1960*)

9. Where would you find details of the following series? Indicate briefly how each index is obtained and comment on the changes which occurred between 1956 and 1960.

Changes in wages, earnings, and retail prices, 1956
Monthly averages January 1956 = 100

	Retail prices	Wage rates	Weekly earnings April 1956 = 100
1956	102	104·7	101
1957	105·8	110	105
1958	109	114	109
1959	109·6	117	114
1960	110·7	120	121

(*University of Bristol 1961*)

10. What statistical sources would you consult and how would you use the available information to compare movements in real income of wage-earners and salaried staff? (*I.O.S. 1962*)

11. The table below shows movements in: (a) weekly wage-rates; (b) average weekly earnings; and (c) average hourly earnings. What are the principal reasons for the series' differing from each other?

	(a)	(b)	(c)
1947	100	100	100
1950	110	120	118
1953	135	152	148

(*University of Bristol 1958*)

12. What are the shortcomings of the Ministry of Labour's Index of Weekly Wage Rates as a measure of changes in pay packets? What other relevant information is there available?   (*I.C.W.A. 1961*)

13. Give a brief survey of the current British statistics of *either* (a) unemployment *or* (b) wholesale prices.

(*University of Liverpool 1961*)

Chapter 17

BRITISH OVERSEAS TRADE

The value of British overseas trade each quarter is very roughly £300–£350 million (f.o.b.: that is, without including insurance, purchase tax, or ship freights) and imports £350–£400 million (c.i.f.: that is, the value as landed at British ports, including insurance and freight). Each quarter there is a "trade gap" in the value of goods, which "invisible" exports (services such as tourism, insurance, and shipping) are hard put to cover.

From the United Kingdom viewpoint exports go to (and imports come from) two "areas," the sterling area and the non-sterling area. The sterling area consists of: (a) the United Kingdom itself, including the Channel Isles; (b) United Kingdom colonies, including protectorates, protected states, trust territories, and mandated territories; (c) all other sterling area countries: the Commonwealth (except Canada), including the independent countries such as Ghana, Malaysia, Zambia and Malawi, the Irish Republic, Burma, Iceland, Jordan, Libya, Muscat and Oman which are in the area.

The phrase "rest of the sterling area" used subsequently merely excludes the United Kingdom, and thus includes (b) and (c). The sterling area itself originated after Great Britain left the gold standard in 1931. Several nations decided to keep their exchange rates stable in terms of sterling, and this continues to be so despite some imperfections. In terms of value of trade, the pattern of United Kingdom trade in March 1963 was:

	(£ million)	
	Exports	Imports
Sterling area	130	127
Western Europe: E.E.C.	69	60
E.F.T.A.	45	45
Others	13	11
North and South America	55	101
U.S.S.R. and Eastern Europe	8	12
Rest of the world	26	28
Totals	346	384

Since January 1963 United Kingdom overseas statistics classification has been brought into line with other countries' practice in accordance with the Revised Standard International Trade Classification of the United Nations. There are now 1312 headings for commodities and the S.I.T.C. Revised is now being used in the "Export List" and the Navigation Accounts, which should simplify international comparisons. Where possible the tables given as examples below adopt the new classification.

BOARD OF TRADE INDEXES OF UNIT VALUE AND VOLUME OF UNITED KINGDOM OVERSEAS TRADE

These indexes are prepared monthly and aim at measuring the monthly change in price and volume of United Kingdom imports and exports, using the Laspeyres fixed-base formula with 1961 = 100:

$$\text{Price (or unit value index)} = p_1 = \frac{\Sigma p_1 q_0}{\Sigma p_0 q_0}$$

and $\qquad q_1 = \dfrac{\Sigma p_0 q_1}{\Sigma p_0 q_0}$ is the quantum

(or volume) index.

Basic data come from the "Trade Accounts," which are available promptly, and since quantity as well as value statistics are given a unit-value figure can be derived which forms the basic data for the unit-value index. The C.S.O. warn users that the goods are heterogeneous, and this may cause some non-comparability over time. Imports are more reliable than exports, being, in the main, easily graded raw materials (see *Economic Trends* for September 1963 for more on this point). The coverage is:

Exports 550 commodities (previously 280), *i.e.* 60% of total exports.

Imports 350 commodities (previously 220), *i.e.* 80% of total imports.

These indexes appear monthly in total and by principal commodity categories, plus an Index of the Terms of Trade, defined as:

$$\frac{\text{Export Unit Value Index}}{\text{Import Unit Value Index}}$$

INDEX OF UNITED KINGDOM IMPORT AND EXPORT UNIT VALUE

(1961 = 100)

	Imports					Exports		Manufactured goods						Terms of trade
	Total	Food, drink, and tobacco	Basic materials	Fuels	Manufacturing	Total	Non-mfg. goods	Total	Chemicals	Textiles	Metals	Machinery and equipment	Other	
Weights	1000	338	230	110	318	1000	129	838	89	67	126	442	114	
1954	104	108	104	110	98	91	105	89	114	95	90	83	87	87
1955	108	109	108	112	106	92	106	90	114	95	93	85	89	86
1956	110	109	111	119	107	95	112	93	113	94	99	88	92	87
1957	111	109	115	138	100	100	122	96	114	96	102	92	94	89
1958	103	104	100	120	96	99	108	97	109	96	103	95	94	96
1959	102	105	98	111	98	98	103	97	108	92	99	97	95	96
1960	102	104	101	104	101	100	102	99	104	96	101	99	97	97
1961	100	100	100	100	100	100	100	100	100	100	100	100	100	100
1962	99	102	96	98	99	101	99	102	98	100	101	103	102	102
1963	103	111	97	97	101	104	103	104	100	102	102	106	104	101
19—														

INDEX OF UNITED KINGDOM IMPORT AND EXPORT VOLUME

(1961 = 100)

	Imports					Exports							
								Manufactured goods					
	Total	Food, drink, and tobacco	Basic materials	Fuels	Manufactured goods	Total	Non-manufactured	Total	Chemicals	Textiles	Metals	Machinery or transport equipment	Other
1954	73	82	96	63	50	82	83	79	57	141	75	75	82
1955	82	88	102	75	63	87	85	86	65	135	86	82	90
1956	81	90	99	71	63	92	89	91	69	129	97	89	90
1957	84	93	103	70	66	93	88	93	74	128	100	91	91
1958	84	98	92	76	67	90	88	90	71	109	93	90	89
1959	90	98	98	88	77	93	90	93	81	109	99	92	91
1960	102	100	107	96	103	98	92	98	93	109	98	97	96
1961	100	100	100	100	100	100	100	100	100	100	100	100	100
1962	103	104	96	113	104	102	110	101	107	99	100	100	103
1963	107	102	101	120	113	108	120	106	113	101	100	107	110
19—													

Note that for imports, the c.i.f. unit values of arrivals obtained from the Trade Accounts in any month will usually be those ruling in the world markets at some earlier date, when the purchase was made—so that there is often a *time* lag between the movements of world commodity prices and the import index.

The Index appears in the *Board of Trade Journal, Economic Trends, M.D.S.*, and is reported in the press. See the *Board of Trade Journal* for 13th September 1963 and *Economic Trends* for September 1963.

BOARD OF TRADE: WORLD PRICES OF IMPORTANT STERLING-AREA EXPORTS

From 1961 this series has been published annually in *The Commonwealth and the Sterling Area Statistical Abstract*. The base date is 1954 = 100, and prices are the average of daily or

INDEXES OF WORLD PRICES OF IMPORTANT STERLING AREA EXPORTS

(1954 = 100)

Year	Wool Merino 64's	Wool Cross-bred 50's	Cotton	Jute	Jute goods	Sisal	Rubber	Hides
1948	74	44	72	95	113	112	64	—
1952	99	83	127	110	137	179	141	104
1953	115	97	90	94	105	109	99	112
1954	100	100	100	100	100	100	100	100
1955	83	98	91	96	91	95	166	88
1956	88	97	83	100	84	92	142	97
1957	98	108	82	114	87	84	129	98
1958	69	76	79	103	83	85	116	96
1959	71	88	68	100	82	106	149	119
1960	69	91	76	142	98	120	159	98
1961	70	90	78	173	113	108	123	84
1962	72	85	79	121	112	119	116	84
19—								
19—								

Year	Wheat	Cocoa	Coffee	Tea	Tin	Copper	Lead	Manganese
1948	—	48	24	—	77	53	96	—
1952	—	61	69	58	134	103	138	100
1953	—	64	74	69	102	102	95	111
1954	100	100	100	100	100	100	100	100
1955	100	64	73	94	103	141	110	104
1956	104	47	74	92	109	132	121	107
1957	100	53	72	84	105	88	100	121
1958	94	76	62	87	102	79	76	120
1959	89	63	47	86	109	96	74	103
1960	90	49	47	88	111	99	75	111
1961	93	40	46	83	123	92	67	113
1962	96	38	43	84	125	94	58	113
19—								
19—								

weekly quotations. These figures could be usefully compared
with raw-material price indexes such as Reuter's and the
Financial Times'.

The items quoted are: wool (the average of Commonwealth
auctions, delivered at London), cotton (Pakistan 289F.
Punjab, saw ginned fine), jute (Mills First, Dundee), jute goods (40 in.
10 oz Hessian, Calcutta), sisal (East African No. 1, London),
rubber (No. 1 R.S.S. spot, London), hides (East African dry
8/12 lb, United Kingdom), wheat (Australian, fair average
quality c.i.f., London (Baltic)), cocoa (Accra spot, New York),
coffee (No. 4 Santos spot, New York), tea (average of auction
prices, London), copper (spot London), lead (London),
manganese (London).

The series was formerly published in the *Board of Trade
Journal*, and details were given in the issue of 13th May 1960.
Since much Commonwealth trade consists of raw materials,
this Index is a reasonable measure of the member countries'
prosperity. Notice the amazing fluctuations in the prices of
many of the food materials.

BOARD OF TRADE UNIT VALUE AND VOLUME INDEXES OF COMMONWEALTH IMPORTS AND EXPORTS

1. *Unit Value Index*

From information supplied in the United Nations' *Monthly
Bulletin of Statistics* and certain Commonwealth journals a
series is compiled for the Commonwealth's foreign trade in
unit-value terms. The countries are Australia, Burma, Canada,
Ceylon, Cyprus, Ghana, India, Eire, Jamaica, Kenya, Uganda
and Tanganyika, Malaya, Mauritius, New Zealand, Nigeria,
Pakistan, Zambia and Malawi, Trinidad, and the United
Kingdom. Imports and exports are shown separately and a
small selection is given below, all converted to 1958 = 100.

	1955	1956	1957	1958	1959	1960	1961	1962	19—	19—
Imports										
Australia	94	96	98	100	101	101	103	103		
Ghana	97	100	101	100	103	106	106	102		
Pakistan	79	84	93	100	97	100	102	101		
United Kingdom	104	106	108	100	99	100	98	97		
Exports										
Australia	112	104	116	100	88	98	92	94		
Ghana	94	76	72	100	89	78	64	58		
Pakistan	108	102	109	100	94	114	158	114		
United Kingdom	93	96	101	100	99	101	102	103		

2. Volume Index

To correspond with the above in quantity terms, a similar series is published in *The Commonwealth and Sterling Area Statistical Abstract*.

	1955	1956	1957	1958	1959	1960	1961	1962	19—	19—
Imports										
Australia	114	108	92	100	101	118	140	114		
Ghana	108	104	113	100	130	145	159	136		
United Kingdom	97	97	100	100	107	121	118	122		
Exports										
Australia	90	99	112	100	114	121	128	144		
Ghana	96	109	121	100	122	141	174	185		
United Kingdom	96	102	104	100	104	110	112	115		

BOARD OF TRADE INDEXES OF STERLING-AREA TRADE WITH ALL COUNTRIES

In *The Commonwealth and Sterling Area Statistical Abstract* are two tables relating sterling-area trade with that of other countries and with each other's. Two series are provided, for prices and for volume.

The source for both tables is the United Nations' *Monthly Bulletin of Statistics*; for the United Kingdom, the trade returns. The indexes for "Total Sterling Area" and "Non-European Sterling Area" are weighted by the values of trade of the individual countries in the current year. The United Kingdom price indexes are compiled with fixed 1954 weights converted arithmetically to a 1958 base. Note that a rise in the terms of trade (import/export prices × 100) is regarded as an adverse movement of prices in the view of the country concerned. N.B. There appears to be no final agreement as to the terms-of-trade formula (*see* page 300).

1. STERLING-AREA PRICES AND TERMS OF TRADE WITH ALL COUNTRIES

(1958 = 100)

Year	United Kingdom			Non-European sterling area, excluding Eire and Iceland			Total sterling area		
	Import prices	Export prices	Terms of trade	Import prices	Export prices	Terms of trade	Import prices	Export prices	Terms of trade
1956	107	96	111	99	107	93	102	102	100
1957	109	101	108	102	107	95	105	104	101
1958	100	100	100	100	100	100	100	100	100
1959	99	100	100	99	103	96	99	102	97
1960	100	101	99	101	104	97	101	103	98
1961	98	102	95	100	100	100	99	101	98
1962	97	103	93	98	98	100	98	101	97
19—									
19—									

2. VOLUME OF STERLING-AREA COUNTRIES' TRADE WITH ALL COUNTRIES

(1958 = 100)

Year	Imports			Exports		
	U.K.	Non-European sterling area	Total sterling area	U.K.	Non-European sterling area	Total sterling area
1956	97	96	97	102	97	100
1957	100	103	101	104	101	102
1958	100	100	100	100	100	100
1959	107	103	106	104	108	106
1960	121	117	119	109	112	111
1961	118	116	118	112	120	117
1962	122	121	122	114	127	122
19—						
19—						

The Board of Trade publishes regular sections in the *Board of Trade Journal* on sterling-area trade, and although tables of index numbers are not included, those given above are scarcely informative enough for any but the most casual user's purpose.

U.S. DEPARTMENT OF COMMERCE FOREIGN TRADE INDEXES

Indexes are compiled by the Bureau of International Commerce of the U.S. Department of Commerce with the intention of helping economists to measure and interpret the flow of U.S. trade with other countries and to understand the factors that influence its variation. Particular reference is made to problems involving the balance of payments, terms of trade, and the competitive position of U.S. industry.

Indexes are prepared of the quantity, unit value, and value of total merchandise exports and imports of each of the five broad commodity categories: Crude materials, Crude foodstuffs, Manufactured foodstuffs, Semi-manufactures, and Finished manufactures.

Data are obtained from the Bureau of Census, export declarations and filed import entries. Selected items include leading individual products in the trade concerned and a variety of typical smaller items. The Indexes cover 60–68% of the total value of imports for consumption and 40–45% of the total domestic exports. Weights are used to incorporate other commodities. Of course coverage ranges widely from category to category: for example, imports of crude foodstuffs 85%; finished manufactures 23%.

From January 1962 a new *reference base* was adopted, 1957–9 = 100, which is used in all currently published series as prescribed by the Bureau of the Budget. This base should not be confused with either the base used in computation or with the weighting periods. Prior to 1958 three separate calculations were made, one for each index but two using the same data. Because the Fisher Ideal formula satisfies the factor reversal test, the product of the two indexes (Unit Value × Quantity) is the same as the index number of Value. We can therefore omit one calculation, which is derived as a quotient of: Value Index/Unit Value. The formula for Unit Value was changed to provide price relatives at the first stage of the calculation:

$$\text{U.V.} = 100 \sqrt{\left[\sum\left(\frac{p_1}{p_0} \times \frac{p_0 q_0}{\Sigma p_0 q_0}\right)\right] \times \frac{\Sigma p_1 q_1}{\Sigma p_0 q_1}}$$

therefore q is derived by dividing the total Value indexes by the corresponding (chained) indexes of Unit Value.

1. *Index of Value*

This is based on the direct ratio

$$\frac{\text{Current value}}{\text{Corresponding average values in base period}}$$

2–3. *Indexes of Quantity and Unit Value*

Unit value is given above and the Quantity Index is thus derived from it. The calculation base changes annually under the chaining procedure and is, in every case, the preceding year. When the three Indexes are calculated the resultant figures are then chained into a series with a common base.

The Indexes are published in *Overseas Business Reports* monthly and in the monthly *Survey of Current Business* showing monthly indexes for total imports and exports. Quarterly and cumulative indexes for total trade and economic class indexes appear in *Summary of Foreign Commerce*. Annual and quarterly indexes of quantity and unit value of exports of manufactured goods are now published in the March, June, September, and December issues of the United Nations' *Monthly Bulletin of Statistics*.

L

Some selections from past data follow.

SELECTED INDEXES OF U.S. EXPORTS AND IMPORTS

(1957–9 = 100)

Year	Total exports (including military grant in aid)			Imports		
	Quantity	Unit value	Value	Quantity	Unit value	Value
1913	29	45	13	28	45	13
1929	46	60	28	57	55	31
1932	24	35	8	34	28	9
1939	38	44	17	46	35	16
1943	103	67	69	48	51	24
1949	75	86	64	59	80	47
1955	88	94	83	81	101	82
1958	96	100	95	96	99	95
1959	94	100	95	113	98	111
1960	108	101	109	109	99	108
1961	107	103	111	107	98	105
1962	112	103	115	122	95	117
19—						
19—						

QUESTIONS AND EXERCISES

1. Describe in some detail the construction and basis of one of the following index numbers:

(a) Index of Industrial Production;
(b) Index of Wholesale Prices of Commodities;
(c) Indexes of Import and Export Prices.

(*I.O.S. 1959*)

2. Describe how the Index of the Volume of Imports is calculated by the Board of Trade. What price index can be derived by relating the Volume Index to figures of the value of imports?

(*University of London 1958*)

3. Explain how the index numbers of Volume and Price of United Kingdom Exports are calculated.   (*University of Manchester 1958*)

4. Define exactly what the official Index of the Terms of Trade measures. Explain the uses and limitations of this index. In what circumstances are other definitions of this concept sometimes needed? How would they be measured?   (*University of Manchester 1959*)

5. What official statistics are published regularly regarding the foreign trade of the United Kingdom? Name the publications and describe briefly the kind of information shown.   (*I.O.T. 1962*)

6. The following indexes give details of United Kingdom trade (published by the Board of Trade):

	Value (£ million)		Volume indexes 1954 = 100		Terms of Trade 1954 = 100
	Imports	Exports	Imports	Exports	
1954	281·2	222·9	100	100	100
1955	323·6	242·1	111·3	107·4	101
1956	323·8	264·3	110·5	113·5	99
1957	339·6	277·1	114·6	115·7	97

Use the figures of Value and Volume of trade in the table to calculate an alternative index number of the terms of trade and compare it with the official index given. Comment. (*University of Manchester 1959*)

CHAPTER 18

BANKING, INDUSTRIAL AND TRANSPORT INDEXES

1. Banking

There is no inclusive series of banking indexes. However, certain indexes are compiled by the British clearing banks, and three are of interest, those from the Bank of England, Lloyds, and the Midland: two are financial, one relates to business activity.

2. Industrial

Many industrial indexes have already been described in earlier pages, but the three mentioned here are of interest and importance. One deals with the difficult problem of measuring capital values with replacements in mind; two deal with building costs, one compiled by the Ministry of Labour and the other by a nationally known British contractor.

3. Transport

There are surprisingly few indexes of transport in the United Kingdom. One series by the Ministry of Transport covers inland transport; the other, tramp shipping. A great deal of statistical work is being done, of course, by the Government and research bodies, and regular reports are available (see, for example, *Statistics of Public Road Passenger Transport*).

THE BANK OF ENGLAND: AVERAGE ESTIMATED CURRENCY CIRCULATION WITH THE PUBLIC

In Great Britain a significant part of the money in existence at any time is that issued by the Mint (coinage) and the Bank of England (notes of various denominations). The greater proportion of trade is carried out with the aid of the cheque system, but for the general public notes and coins are of more importance.

Each week the "Bank Return" is published, showing the issue position of the Bank. At the end of 1962 the total of notes and coin was £2,815 million, of which £2,469,100,000 consisted of Bank of England notes, £214 million coin, and the remainder

Scottish and Irish notes. Of this an estimated £2,222 million was held by the public.

Each month the Bank of England supplies the *Monthly Digest of Statistics* with a series on currency which includes one Index table, "Average Estimated Currency in Circulation with the Public" on the base of 1954 = 100. It relates to the total note issues of the Bank of England, the Scottish banks, and those of Northern Ireland, plus the estimated total of the United Kingdom silver, cupro-nickel, bronze, and nickel–brass coins in circulation, less notes and coin held by the Bank of England Banking Department and by the Scottish and Ulster banks (as published in the London and Belfast gazettes and by the London clearing banks).

Notice the great rise between 1938 and 1948, and the steady circulation increase from 1954 to date. There is now five times the currency in circulation there was in 1938. Notice also the seasonal nature of demand for cash.

UNITED KINGDOM AVERAGE ESTIMATED CURRENCY
CIRCULATION, WITH INDEXES

1. *Annual index 1938–63*

Year	£ million	Index (1954 = 100)	Year	£ million	Index (1954 = 100)
1938	442	28·5	1959	1969	127
1948	1229	79·2	1960	2062	133
1954	1551	100	1961	2151	138·7
1955	1657	106·8	1962	2160	139·3
1956	1765	113·8	1963	2220	143·1
1957	1842	118·8	19—		
1958	1905	122·8	19—		

2. *Monthly index 1960–3*

Year	£ million	Index (1954 = 100)	Year	£ million	Index (1954 = 100)
			1960		
Jan.	1971	127·1	July	2117	136·5
Feb.	1983	127·8	Aug.	2106	135·8
Mar.	2014	129·8	Sept.	2078	134
Apr.	2053	132·4	Oct.	2073	133·6
May	2048	132	Nov.	2088	134·5
June	2075	133·8	Dec.	2149	138·6

Year	£ million	Index (1954 = 100)	Year	£ million	Index (1954 = 100)
			1961		
Jan.	2065	133·1	July	2195	141·5
Feb.	2075	133·8	Aug.	2204	142·1
Mar.	2111	136·1	Sept.	2160	139·3
Apr.	2125	137	Oct.	2156	139
May	2147	138·4	Nov.	2166	139·7
June	2160	139·3	Dec.	2236	144·2
			1962		
Jan.	2160	139·3	July	2170	139·9
Feb.	2138	139·1	Aug.	2177	140·4
Mar.	2160	139·3	Sept.	2138	137·8
Apr.	2180	140·6	Oct.	2135	137·7
May	2145	138·3	Nov.	2144	138·2
June	2149	138·6	Dec.	2222	143·3
			1963		
Jan.	2148	138·5	July	2278	146·9
Feb.	2152	138·7	Aug.	2259	145·6
Mar.	2164	139·5	Sept.	2231	143·8
Apr.	2201	141·9	Oct.	2228	143·6
May	2194	141·4	Nov.	2240	144·4
June	2210	142·5	Dec.	2334	150·5

LLOYDS BANK INDEX OF CLEARING-BANK DEPOSITS

Lloyds Bank Ltd compile this index with the object of emphasising the underlying trend in clearing-bank net deposits, without the distortions regularly recurring each year at such times as the end of December (due to Christmas shopping) or in the last quarter of the financial year, January to March (due to tax payments, etc.).

The Index is based on 1954 = 100 and relates to clearing-bank net deposits, which are gross deposits *less* balances with and cheques in course of collection from other banks, and cheques in course of collection on banks' own branches—"items in transit." These deductions provide the figure of net deposits.

The Index was first issued in 1948, based on 1938 = 100, and has been revised from time to time.

A significant feature of the Index is the attempt to eliminate the well-marked seasonal fluctuations by the normal statistical methods mentioned in the first part of this book.

Each month the result is circulated to City editors and others interested in City, banking, and financial matters, and it is published in the *Financial Times* and other publications.

For interest's sake, the following figures show changes in net deposits on different bases:

1. *1938 = 100:* from 1936 to late 1939 deposits were (comparatively) steady, but a rapid rise took place from 1940 (January 104) to the end of 1949 (260), with two interruptions in late 1941 (on the introduction of tax reserve certificates) and late 1945 (due to the thanksgiving savings drive).

2. *1948 = 100:* monetary controls and decontrols have been a feature of the economic scene since the end of the war, and deposits are affected. The Index fluctuated accordingly, reaching peaks of 110 (in late 1954), but falling to 105 or below during parts of 1956.

LLOYDS BANK INDEX OF CLEARING BANK DEPOSITS

Seasonally adjusted (1954 = 100)

		March	June	September	December
	1955	101	98·4	97·6	95·9
	1956	95·9	95·3	96·5	97
	1957	96·9	98·2	98·6	99·8
	1958	100·1	100·2	101·7	103·4
Revised	1959	104·1	104·1	108	110·7
Revised	1960	109·5	109·1	110·5	110·6
	1961	111·8	113·7	112·8	112·5
Revised	1962	115·1	115·4	116·3	117·2
	1963	119·7	120·1	122·4	123·8

(Revised as to July 1963)

MIDLAND BANK INDEX OF BUSINESS TURNOVER

This index is compiled by the Intelligence Department of the Midland Bank Ltd, London. It was first announced in the annual statement for 1957 by the Chairman, Viscount Monckton:

"In accordance with restrictive monetary policy, deposits have once again shown, on averages for last year and 1956, only a trifling growth. Their composition, however, has changed: a considerable shift has taken place from current account balances to deposit accounts in response to the attraction of interest rates higher than anyone would have thought likely a few years ago.

"Over a longer period one feature of the statistics is a remarkable degree of stability in the supply of the more liquid form of 'bank money'—current account balances. We have related these figures to broad indexes of business turnover and a new series has been created. The results indicate the fluctuations in turnover arising out of the day-to-day conduct of the country's industry and trade."

The index may be taken to represent the course of "business turnover" through drawings on current account (either cash over the counter or by cheque and other transfers to bank accounts in the ordinary course of industry, trade, and day-to-day disbursements).

Note that it measures fluctuations in *actual* turnover, not the *rate* of turnover. However, if we show also a series of aggregate credit balances on current accounts with the clearing banks expressed as a quarterly index number, we can derive from this and the new Index an index of rate of turnover. The Indexes of Credit Balances on Current Accounts (1950 = 100) for the period 1946–57 are:

1946	85	1950	100	1954	103
1947	93	1951	102	1955	102
1948	97	1952	99	1956	98
1949	99	1953	100	1957	98

Data are obtained from the annual totals of turnover on current account with the Midland Bank after deducting from these totals the figures for a few branches in the City of London which are heavily affected by purely financial operations, especially the money market. It is calculated on a working-day basis; some differences in the number of working days become important. Some tendency has been found for a seasonal pattern to emerge, affected by such events as the variable date of Easter.

In the *Midland Bank Review* of May 1963 an article described the changes made in the light of experience in the five previous years, which mainly involved a change in the base and seasonal correction. The Midland's 2400 branches are widely spread throughout the country, and it is reasonable to suppose that its turnover figures are representative of the whole banking system.

The Index has now been rebased on 1962 = 100 and will be published quarterly on that base; it has been calculated yearly back to 1950. Quarters in banking are three-month periods mid-March — mid-June — mid-September — mid-December — mid-March. This means that in the Index Christmas always falls in the last quarter, mid-December to mid-March, and Easter in the next, first, quarter. Seasonal influences affect turnover, and the compilers now smooth these regular fluctuations statistically (both seasonally adjusted and unadjusted figures will continue to be shown).

The Index appears as a printed press release two or three weeks after the end of the quarter, and is charted in the monthly *Midland Bank Review.*

MIDLAND BANK INDEX OF BUSINESS TURNOVER

1. *With base 1950 = 100*

Quarters:	1	2	3	4	Over whole year
1950	99	100	95	104	100
1951	112	116	108	113	113
1952	121	121	109	115	117
1953	123	120	112	122	119
1954	125	130	122	131	127
1955	138	137	133	143	138
1956	144	143	135	139	141
1957	153	154	148	154	152
1958	161	159	151	160	158
1959	169	173	167	172	170
1960	186	186	183	187	186
1961	198	201	199	207	201
1962	216	221	218	227	221

2. *With base 1962 = 100 (seasonally corrected figures in brackets)*

Quarters:	1	2	3	4	Over whole year
1950					47
1951					53
1952					55
1953					56
1954					60
1955					65
1956					66
1957					71
1958					74
1959	79 (77)	80 (80)	78 (79)	81 (83)	80
1960	89 (86)	87 (87)	86 (87)	87 (89)	87
1961	94 (91)	94 (93)	94 (95)	94 (96)	94
1962	99 (96)	100 (99)	100 (101)	104 (107)	100
1963	102 (99)	109 (108)	108 (110)	115 (117)	108
19—					

MINISTRY OF PUBLIC BUILDING & WORKS: INDEX OF THE COST OF NEW CONSTRUCTION

This index is a component of the Board of Trade Wholesale Price Index Series, and is intended to show changes in the cost of new construction work. The series was introduced in the *Board of Trade Journal*, 12th May 1956, and is substantially the same today except for the S.I.C. changes and the base date, which (in common with the remainder of the Wholesale Price Index) is 1954 (yearly average) = 100. Weighting is incorporated by using the gross value of building and civil engineering work done in 1954 as weights; "new housing" has 53% of the weights and "other new work" 47%.

Calculations are made using the Laspeyres formula for both the individual indexes and the final composite index. The statistical problems presented in preparing index numbers for building costs are very much more difficult than those arising with basic materials or with those manufactured goods for which prices of standard products can be regularly collected. The cost of a building is determined by the cost of materials and labour and by overheads and profits. If the proportion of the end cost which is to be attributed to each item at base date is known, and the movement of each item is also known, it is possible to construct an index number. These numbers should reflect changes in the average cost of new building and civil engineering work as defined by the output figures collected in Census of Production returns. For full details of calculation refer to the *Board of Trade Journal*, 12th May 1956.

Publication is in the *Board of Trade Journal* and *Monthly Digest of Statistics*. Twice a year the value of work done by the

INDEX OF COST OF NEW CONSTRUCTION
Average costs for the quarter (1954 = 100)

Quarters:	1	2	3	4	Over whole year
1957					114
1958					115
1959					113
1960					114
1961	116	117	117	120	118
1962	121	122	123	123	122
1963	125	126	126	126	126
19—					

construction industries is also published in *Monthly Digest of Statistics* and details of earnings twice yearly in *Ministry of Labour Gazette.*

Much building work is, of course, non-standard, and it is difficult to assess changes in values of the product. An attempt is made, however. For example, if a contract for an "average" building were set today at a fixed price the Cost Index would reflect the change in the contract price for the same building at a different date.

MINISTRY OF PUBLIC BUILDING & WORKS: INDEX OF THE AVERAGE PRICE OF NEW HOUSES FOR PRIVATE OWNERS

In the *Monthly Digest of Statistics*, in the table "Index Numbers of Wholesale Prices," is a series with the above title. It is based on 1958 = 100 and covers only houses on which building societies have advanced mortgages during the period. The cost of land is included.

INDEX OF THE AVERAGE PRICE OF NEW PRIVATE HOUSES
(1958 = 100)

Quarters:	1	2	3	4	Over whole year
1957					96
1958					100
1959					101
1960					106
1961	112	115	117	119	116
1962	121	123	124	126	124
1963	129	131	133	135	132
19—					

HOLLAND & HANNEN AND CUBITTS LTD
THE CUBITT INDEX

Construction work (house building included) accounts for half the total capital investment in Britain and thus changes in building activity have important repercussions on all economic affairs in the country. Cubitt's devised a series of indexes to bring together masses of statistics compiled by local authorities, industrial organisations, etc. Publication is in *The Cubitt Magazine* (quarterly), starting with the winter 1962–3 issue.

The Index aims at showing two things clearly:

1. The level of construction activity.
2. The movement of costs.

It is designed as a pointer to future trends in the industry.

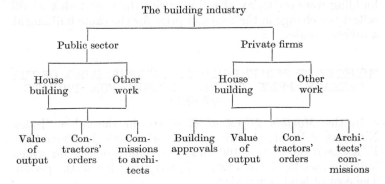

For No. 2, Costs, one index shows quarterly changes in the cost of a new house for private owners. The other index shows the cost factors for offices, factories, houses, flats, and civil engineering together.

1. *Level of construction activity*

A series of charts is given, in monetary terms, showing the value of output, new orders obtained by contractors, new commissions for private architects, the value of work entering the working drawing stage, and houses completed.

2. *Construction Costs Indexes*

These are made up of three elements: (*a*) materials, (*b*) labour, and (*c*) overheads. (*c*) varies widely, so only (*a*) and (*b*) are used in the Indexes, which relate to average costs for a number of different types of construction. Changes in construction prices cannot be indicated, since the end prices of building, including land values, overheads, and profit margins, are not given.

The base date is 1956 = 100. The pattern as published is of seven charts, grouped as follows.

House building costs

Two charts, one showing materials and the other, total costs. The materials sector is based on the Board of Trade House Building Materials Index.

Other new building costs

Four charts covering foundations, structure, finishes, and services, information being taken from contract prices published in the press, etc.

Labour and productivity

One chart, "labour" being based on the average weekly earnings in construction. "Productivity" is based on the total value of output adjusted for price changes, the changing labour force, and the average hours worked per week.

The following data are taken from the actual published charts. Since 1960 quarterly indexes have been made available.

CUBITT INDEX OF CONSTRUCTION COSTS
(1956 = 100)

Year	Housebuilding costs		Other new building				Labour and productivity	
	Materials	Total	Founda-tions	Structure	Finishes	Services	Labour	Pro-ductivity
1956	100	100	100	100	100	100	100	100
1957	102	103	104	102	103	105	104	102
1958	102	105	108	104	101	97	108	106
1959	102	107	108	103	98	99	115	114
1960	104	109	105	106	102	101	116	118
1961	108	115	110	108	105	102	124	122
1962 (quarters)								
1	109	118	112	109	105	102	132	127
2	110	119	112	110	105	103	134	127
3	110	121	112	110	105	103	136	127
4	111	122	112	110	105	103	138	127
1963 (quarters)								
1	111	122	112	112	106	104	138	116
2	111	122	112	112	106	105	138	128
3	112	122	118	114	105	104	138	133
4	112	122	118	115	107	104	138	138

CO-OPERATIVE PERMANENT BUILDING SOCIETY INDEXES OF HOUSE PRICES

Three indexes are published in the *Occasional Bulletin* of the C.P.B.S. along with information about average house prices.

1. *Index of Second-hand House Prices*

Information comes from records of mortgage approvals kept at head office, including the location of the property, the selling price, the estimated (or notional) 1939 value. The data are extracted monthly and then summarised quarterly, using simple aggregates of prices; *i.e.* within each price range, each region, and each class of property the total 1939 values are divided into the total of the vacant possession prices (× 100). The index numbers are then adjusted to the base (quarter ended 31st December 1962 = 100).

2. *Index of New Houses*

This is based on average prices at which newly built houses mortgaged to the Society were purchased, exceptionally high priced properties excluded. It has the same base.

3. *House Building Costs (Wages and Materials)*

This index is calculated from movements in the costs of labour and materials; no allowance is made for changes in productivity. Grade A rates of building workers are used, adjusted to a 31st December 1962 (last quarter) base, assuming that wages account for one-third of total building costs; and materials used in house-building, adjusted to a 31st December 1962 (last quarter) base. The Index is compiled by combining wage and materials indexes in the ratio of 1 : 2.

CO-OPERATIVE PERMANENT INDEX OF HOUSE PRICES AND
HOUSE BUILDING COSTS IN GREAT BRITAIN

(Quarter ended 31st December 1962 = 100)

Quarter ended 31st Dec.	Existing houses			New houses	House-building costs
	Up to £2000 (London £2500)	£2000– £3000 (London £2501– £3500)	Over £3000 (London £3500)		
1952	78	75	66	67	74
1953	77	73	66	67	75
1954	76	72	64	67	78
1955	79	74	67	70	83
1956	82	77	69	74	86
1957	83	77	68	76	89
1958	83	79	73	77	89
1959	86	82	76	81	90
1960	90	90	86	87	93
1961	94	96	97	96	98
1962	100	100	100	100	100
1963	106	105	108	107	103
19—					

In the *Occasional Bulletin* a map is given which shows regional variations. For example, the least growth in prices (between end of 1958 and 31st December 1963) was in the North East (125); the greatest, in London and the South East, where there was a 60% increase.

For a thought-provoking analysis of house-purchase economics, see *The Financial Times* for 17th November 1962. See also *Occasional Bulletin*, February 1964.

"THE ECONOMIST" INDEXES OF CAPITAL REPLACEMENT COSTS

Published on a subscription basis by *The Economist* Intelligence Unit Ltd, this series is intended to provide a continuous survey of the prices of a wide range of capital goods to determine (*a*) what sum should be set aside to replace assets; (*b*) the right values to place on assets for insurance and other purposes such as for buildings, plant, and equipment.

The base is 1938 = 100 (steelworks plant 1945), and in the calculation of the index numbers over 200 items of equipment are included through the co-operation of more than 120 British manufacturers of plant and machinery, trade associations, and other bodies.

The 200 sets are combined to form standard series for convenient groups of plant and machinery (*a*) by averaging the separate quotes for the same item, then (*b*) different items in the group (*e.g.* the machine tools group) are combined to form a group series by weighting each of them according to the value of home deliveries from British factories in 1948.

The equipment is mainly standard, but improvements in design are incorporated. The Index can be applied by each company according to the year the equipment was acquired. The standard series are:

1. Industrial plant.
2. Chemical and allied plant (*e.g.* valves, pumps, and specialised items).
3. Clothing manufacturing machinery.
4. Commercial vehicles.
5. Electrical installations (including all kinds of motors, transformers, etc.).
6. Food manufacturing equipment (flour milling, bakery, canning).
7. Foundry plant.
8. Industrial buildings (most kinds of non-residential building).

9. Industrial pumps.

10. Machine tools (lathes, milling, drilling, and boring machines, and presses).

11. Mechanical handling gear (conveyors, etc.).

12. Office equipment (furniture, typewriters, and calculation machines).

13. Passenger cars (twelve cars often used in business).

14. Printing machinery.

15. Railway equipment (locomotives and costs of laying sidings).

16. Tanning manufacture.

17. Textile manufacture.

18. Welding equipment.

19. Steelworks plant.

MINISTRY OF TRANSPORT
ROAD TRANSPORT STATISTICS

The Ministry carried out a census of road-haulage vehicles in 1959 to discover details of the goods carried and to see how the industry was developing. From 1958 regular traffic counts have been taken to discover changes in total traffic, *i.e.* to measure the industry's output (see an article by K. F. Glover in the *Journal of the Royal Statistical Society*, Part 2, 1960, for a full coverage of these developments).

The traffic system covers eight divisions of roads: trunk, first, second, and third class roads, both urban and rural, and 50 points were selected. Each category of road is weighted by the total length of that category of road in Great Britain. Separate records are made of the various kinds of vehicle. Counts are made on Fridays, Saturdays, Sundays, and public holidays, designed to estimate changes in aggregate vehicle miles performed on roads from one month to the next by each category of road vehicle. The sampling error is believed to be not great. No night counts are taken, on the assumption that the traffic passes in the same proportions as in the daytime.

The Ministry of Transport publishes three series of index numbers. As a result of a traffic survey undertaken by the Road Research Laboratory in 1959–60 at 1100 points distributed over all roads in Great Britain except motorways, revised estimates of vehicle miles in 1960 were obtained for all classes of vehicle except public service vehicles. The P.S.V. figure was also revised, but on the basis of the returns obtained by the Ministry from operators, not the traffic counts.

The effect on each individual vehicle class except P.S.V.s of this revision was to multiply the earlier estimates of vehicle miles by a constant factor throughout the period 1956 to the present. Consequently, index numbers shown in the *Monthly Digest of Statistics*, which are referred to the 1958 base, are unchanged for these vehicle classes. For P.S.V.s, however, there was in effect a different factor available for each of the years 1958–60 and the index numbers had to be recalculated. This gave rise to consequential changes in the "All Road Traffic" and "All Motor Traffic" indexes, but in no case do they exceed half a unit in the last digit.

Index of Vehicle Miles Travelled on Roads in Great Britain

This index was introduced in March 1959 and is derived from data from traffic counts, both automatic and manual, which are made by the Road Research Laboratory and the Ministry, as described above.

The purpose of the Index is to provide interested bodies with an indication of traffic trends; it is also used in conjunction with road accident and other statistics. The base for this and the following indexes of road traffic is 1958 monthly average = 100.

INDEX OF VEHICLE MILES TRAVELLED ON ROADS IN
GREAT BRITAIN

Year	All road traffic	Pedal cycles	Motor traffic							
			All motor traffic	Cars	Mopeds	Motor scooters	Other motor cycles	Buses and coaches	Light vans	Other goods vehicles
1959	110	96	112	112	112	150	108	198	116	108
1960	115	85	120	122	147	183	103	100	125	113
1961	123	76	130	130	140	194	95	102	135	117
1962	126	68	135	146	135	189	81	101	136	120
1963	131	56	142	158	122	162	70	102	145	124
19—										

For interest, the following selections of monthly data are given:

	1962												1963 First half					
Pedal cycles	56	51	59	66	72	80	86	77	73	64	52	42	37	40	51	62	67	69
Scooters	139	123	161	204	203	253	253	257	218	200	157	99	82	71	143	169	197	221
Buses	96	86	99	88	106	112	123	118	107	101	86	91	92	85	97	90	109	115

Index of Ton-miles of Inland Goods Transport

This index covers transport by road and rail and is of considerable interest to the Ministry as an aid when comparing the relative needs of these two forms of transport.

Part of the information is derived from traffic counts and appears in the *Monthly Digest of Statistics*. It is the first attempt to measure completely the volume of all inland goods traffic (since road statistics are poor). There exist about half a million operators, many of whom do not keep the right type of records.

The Ministry is interested in tracing fluctuations in the total volume of traffic carried by road and rail. The Index is also useful as a general economic indicator reflecting a wide range of goods activity.

The railway figures are derived from statistics compiled by the British Railways Board.

Index numbers for both rail and road transport are obtained by dividing each month's figures of ton miles on road and rail respectively by the monthly average in 1958. The results are adjusted to eliminate the effect of variations in the length of calendar months.

See, for discussion of these two indexes, the article by K. F. Glover in the *Journal of the Royal Statistical Society*, Part 2, 1960; *Economic Trends* for February 1960; *Journal of the Royal Statistical Society*, Series A, Vol. 117, Part 3, 1954; *The Transport of Goods by Road*, H.M.S.O., 1959.

INDEX OF TON-MILES OF INLAND GOODS TRANSPORT

	Total	Rail	Road		Total	Rail	Road
1959	103	97	108				
1960	110	103	115				
1961	110	96	120				
1962	108	89	123				
1963	112	91	127				
1962 Jan.	107	93	117	1963 Jan.	100	88	109
Feb.	109	97	118	Feb.	101	95	106
Mar.	113	97	125	Mar.	111	93	125
Apr.	108	89	123	Apr.	115	94	130
May	112	92	127	May	119	95	137
June	111	90	126	June	113	86	133
July	110	81	132	July	114	83	137
Aug.	100	74	119	Aug.	107	78	128
Sept.	110	85	129	Sept.	116	92	134
Oct.	113	92	129	Oct.	120	98	137
Nov.	110	94	122	Nov.	121	102	134
Dec.	99	87	108	Dec.	108	92	119

Index of Bus and Coach Stage Fares

This index appeared for the first time in *Statistics of Public Road Passenger Transport in Great Britain 1958–9*, published by the Ministry of Transport in association with the other transport bodies. It is published in regular issues of the above digest and provides the Ministry of Transport with a measure of price changes in public road passenger transport. It is also of value to the Central Statistical Office when they prepare tables on national income and expenditure.

It is a weighted average index whose weights are the total stage receipts in that year of the operators of large fleets of public service vehicles, *i.e.* those operating 100 or more buses and coaches. When the stage service fares of these larger operators are changed the Ministry is notified of the total stage receipts of the undertaking in the latest full year at the old fares and the estimated change in receipts in a full year which would result from the alteration in fares if there were no change in the volume of traffic.

INDEX OF BUS AND COACH STAGE FARES

		Total	London Transport	Local authorities	Other operators
1954	end June	100	100	100	100
	end Dec.	103	109	102	101
1955	June	108	113	105	107
	Dec.	109	118	105	108
1956	June	114	118	110	114
	Dec.	—	—	—	—
1957	June		Hydrocarbons Act 1956		
	Dec.	128	127	128	127
1958	June	128	127	130	128
	Dec.	128	127	130	128
1959	June	130	127	132	130
	Dec.	132	136	133	130
1960	June	136	147	135	131
	Dec.	141	147	139	139
1961	June	142	154	140	139
	Dec.	148	154	150	145
1962	June	153	169	151	147
	Dec.	158	170	159	152
1963	June	159	173	160	152
	Dec.	163	173	165	158
19—	June				
	Dec.				

Apart from London, there are ninety urban bus systems owned and operated by local authorities. In 1957, 4800 million passenger journeys were made on buses and coaches (London Transport Executive excluded). "Stage" services are typically the short-distance ones marked by bus stops, as distinct from the long-distance, non-stop "express" services.

The tendency in recent years has been for fares over shorter distances to be increased by more than the average shown by the Index, while fares over longer distances have therefore increased by smaller amounts.

CHAMBER OF SHIPPING OF THE UNITED KINGDOM TRAMP SHIPPING INDEXES

The Chamber of Shipping compiles two sets of indexes whose aim is to provide a measure of the changes in dry cargo shipping freights (*i.e.* excluding tankers). Freight rates have always been of interest to economists, and in 1923 an indicator was begun by *The Economist* (back-dated to 1898) which continued to 1939; *Lloyds List* included one from 1929 to 1939, but neither has been resumed. The *Norwegian Shipping News* issues two indexes, one for tramp voyage rates and the other for time charter. The former aims at world-wide coverage based on freights on 23 routes; the latter covers vessels in the 9000–11,000-dwt class (excluding charters in excess of one year). Other compilers at present include the Danish Government, the Swedish Board of Trade, and the Svenska Handelsbanken.

Index of Tramp Shipping Freights

Based originally on Average 1920 = 100 and being first published in 1921, the Index was rebased and modernised later, with 1948 = 100. It was rebased again in 1952, and in 1958 an enquiry was instituted by the General Council of British Shipping to discover the contribution made by the shipping industry to the country's balance of payments in that year. This was an opportunity to revise the Index, especially as the enquiry was supplemented by information from deep sea tramp owners. A revised index was introduced, using Average freights in 1960 = 100 and based on the pattern of trade as shown by the invisible exports enquiry. As freights (*i.e.* payments made to ship owners by shippers for the carriage of their goods) were so much lower in 1960 than in 1952 an approximate comparison of the index numbers with 1952 = 100 can be made by using the figure 74·2% to adjust the new figures to those on the old basis.

More than 93% of the total freight of British tramp owners on voyage charter is earned by carrying coal, grain, sugar, ore, fertilisers, timber, and sulphur, and these are the items used (esparto has recently been excluded and replaced by sulphur). To each item is attached an index number which is the weighted arithmetic mean of the price relatives for the trade routes in which fixtures were reported during the month. The weights are: coal 125, grain 316, sugar 150, ore 112, fertiliser 132, timber 135, and sulphur 30, making a total of 1000. For each of these items the main movements of traffic have been ascertained, and these are weighted, *i.e.* for each commodity several routes are chosen and given a weight (totalling 1000 for each commodity). As examples consider coal and sugar:

Main movement	Representative route chosen	Weight
	Coal	
(a) United Kingdom–Portugal	British Channel–W. Italy	46
(b) Poland–River Plate	—	123
(c) U.S.A.–Japan	Hampton Roads–Japan	329
(d) U.S.A.–N.W. Europe	Hampton Roads–Antwerp/ Rotterdam	502
		1000
	Sugar	
(a) Queensland–United Kingdom		204
(b) Mauritius–United Kingdom		332
(c) Cuba and San Domingo– Japan		295
(d) Cuba–United Kingdom, etc.		169
		1000

For each trade route the arithmetic mean of the freight rates for fixtures reported each month is calculated. The arithmetic mean for the year 1960 of these monthly averages forms the basis of comparison of freight rates in that trade route.

The Index Number of Tramp Shipping Freights is the weighted arithmetic mean of the commodity indexes for the month, weights being in proportion to the freights earned. This takes account of the differing lengths of haul as well as the amounts of cargo carried. Quantities as such cannot be included because they are too difficult to define.

For a full explanation see the two reports of the Freight Index Committee in 1952 and 1953, which were adopted and an index calculated with the base of 1952 = 100; and the Revisions published in May 1961 altering the base to 1960 = 100.

The Index is one of the few pieces of information regularly reported in the *Monthly Digest of Statistics* which is not derived from Government sources. It is also the only shipping freight index now produced in Great Britain to provide the chamber with information for its day-to-day work.

INDEX OF TRAMP SHIPPING FREIGHTS

Quarters only given here (1960 = 100)

Group	Weight	1960				1961				
		Mar.	June	Sept.	Dec.	Mar.	June	Sept.	Dec.	Year
Coal	125	97·5	100	100	100	99·7	121·5	121·2	103·1	110·4
Grain	316	106·7	90·6	97·9	106·9	105·5	102·9	106·3	99·6	106·2
Sugar	150	101·2	96·3	95·8	109·1	104·1	117·8	121·7	117·4	112·1
Ore	112	109·4	99·5	88·4	99	101·1	97·6	95·2	93	100·2
Fertilisers	132	95·8	103·7	97·5	99·3	101·5	121	112·6	102	108·4
Timber	135	99	91·5	97	114·9	104	98·6	108·7	92·8	103·2
Sulphur	30	103·8	93·2	93·5	98·5	—	104·8	114·8	94·8	107·3
All items	1000	102·5	95·6	96·5	105·3	103·2	108·7	110·6	101·2	106·8

Group	1962					1963				
	Mar.	June	Sept.	Dec.	Year	Mar.	June	Sept.	Dec.	Year
Coal	89·6	75·6	73·5	75·7	82·9	89·4	96·3	98·7	122·2	101·4
Grain	101·4	84·4	77·2	89·6	90	102·3	103·8	124·3	134·7	113·6
Sugar	108	91·1	85·7	98·4	97·1	104·2	120·7	120·2	131·5	116·8
Ore	85·3	75·3	72·5	69·4	77	86·7	96·9	90·3	110·7	96·4
Fertilisers	101·1	95·9	90	—	99·2	88·4	112·1	96	—	99·5
Timber	88·1	80·5	91·3	101·4	90·1	103·5	106·6	109	126·9	109·8
Sulphur	87·4	87·4	74·9	74·9	82·3	101·3	97·8	107·8	—	104·9
All items	96·9	84·4	81	87·8	89·1	97·5	105·9	110·4	127·8	109

Index of Tramp Time Charter Rates

Since the 1952 Index the number of oil-fired steamers has decreased, and so the Index is restricted to motor ships. The lower and upper deadweight limits are 9000 and 11,000 tons. The calculations are based on reported fixtures for round voyages or for time charters not exceeding about nine months. The arithmetic mean of the rates for fixtures of motor ships reported in each month is calculated, and the A.M. for 1960 of these monthly averages forms the basis of comparison. A linking factor between the 1960 and 1952 indexes is 65·4.

Only sterling quoted fixtures are used. For voyage charters the actual date of the fixture, irrespective of the expected loading date, is that which determines its place in the Index, data being reported in the shipping press.

The Index reflects the level of the market rate over the period it covers and bears no relation to profitability or to the costs of operation. Freight rates fluctuate according to supply and demand—if there are more ships than cargo the rate slumps. Operating costs are not, of course, governed by supply and demand like ships and cargoes, and indeed in recent years have risen inexorably. In short, the Index is a record of freight-rate movements, not a measure of profitability.

It is published about the first week of the month for the preceding month in the form of a statement issued to the press. Copies go to other interested persons on a circulation list.

INDEX OF TRAMP TIME CHARTER RATES FOR MOTOR VESSELS

Quarters only given here (1960 = 100)

	March	June	September	December	Year
1960	107·4	102·7	94·3	101·9	100
1961	109·5	111·2	118·3	99·4	111·6
1962	97·3	91·4	77·9	80	89·1
1963	93·1	93·5	114·5	131·4	104·8
19—					

QUESTIONS AND EXERCISES

1. Give an outline of the purpose and method of construction of one of the following index numbers: (a) index of retail prices; (b) weekly wage-rates; (c) tramp shipping freight rates.   (I.O.T.)

2. The following data show passenger journeys originating on British Railways in millions:

	1956	1957	Average seasonal variation (%)
1st quarter	232	266	−4
2nd quarter	249	266	−2
3rd quarter	281	309	+14
4th quarter	243	236	−7

Devise a series of quarterly index numbers, corrected for seasonal variations, with the first quarter of 1956 = 100. Graph your results.

(I.O.T. 1959)

3. How would you set about constructing an index of business conditions in Britain?   (A.C.C.A.)

4. What is the purpose of economic index numbers? Discuss some of the general problems of constructing and using such measures, illustrating your answer by reference to published official statistics.

(University of Manchester)

CHAPTER 19

BACKGROUND INFORMATION

IN this final chapter several incidental topics which have occurred from time to time in the preceding pages are dealt with more fully, so that the reader may not be left in doubt: the major examining bodies, the governmental and private sources of statistics, the use of computers, the construction of graphs, and the bases of the Standard Industrial Classification and the 1947 Statistics of Trade Act.

The second part of this book has provided details of published indexes. One important feature of the subject still remains: critical analysis. This, I hope, will be the task of the reader. Statistics are meant to be used in the clarification of problems in the sense that they furnish the required background information. The study of any index's performance should illuminate somewhat the background problem, but space is not available in this book nor, I think, would a comprehensive analysis be possible in any reasonable span of pages.

EXAMINATIONS IN STATISTICS

The following list includes most of the professional bodies which set examinations in statistics, and a selection of university syllabuses.

Professional examinations

1. *The Institute of Statisticians Ltd*
   55 Park Lane, London, W.1

There are three levels of examinations for this body, one of whose main objects is to train statisticians. Index numbers appear in the syllabuses of each level of examination. The Institute's journal is *The Incorporated Statistician*.

2. *Royal Society of Arts*
   18 Adam Street, Adelphi, London, W.C.2

The Society aims at the advancement, development, and application of every department of science in connection with the arts, manufacturing, and commerce. Examinations are held at three levels four times a year and statistics are examined at the second and third. Index-number theory is included in Stage 2, and applications in both stages. Individual subjects may be taken.

3. *Institute of Commercial and Technical Representatives Ltd*
   Queens House, 180 Tottenham Court Road, London, W.1

Formed under the auspices of the United Kingdom Commercial Travellers' Association in 1962, the Institute sets exams at graduate and associateship levels. Statistics appear in the group of graduate subjects and the syllabus includes elementary treatment of index numbers.

4. *The Association of Certified and Corporate Accountants*
   22 Bedford Square, London, W.C.1

A major accounting body, the Association conducts intermediate and final examinations, of which "Economic and Business Statistics" is a three-hour paper at intermediate level (Section 2).

5. *The London Chamber of Commerce Incorporated*
   69 Cannon Street, London, E.C.4

There are examinations at three levels; "Business Statistics" appears in the intermediate and higher levels, and index-number theory and applications appear at both levels.

6. *British Institute of Management*
   80 Fetter Lane, London, E.C.4

The examination for the Diploma in National Scheme of Management Studies includes Part C, "The Tools of Management," of which Part C2, "Statistical Method," covers both the theory and applications of index numbers at intermediate level.

7. *Institute of Marketing and Sales Management: College of*
   Marketing
   (*Formerly the Incorporated Sales Managers' Association*)
   51 Palace Street, Westminster, London, S.W.1

The qualifying examination includes a paper on "Statistical Method," which has questions on index numbers, theory and applications. An interesting paper appears in the Diploma examination, Part 1, "Market Research," which in the section devoted to sampling incorporates index numbers and requires a knowledge of published statistics.

8. *Institute of Cost and Works Accountants*
   63 Portland Place, London, W.1

This body examines in statistical method at the final examination and the advanced fellowship examination in management accountancy. The syllabus for both corresponds with that of the British Institute of Management National Scheme intermediate, and thus involves knowledge of both aspects of index numbers.

9. *Institute of Personnel Management*
   80 Fetter Lane, London, E.C.4

10. *Institution of Works Managers*
    34 Bloomsbury Way, London, W.C.1

11. *Office Management Association*
    58 Victoria Street, London, S.W.1

12. *Purchasing Officers' Association*
    York House, Westminster Bridge Road, London, S.E.1

The four bodies above, 9–12, set a common examination syllabus as for the National scheme, at Intermediate level, including statistical method.

13. *Corporation of Secretaries*
    Devonshire House, 13 Devonshire Street, London, W.1

Final examination, Economics (Money and Banking), expects a knowledge of index numbers as part of the study of changes in the value of money.

14. *The Institute of Bankers*
    Lombard Street, London, E.C.3

The Institute examines at two levels and index numbers appear in the syllabus of Part 1, "Economics."

15. *Institute of Transport*
    80 Portland Place, London, W.1

The Institute examines in "Elements of Statistics" in Part 1 of the graduateship examination. Index-number theory and applications are included.

16. *Local Government Examinations Board*
    41 Belgrave Square, London, S.W.1

The administrative examination contains statistics at intermediate level (optional): "index numbers as weighted averages of percentages, relatives, crude and standardised death rates."

17. *Building Societies' Institute*

7 Aldford Street, London, W.1

This body has a full paper on statistics in its final examination, and questions on indexes are frequently set.

University examinations

Most universities examine in statistics, but for the majority of degrees the subject is of a very mathematical nature. I have selected here syllabuses of as many degrees as possible in which "Economic Statistics" is a subject. I do not claim that the list is comprehensive.

1. *University of London*

B.Sc. (Economics) old regulations (Part I being held until 1965, Part II up to 1967). *Part I:* one of eight papers, selected as an alternative according to the subject being taken in Part II, which may be (*a*) Elementary Statistical Method and Sources, or (*b*) Elementary Statistical Theory. In the former paper index-number theory and sources figure prominently, but not in syllabus (*b*). *Part II:* a special subject is chosen, in several of which there is a paper on statistics. In Special subject 2, "Statistics," Paper III deals with economic problems statistically; Papers IV and V(*c*) "Economic Statistics" include index numbers. Paper (*d*) requires a considerable knowledge of index-number problems and applications. These papers are included in other Special subjects, such as: 1. "Economics," 2. "International Economics," 4. "Industry and Trade."

2. *University of Southampton, Faculty of Social Sciences*

(*a*) B.Sc. (Social Sciences): statistics forms a final subject if the student has reached a good "A" level standard beforehand.

(*b*) Diploma in Public Administration: statistics is a subject of study in the second part of this two- or three-year course.

3. *University of Liverpool, School of Economics*

B.A. (Special Studies): "Elements of Economic Statistics" is taken in the final, Part 1, and for those specialising in economics a paper in advanced economic statistics is an alternative. For the B.Com. degree similar papers are taken.

4. *University of Bristol*

For the B.A. an optional course in statistics covers theory and applied aspects and includes index numbers. At a more advanced level the B.A. in Economics (Special) course covers statistics, including econometrics.

5. *University of Manchester*

B.A. (Econ.): papers in economic statistics are set, in which questions involving a knowledge of index-number theory and applications are often included.

6. *Queen's University of Belfast*

B.Sc. (Econ.): Paper F (Economics) contains questions relating to economic statistics, including index numbers. The paper "Statistics" is more purely mathematical.

7. *University of Birmingham*

The examination Statistics I for B.Com., D.P.A., etc., is an elementary paper including questions on averages, indexes, and sampling. The paper "Economic Statistics" III for the B.Soc.Sc. degree is an interesting one in which economics and statistics are linked closely together as a basis on which to analyse (for example) production and consumption functions.

8. *University of Exeter, Faculty of Social Studies*

(a) D.P.A. Part 1: includes "Elementary Statistics."
(b) B.A. General (Social Studies): includes "Applied Statistics" and "Statistical Sources."
(c) B.A. Hons. (Social Studies): includes "Statistical Methods and Sources."
All these contain questions on index numbers.

9. *University of Leicester, Faculty of Social Science*

Special Degree: includes an optional course in the third year in economic statistics: "statistical treatment of economic problems, including income and expenditure, index numbers and time series."

10. *University of Edinburgh*

"Elements of Statistics" is a compulsory subject in the Honours examination in Economic Science.

11. *University of Glasgow*

First Year Certificate in Industrial Administration: includes a paper on statistics, including questions on index numbers.

12. *University of Leeds*

B.Com.: has a special subject "Economic Statistics." The syllabus for Paper 2 requires a knowledge of index numbers.

REGULAR STATISTICAL SOURCES

Governmental sources

Reference should be made to *Government Statistical Services* (H.M. Treasury), in which the principal publications and subjects are given. Of course, most publications listed below are not exclusively concerned with index numbers. But my selection covers most of the journals which will be useful.

General statistical publications

1. *Monthly Digest of Statistics:* published monthly by the C.S.O., this provides monthly data, including the Index of Industrial Production, textile index numbers, retail sales and stocks, road transport statistics, foreign trade, wages and hours of work, the Retail and Wholesale price indexes, and agriculture; all in tabular form. The regular user of the *Monthly Digest of Statistics* should provide himself with a copy of the Supplement, which is revised each January and describes the background of many statistical series in the *Monthly Digest of Statistics* itself.

2. *Annual Abstract of Statistics:* this publication, with its extensive runs of series, can be of great value to researchers requiring yearly data. Together with the *Monthly Digest of Statistics*, it can be found in most public reference libraries. The contents include details of national expenditure (spending, hire purchase, etc.), the national product (stocks, output, etc.), income, labour, finance, population, and other economic and social matters.

3. *Economic Trends:* published monthly by the C.S.O., this publication provides charts and statistics illustrating trends in the British economy in summary form, cross-referenced to appropriate tables in the *Monthly Digest of Statistics*. Two major features are worth noticing—first, that charts are given as well as tables (these do not appear in *Monthly Digest of Statistics* or *Annual Abstract of Statistics*) and, second, that all major changes in statistical series are discussed in detail so that

regular reference to this journal will ensure that all changes are noticed.

Agricultural

1. *Agricultural Price Indexes*: a monthly pamphlet from the Ministry of Agriculture.

2. *Agricultural Statistics for the United Kingdom*: published annually by the Ministry of Agriculture, a comprehensive review of all agricultural matters.

3. Agricultural prices are featured in the *Monthly Digest of Statistics*.

Banking and finance

1. *Financial Statistics:* this monthly publication covers exchequer, banking, overseas finance, and other financial matters, including the series "Industrial Security Prices and Yields," indexes published by *The Times, Financial Times*, and the *Financial Times*–Actuaries'. The journal is of value in giving brief explanations of the function and composition of financial "houses" such as discount houses.

2. *Board of Trade Journal:* weekly from the Board of Trade. For a full description see "Distribution" below. Each quarter the *Board of Trade Journal* publishes articles on finance houses and instalment credit, including hire-purchase index numbers.

3. The Bank of England Index of Notes in Circulation with the Public is included in the *Monthly Digest of Statistics* as part of one of the tables.

Distribution

The Board of Trade publishes two regular periodicals of direct interest in this context:

1. *Board of Trade Journal* (weekly).
2. *Report on Overseas Trade* (monthly).

The first is perhaps the most interesting commercial publication of H.M. Government, being well edited and produced, with regular articles on home and foreign trade, although the main bias is towards the promotion of British export trade. The regular index numbers of the Board of Trade (including the components of the Index of Industrial Production and the Index of Wholesale Prices) are periodically published in it, usually with full explanatory matter. The series concerning distribution are "Monthly Sales and Stocks of Retail Establishments" and "Hire Purchase and Other Instalment Credit." A recent innovation is the table "The Economy—Selected Indicators," which assembles in summary form on one page indexes and monetary data on a wide range of economic topics such as prices, labour, industrial production, and overseas trade.

The Board of Trade has power to conduct a census of distribution from time to time, and details appear in the *Board of Trade Journal*. For example, the second full-scale census was taken in 1961 (the first was in 1950, and a limited sample in 1957). First results appeared in the *Journal* of 8th February 1963 in ten pages, including tables. The full census reports will be in three volumes, giving valuable information as to the growth or decline of various sections of distribution, including department stores, mail order, and self service, as well as results of individual retail trades (grocery, clothing, bookselling, for example).

Labour

1. *Ministry of Labour Gazette:* contains, in addition to regular monthly, quarterly or annual statistics, articles on a variety of industrial topics like safety and wage agreements. Its regular index series are the Index of Retail Prices, Index of Weekly Rates of Wages, Normal Weekly Hours and Hourly Rates, and Index of Hours Worked. It is published monthly.

2. *Annual Report of the Ministry of Labour.*

3. *Time Rates of Wages and Hours of Work:* annual.

4. *Statistics on Incomes, Prices, Employment and Production:* a quarterly which first appeared in 1962, produced by the Ministry in association with other departments and designed to provide information needed for negotiation or arbitration, such as wages, hours, prices, profits, and relevant subjects. Several indexes are shown that relate to hours and wages.

These four sources are all published by the Ministry of Labour, the Government department chiefly responsible for issuing data on work, hours, wages, employment, accidents, and training, as well as the Index of Retail Prices. For a complete list of statistics published by the Ministry up to September 1961 see the *Ministry of Labour Gazette* for that month. The international situation can be understood by regular reference to I.L.O. publications and the U.N. *Monthly Bulletin of Statistics*.

National income and expenditure

The major document is the *National Income and Expenditure* Blue book published annually by the Central Statistical Office.

This contains annual estimates for ten years of the national product, income, and expenditure of the United Kingdom; the economics student should use it after referring to the H.M.S.O. publication *National Income Statistics: Sources and Methods* (1956). There are ten divisions plus definitions, and index numbers appear in certain tables, chiefly "Prices and Costs," some at constant prices, and "Consumers' Expenditure." The bulk of tables are of data in monetary units.

Prices

1. Index of Retail Prices: monthly in the *Ministry of Labour Gazette* in detail with a commentary. A table of retail price indexes overseas is also given. The Index appears, with comparisons from earlier periods, in the *Monthly Digest of Statistics* and *Economic Trends*; it is widely reported in the press. Because of its close link in the public's mind with the cost of living, it receives more publicity than any other index.

2. Index of Wholesale Prices: appears monthly in the *Board of Trade Journal* in full detail and with a commentary. It also is widely reported in Government publications, including *Economic Trends*, the *Monthly Digest of Statistics*, and the *Annual Abstract of Statistics*; it receives mention in some parts of the press.

3. Index Numbers of Imports and Exports: price and volume statistics are given in detail in regular tables of the *Board of Trade Journal*, and useful graphs and tables in *Economic Trends*. Most of the figures derive from *Accounts relating to the Trade and Navigation of the U.K.*, and are also shown in the *Monthly Digest of Statistics* and in *Annual Abstract of Statistics*. The Board of Trade publishes a useful *Report on Overseas Trade* monthly, which gives, in more detail than is possible in the *Board of Trade Journal* or *Monthly Digest of Statistics*, information on imports and exports by type, direction, in sterling, and index numbers. Indexes are: (*a*) Volume of External Trade: import totals by months; (*b*) Volume of U.K. Exports, by classes of product; (*c*) Volume of U.K. Imports: by classes of product; (*d*) Import and Export Prices, by months and years, including terms of trade.

For Commonwealth matters, the annual report entitled *The Commonwealth and the Sterling Area Statistical Abstract* is highly informative. Tables cover all aspects of trade, including production, consumption, prices, population, and balance of payments.

4. Indexes of Agricultural Prices are given in the *Monthly Digest of Statistics*—for reference see *Economic Trends* 100

(February 1962). Indexes are given for prices and materials consumed.

Production

Statistics are produced and issued by the C.S.O. and associated Government departments and are the source of much discussion by economists and planners—such as N.E.D.C., or "Neddy." The most important is the Index of Industrial Production, which appears monthly in the *Monthly Digest of Statistics* and annually in the *Annual Abstract of Statistics*. A summary table is given regularly in the *Board of Trade Journal*, which also announces the publication of volumes of the Census of Production Report. The Index is given with accompanying charts in *Economic Trends*.

Transport

A large quantity of transport statistics is published by various authorities, but not many indexes. The Ministry of Transport Index Numbers of Inland Goods Transport appear in the *Monthly Digest of Statistics*.

Miscellaneous

A series has been published in recent years called *Studies in Official Statistics*, some of which are devoted to a full description of a particular index. No. 1, "Labour Statistics"; No. 2, "Census Reports of Great Britain, 1801–1931"; No. 3, "Local Government Statistics"; No. 4, "Agriculture and Food Statistics"; No. 5, "New Contributions to Economic Statistics" (reprints from *Economic Trends*); No. 6, "Method of Construction and Calculation of the Index of Retail Prices" (but add Cmd 1657 (1962) to this); No. 7, "The Index of Industrial Production, 1959" (but add reference to *Economic Trends* for March 1962); No. 8, "Input–Output Tables for the United Kingdom, 1954."

Nos. 2 and 3, however, do not contain any index numbers.

To ensure that changes in index series are not missed, regular reference should be made to the *Board of Trade Journal*, the *Ministry of Labour Gazette*, *Economic Trends*, the Treasury bulletins on industrial topics, and the annual Supplement to the *Monthly Digest of Statistics*.

M

Private sources

Prices (non-investment)

1. The Comtelburo Statistics Service: provides monthly statistics on commodity prices as well as Reuter's daily Index of Staple Commodity Prices.

2. *The Financial Times:* quite apart from share prices, this daily newspaper covers a wide range of price indexes, including regular tables on the *Financial Times* Commodity Index and several other commodity indicators.

3. *The Statist:* this weekly publishes the Sauerbeck–*Statist* Indexes of Wholesale Prices and Silver Prices once a month. An article on these indexes appears annually in the *Journal of the Royal Statistical Society.*

4. *The Economist:* every week the *Economist* Commodity Price Indicator and the Share Price Index are given. In addition, *The Economist*, either weekly or less frequently, covers many Government and private indexes. See the statistical pages at the end of each issue.

5. *The Commonwealth Economic Committee Intelligence Bulletin:* there is one index (Butter Sales) among many statistics on dairy products in this monthly publication.

Prices (investment)

Since share prices fluctuate rapidly, daily newspapers report many of these indexes. A full description of sources is given in the appropriate chapter. In summary, the major sources are: the *Financial Times, The Times, The Wall Street Journal, The Investors' Chronicle, The Economist, The Statist, The Stock Exchange Gazette*, the *Daily Mail*, the *Sunday Times*, and *The Observer.*

Stocks and production

1. *Times Review of Industry and Technology:* each quarter this monthly publication contains the London & Cambridge Economic Service Production Indexes.

2. Governmental Indexes: these are reported in responsible journals and dailies.

Labour

The Guardian: the *Guardian* Wage Indexes are published monthly.

General comments

There are many more publications than have been mentioned. One useful source of information on all economic matters is the regular bank review. Each of the major British banks publishes one, usually quarterly, and it should be emphasised that these have basically nothing to do with banking, being a service by the banks to further knowledge of economic matters. Articles are written by leading industrial, commercial, and educational authorities and cover a wide range of topics. In addition, several bank reviews contain statistical sections.

Many libraries subscribe to the "academic" journals, of which there are many—British, American, and others. The articles are of a high standard and frequently break new territory. Consequently, the degree of knowledge expected of the reader by the author is high. However, such publications as the journals of the Royal Statistical Society and the Institute of Statisticians should be required reading.

RAPID PROCESSING OF STATISTICS

The demand for more speed in the processing and presentation of statistics has caused both governmental and private compilers of index numbers to adopt, or consider adopting, mechanical or electronic devices to aid them in their efforts to produce their eagerly awaited indexes.

An interesting table was published in *N.I.E.S.R. Review* in May 1963, showing various well-known statistics and the time lags involved before they are presented to readers. For example, *The Bankers' Magazine* Security Prices Index (monthly) takes a week, The Index of Industrial Production (monthly) two or three months, and the Midland Bank Turnover Index (quarterly) four or five weeks.

The following notes relate to the use of electronic computers, although it should be noted that the bulk of statistical work is done with the aid of hand accounting machines or (less often) punched-card set-ups. Indeed, I know of at least one very famous index which is compiled without machinery of any kind by one man in his spare time! Many statisticians regard electronic equipment with suspicion, but the advice of organisation and methods departments which investigate the advantages and disadvantages of such equipment may convince these people that in certain cases the very fact that work can be done so much faster will enable them and their management to concentrate on the use and analysis of statistics rather than spend their lives simply producing them. As illustrative proof, the following is from the Congress of the United States, Sub-Committee on Economic Statistics of the Joint Economic Committee hearing on the 24th January 1961:

> Representative Curtis: Would you say it is true that a great deal of the advancement in economic statistics comes from the advancement in electronic data processing equipment?
>
> Mr Bowman (U.S. Bureau of the Budget): It has been a main element in getting things out more promptly, and also to handle complicated tabulations . . . the Census of Population this time was completely tabulated on electronic data processing equipment . . . the data for 1960 will be available in half the time that it took for the 1950 census.

A computer is a set of electronic devices into which data are fed together with certain instructions, or "programmes." The information emerges in very quick time. Provision is made for information to be stored and withdrawn from store during the calculations as required. The machine cannot, of course, "think," but it can obey instructions rapidly in logical sequence and, where properly used, has the following possible advantages, as listed by J. Batty:

1. It avoids clerical drudgery, by providing more information with less work. Some tasks which are now regarded as necessary could not be done without using computers (e.g. the railways' summer train planning schedules).

2. Speed is measured in minute fractions of a second for each complete operation, and with share-price calculations, for instance, this is essential.

3. Complicated calculations can be carried out rapidly and with great accuracy, e.g. the calculation of share yields and indexes.

4. Sampling surveys can be processed in a reasonable span of time, allowing market-research efforts to be applied while they are still up-to-date.

5. Information can be stored until it is required and used to provide standard information (such as basic weights, etc.), which can be mixed with current data being fed in.

These are only a few of the uses of computers which I feel are especially important. The three basic benefits, as listed by P. G. Barnes, are speed, complexity of calculation, and control.

The Sub-Committee of the Joint Economic Committee quoted above heard a statement from Dr Ewan Clague, of the U.S. Department of Labor. The Bureau of Labor Statistics had its first computer in 1958, a second in January 1961, and in May 1961 was considering a third, more advanced, model.

Dr Clague pointed out that the equipment cannot be much help in certain problems, such as recognising that there *are* problems and selecting the right approach to a solution. Results can be no better than the quality of data fed in. Programmes are costly and time-consuming (although standard programmes can sometimes be used). The use of computers may save time, but often more workers and effort follow their adoption because (*vide* Parkinson's Law) work will expand to benefit by the facilities the equipment provides.

The Bureau can prepare complicated indexes from the computers, which compare current and previous data, weight the results, and calculate averages and the indexes. In addition, the final results emerge from the equipment in such a form as to be suitable for photo-offset process printing direct.

Several United Kingdom Government Departments have computers, and their use is spreading. The Board of Trade (which already own an N.C.R. computer) is adding a Leo III for statistical work. Commercial compilers of statistics often use the benefits of computer service centres and "buy time" from expensive equipment. They pay the charge but do not have to find the equipment, staff, or room space. In addition, costs can be budgeted and paid for as they arise without the necessity of large outlays at any one time. Of course, the service centre will have experts available whose advice is part of the service. One such service is that of the National Cash Register Company Financial Computing Centre in London. The Centre houses several computers, two of which are used to compile well-known indexes. The National-Elliott 803 has the daily task of receiving and processing Stock Exchange data on behalf of the *Times* and the *Financial Times*–Actuaries' indexes. The National-Elliott 405 helps compile the indexes of share prices for the *Engineering News* and *Electronics Weekly*. In the case of the 803, messengers rush round to the Centre early in the evening with stock-exchange results, and after a quick cup of tea they are ready to dash back to their newspapers with the results. The *Times* index takes one hour for the prices to be punched in and five minutes to be calculated; the *Financial Times*–Actuaries' takes ten minutes more, since yields are calculated in addition to price indexes! The speeds are measured in milliseconds (thousandth parts of a second). Any short arithmetic instruction takes 0·576 milliseconds; division or multiplication can take up to 12·384 milliseconds.

Programmes have been prepared by the staff of the Computing Centre, who are responsible for incorporating changes into the indexes (*e.g.* on the occasion of a take-over bid).

ILLUSTRATION OF INDEX NUMBERS: GRAPHS

"The job of the economic statistician," says C. T. Saunders, "is not to display the maximum number of figures, but to present those facts which will give users such insight into the economic situation as statistics can provide." Graphical presentation of data is an essential part of any time-series analysis. Not many readers can visualise several series of data over several years without a graph to display their features, which is something a table of numbers cannot do.

When plotting actual data as distinct from textbook examples, it is often found that the orderly controlled curves may be missing. As Moroney says, "the physicist as a student meets with nothing but nice smooth curves in his experiments —by kind arrangement of his tutors. When he gets out doing research in an industrial laboratory, all too often his graphs are like plum puddings, through which he helplessly and hopelessly tries to draw a trend line."

The curves

Although graphs are drawn on a framework involving two axes with four quadrants, index-number charts normally use only the positive quadrants, where both axes start at zero and move in the positive direction.

The axes are labelled; X usually has the independent variable scale along it, Y the dependent variable. For index number presentation, the X axis is divided into years or months, etc., and the Y axis is numbered around the 100 mark for the index numbers themselves.

Any lines joining points are known as curves, whether straight or not. A straight line joins points if the data is discrete, that is, the items are independent and do not flow into each other by graduations. The process of interpolation is not possible, in other words, you cannot read off intermediate positions on such a chart. Smooth lines are used for joining points where the data are continuous, and in most index numbers series this will apply. For example, when plotting retail price data at quarterly intervals you can read off intermediate positions provided that due allowance is made for seasonal influences.

The scale

Two scales are used along the dependent variable, natural and logarithmic. Natural scale is the more usual, since it is simple and most readers are used to it. A rise of (say) £50 or two points of an index number will show by a rise of a given number of squares on the graph, irrespective of whether the rise is from £75 to £125, from £725 to £775, or from 375 to 377 in index numbers.

Using the log, or "ratio," scale the actual rises assume less significance than the rate of change or speed of the rises. A rise from £75 to £125 represents a greater speed of increase than the same amount of rise between £725 and £775, and on log scale this would show clearly by the slope of the line. Some compilers of index numbers use log scale charts, but in general natural scales are used. Two other features of log scales do not apply to index numbers: the benefit if the data are widely spaced (the classic example being wholesale and retail prices in the great German inflation after the first world war), and the advantage of the graph is to show several variables measured in different units, e.g. a graph showing sales in units, in money, and hours worked by the office. Most tables using index numbers do not have such a wide spread of data and the problem of mixed units cannot arise.

Rules

1. Choose graph paper of the right size: all shapes and sizes are available to suit special requirements.

2. Decide on the scales in advance, allowing room at top and bottom for later items (unless the chart is historical and thus complete in itself).

3. If the Y scale does not start at zero, make it quite clear. Since 100 is a significant number, rule a heavy line across the chart. If log scales are used do not measure from zero (the log of zero is minus infinity).

4. Do not plot more than three or four curves on one graph. Do not use coloured inks if the graph is to be reproduced by photographic processes—use various kinds of broken, pecked, or dotted lines, etc.

5. Label the graph carefully: a short title, a heading for each axis, proper scales, source, and a (very) few footnotes if they are really necessary. Label with the titles written horizontally.

Mary Spear makes some important points to encourage the use of index-number charts when certain kinds of data are to be illustrated.

First, when two or more series of a similar type of data but of very different magnitudes are given indexes provide the ideal solution. As an example, take the number of current road-vehicle licences in Great Britain (given here in thousands):

Annual census	Cars	Tramcars	Ambulances and fire engines
1957	4187	1·6	14·4
1958	4549	1·3	14·5
1959	4966	1·1	14·7
1960	5526	0·7	14·8
1961	5979	0·4	14·8

(*Source: Ministry of Transport*)

To plot these on natural scale on one chart would prove
difficult, but if converted to index numbers the data are visible
at a glance and compact; if the original series is required the
table should be kept near the chart.

Annual census	Cars	Tramcars	Ambulances and fire engines
1957	100	100	100
1958	108·6	89·5	100·7
1959	118·9	68·6	102·1
1960	132·3	43·8	102·8
1961	142·8	25	102·8

Second, when two series of related data, measured in different
units, are given. Two charts can be shown, but for comparison
one chart with index numbers is better. For example, take
United Kingdom airline traffic figures.

Year	(a) Aircraft miles flown (000's)	(b) Passengers carried (000's)	(c) Freight carried (short tons)	Index numbers 1956 = 100		
				(a)	(b)	(c)
1956	6500	288	8,500	100	100	100
1957	7100	331	9,400	109	115	111
1958	7250	332	11,600	112	115	137
1959	7650	392	16,200	118	136	190
1960	8900	490	20,000	140	170	235
1961	9700	570	21,110	150	197	250

(*Source: Ministry of Aviation*)

A glance at the graph showing the data as index numbers on
a common base is more revealing than the tables if an impression
is all that is required. The miles flown by aircraft have increased

less quickly than revenue items, indicating a more successful load factor and possibly larger aircraft.

It is important to show a reliable base date. Mary Spear uses a table showing Government purchases of goods and services in the U.S.A. between 1939 and 1945, and indicates how different bases can give different impressions. The table is as follows:

Year	(a) Billions of dollars	(b) Index 1939 = 100	(c) Index 1944 = 100
1939	13·1	100	13·6
1940	13·9	106·1	14·4
1941	24·7	188·5	25·6
1942	59·7	455·7	61·9
1943	88·6	676·3	91·8
1944	96·5	736·6	100
1945	82·8	632	85·8
1946	30·7	234·3	31·8
1947	28·8	219·8	29·8
1948	36·7	280·1	38·0
1949	43·5	332·0	45·1

If 1939 = 100 is chosen all future data are far above the values at the base date, but if 1944 is chosen all values save for that one extreme year are well below the base-date values. This emphasises the need to choose a base carefully. Plot the two series side by side, with a common line at 100, and the differences are obvious.

Charts for investors

Investors rely for their prosperity on their anticipations of the near future, and index numbers of share prices are often published with graphs to aid the interpretation of trends. Investors aim to buy shares when the price-index curve has reached its lowest level and to "unload" them when the peak has been attained; but few are prepared to claim that charts can show with reasonable certainty that those points have been reached. Graphs of share prices follow the normal construction rules.

On 4th February 1963 there appeared in *The Times* the first of a series of graphs, to be published at intervals, designed to show how share prices have moved in all parts of the world where stock exchanges exist. Each graph is to cover three years and one month, the three years being shown weekly and the most recent month daily, using an extended scale.

Each chart contains graphs representing the movement of four or five equity indexes, which are technically most nearly comparable with *The Times* index. The object is to show, as simply as possible, what has happened to prices since the beginning of 1960, and thus all indexes are recalculated on a base of 1st January 1960 = 100. Each chart has with it a commentary describing the reasons for important movements. Reference should be made to such journals as *The Economist* and *The Investors' Chronicle* for useful charts.

THE STANDARD INDUSTRIAL CLASSIFICATION

The growing confusion of statistical information collected by Government departments led, after the second world war, to the issue of the Standard Industrial Classification, whose object was the promotion of uniformity and comparability in official statistics.

The first issue was in 1949 and this basis is still retained. The latest major revision was that of 1958, and changes were made following the changing pattern of the structure and organisation of British industry. The new edition was prepared by an inter-departmental committee, formed of the main departmental committees which collect statistics.

There is an International Standard Industrial Classification of all economic activities, published by the United Nations, which is followed by the United Kingdom classification.

The first revision to the 1958 Standard Industrial Classification was made in 1963 (Standard Industrial Classification Amendment List 1), revising details within various list headings but not affecting the basic structure. The latter is as follows:

1. The Classification is based on industries, not on occupations. Thus all who are employed in a "unit" of an industry would be included. The classification covers nationalised as well as private industry.

2. The "unit" is usually the whole premises at one address, unless each department of the building can be separately classified.

3. Industries are classified under 152 "minimum list headings" (M.L.H.), which are grouped into 24 "orders" (by Roman numerals), and in turn these can be placed into eight divisions.

Standard Industrial Classification, revised 1958

Division	Minimum list heading	Order	Title
0	001–003	I	Agriculture, forestry, and fishing
1	101–109	II	Mining and quarrying
2–4			*Manufacturing*
	211–240	III	Food, drink, and tobacco
	261–277	IV	Chemicals and allied industries
	311–322	V	Metal manufacture
			Engineering and allied industries
	331–369	VI	Engineering and electrical goods
	370	VII	Shipbuilding and marine engineering
	381–389	VIII	Vehicles
	391–399	IX	Metal goods not elsewhere specified
			Textile, leather, and clothing
	411–429	X	Textiles
	431–433	XI	Leather, leather goods, and fur
	441–450	XII	Clothing and footwear
			Other manufacturing
	461–469	XIII	Bricks, pottery, glass, cement, etc.
	471–479	XIV	Timber, furniture, etc.
	481–489	XV	Paper, printing, and publishing
	491–499	XVI	Other manufacturing industries
5	500	XVII	Construction
6	601–603	XVIII	Gas, electricity, and water
7	701–709	XIX	Transport and communication
8	810–832	XX	Distributive trades and services n.e.s.
			Financial professions, and miscellaneous services
	860	XXI	Insurance, banking, and finance
	871–879	XXII	Professional and scientific services
	881–899	XXIII	Miscellaneous services
9	901–906	XXIV	Public administration and defence

Each M.L.H. has various groups, each identified by the M.L.H. number. For example:

Order III, M.L.H. 240, Tobacco: manufactured tobacco, cigars, cigarettes, and snuff.
Order V, M.L.H. 312, Steel tubes: manufacture of all types of steel tube and pipes and fittings, therefore including conduits, gas cylinders, and flexible tubes.

Order XX, M.L.H. 820, Groceries and provisions, has seven sub-groups: other food, confectionery, tobacco and newspapers, clothing and footwear, household goods, other non-food goods, general stores, etc.

The student should refer to the *Ministry of Labour Gazette* of February 1959 (p. 55) and February 1960 (p. 56); each annual Supplement to the *Monthly Digest of Statistics*; *The Standard Industrial Classification*, published for the Central Statistical Office by H.M.S.O., 1958; S.I.C. Amended List 1 and the Alphabetical List Amendment, both also published for the C.S.O. by H.M.S.O.; and *Economic Trends* for October 1958.

THE STATISTICS OF TRADE ACT, 1947

In order to enable certain Government departments to obtain more readily the information they need for the appreciation of economic trends, this Act was passed by Parliament, the first in the United Kingdom to give general powers for the collection of statistics. It ensures that the work of the various departments is facilitated because the necessary statistics are regularly submitted by those institutions, companies, and so on from whom they are required. The Act also obliges the Board of Trade to take a yearly census of production and empowers it to take a census of distribution in any prescribed year.

Some of the details which can be requested include the nature of the business, details of persons employed, their remuneration, hours of work, sales and deliveries of goods, financial statistics, and capital. It is accepted practice never to publish information which would disclose the identity of the firm or persons making a return, nor to divulge figures relating to individual firms or persons to the tax authorities or police, except for prosecutions under the regulations authorising the collection of the statistics. For example, see sections 9 (1) and 9 (5) of the Act.

The Act appears to be functioning efficiently—at any rate there have been no legal cases arising from it so far as I am aware. For reference, apart from the Act itself, see Butterworth's Annotated Legislation Service, Statutes Supplement No. 44, pp. 95–100 and 106–18, published in 1948, which contains an explanation of the Act and notes to sections.

QUESTIONS AND EXERCISES

1. Name the sources which you would consult for information concerning: (a) wholesale prices; (b) retail prices; (c) wage rates. Indicate the main features of the information given.

(London Chamber of Commerce 1962)

2. Summarise the general information to be found in the *Board of Trade Journal*. *(London Chamber of Commerce 1960)*

3. What basic information relating to any one single industry can be found in the *Monthly Digest of Statistics*? Set out your answer in three sections: (a) Employment; (b) Output; (c) Prices. For each of these give some concrete examples and indicate how the figures are collected.

(I.C.W.A. 1959)

4. Write a brief note on four of the following. Give an example of how each of the four can be of use in a practical business situation:

(a) Census of Production.
(b) Index of Production.
(c) *Ministry of Labour Gazette.*
(d) *Monthly Digest of Statistics.*
(e) Census of Population.
(f) *Annual Abstract of Statistics.*
(g) *Board of Trade Journal.*

(I.C.W.A. 1958)

5. Indicate the source, coverage, and the weaknesses of four of the following official statistics:

(a) Monthly Retail Trade Indexes prepared by the Board of Trade.
(b) Index of Industrial Production.
(c) Personal savings.
(d) Household expenditure.
(e) United Kingdom transactions with the rest of the world in the Investment Account of the Balance of Payments.

(I.O.S. 1962)

6. Give an account of the information collected and published by the Board of Trade on *either* retail sales *or* hire purchase. *(I.O.S. 1962)*

7. What *original* official sources (not C.S.O. publications) would you consult to find the following statistics?

(a) Average weekly earnings in the principal industries.
(b) Monthly changes in retail sales in Great Britain.

(I.M.S.M. 1961)

8. "The collection of accurate statistical data upon a large scale is only possible with exact definitions of terms, *e.g.* classes, units, etc." Comment with illustrations. *(I.M.S.M. 1962)*

9. Discuss the value of the logarithmic scale in the graphical presentation of a time series. Illustrate your answer by drawing one or more graphs of the following data:

Industrial Production (1953 = 100)

	1954	1955	1956	1957	1958	1959	1960 (Est.)
United Kingdom	108	114	114	116	114	121	130
Japan	108	116	144	167	168	208	257
U.S.A.	93	104	109	110	102	116	119

(University of Liverpool 1961)

10. Draw a graph of the two series, using a logarithmic scale. Draw a second graph of the two series with an arithmetic scale. Comment briefly on the differences between the slopes of the lines of the two charts and state, with reasons, which chart gives the better representation.

Vehicles with current licences in Great Britain (000's)

1951	1952	1953	1954	1955	1956	1957	1958	1959	1960
All motor vehicles									
4625	4904	5286	5775	6412	6920	7427	7904	8606	9384
Private cars									
2380	2508	2762	3100	3526	3888	4187	4549	4966	5526

(I.O.T. 1962)

11. Plot the following data:

Year: 1, 2, 3, 4, 5, 6, 7, 8, 9, and 10
Production of x *for respective years:* 12, 35, 58, 81, 104, 127, 150, 173, 196, and 219

(a) on a natural scale; (b) on a semi-logarithmic scale. State briefly the advantage of each method of plotting in the interpretation of the data. *(I.C.W.A. 1961)*

12. Explain the difference between a semi-logarithmic scale and a natural scale chart. Give an example to indicate when each would be used. *(London Chamber of Commerce 1962)*

13. What are the objectives of a Standard Industrial Classification? Give an outline of the history of the United Kingdom Standard Industrial Classification, and describe the current system briefly, indicating the main principles on which it is based.
(University of Bristol 1960)

14. Describe broadly the basis of the Standard Industrial Classification and explain some of the difficulties in applying it generally to all Government statistics. *(R.S.A. 1960)*

15. You are asked to construct a monthly index of house prices in your locality from information that is readily available at negligible cost. Describe in main outline the method you would use, discussing particularly:

(a) the meaning of the price quotations you would use;

(b) the need for a standard classification of houses according to their types and which would be used from month to month to ensure comparability in the price quotations used for relatives;

(c) the possibility of using a weighted rather than an unweighted average of price relatives.

Comment on the reliability which you would expect the index to possess. (*University of London 1962*)

BIBLIOGRAPHY

DURING my work on this subject I have read many books and articles, and I list below those which have been especially valuable. The editions quoted are those I used, but many will have been re-issued more recently. I am grateful to authors and publishers for permission to use copyright material.

Ministry of Agriculture, *Agricultural statistics.* H.M.S.O.
R. G. D. Allen, *Statistics for economists.* Home University Library, Hutchinson, 1951
H. Arkin and R. Colton, *Statistical methods.* Barnes & Noble, 1958
F. E. Armstrong, *The book of the Stock Exchange.* Pitman, 1958
H. B. Arthur, "Weighted aggregate sand index numbers." *Journal of the American Statistical Association,* No. 1983, June 1937
T. S. Ashton, "The work of Stanley Jevons and others" in *The Manchester Statistical Society 1833–1893,* ed. P. S. King, 1934
The Bankers' Magazine
P. G. Barnes, "Computer service bureaux." *Office Magazine,* May 1963
J. Batty, *Management accountancy.* Macdonald & Evans, 1963
Belfast Newsletter, issues in 1959 and 1960
Belfast Telegraph, issues in 1959 and 1960
C. A. Blyth, *The use of economic statistics.* Allen & Unwin, 1960

Board of Trade Journal:

1. Catering: 29th December 1961, 21st September 1962
2. Census of Distribution: 8th February 1963 and later issues
3. Foreign trade: 10th December 1955, 19th May 1956, 2nd May 1958
4. Hire purchase: 9th December 1960, 10th February 1961, 17th August 1962
5. Industrial production: 8th May 1959, 22nd July 1960
6. Northern Ireland retail sales: 18th March and 20th May 1960
7. Retail sales: 5th May 1956, 19th December 1958, 6th February 1959, 1st January 1960, 10th February 1961, 9th June 1961, 6th July 1962
8. Retail stocks: 19th December 1958
9. Wholesale prices: 12th May 1956, 21st March 1958, 16th January and 13th February 1959, 26th February 1960, 12th May 1961
10. Wholesale textiles: 10th January 1953, 4th March 1960

Board of Trade, *Report on wholesale and retail prices.* H.M.S.O., 1903
Sir A. L. Bowley, *An elementary manual of statistics.* Macdonald & Evans, 1951

Sir A. L. Bowley, "Francis Ysidro Edgeworth." *Econometrica* 2, 1934

Bureau of Labor Statistics (U.S.A.):
  Consumer Prices: *Bulletins* 699, 966, 1165, 2477
  Wholesale prices: *Bulletin* 1168

Carter and Roy, *British economic statistics.* Cambridge University Press, 1954

Chamber of Shipping of the United Kingdom:
  Tramp shipping freights, 1953
  Tramp freight index (revised basis), 1961

W. G. Cochran, *Sampling techniques.* John Wiley, 1953

Commercial and Financial Chronicle (U.S.A.), "Standard & Poor's indexes," 8th May 1952

L. Connor, *Statistics in theory and practice.* Pitman, 1947

L. Connor and A. J. H. Morrell, *Statistics in theory and practice.* Pitman, 1957

T. G. Connolly and W. Slukin, *Statistics for the social sciences.* Cleaver Hume Press

Cost of Living Advisory Committee:
  Report into household expenditure in 1953–1954. H.M.S.O. 1957
  Report on the revision of the Index of Retail Prices. Cmd. 1657, H.M.S.O. 1962
  See also Cmd. Papers 7077, 8328, 8481, 9710

Honor Croome, "Public opinion and the cost of living index." *Westminster Bank Review*, November 1956

Council on Prices, Productivity and Incomes, Third *Report.* H.M.S.O. 1950

F. E. Croxton and D. J. Cowden, *Applied general statistics.* Pitman, 1960
  Practical business statistics. Prentice-Hall, 1960

C.S.O., *National income statistics, sources and methods.* H.M.S.O.

C.S.O., "The Industrial Production Index." *Studies in official statistics* No. 7. H.M.S.O. 1960

F. N. David, *A statistics primer.* Griffin, 1953

W. E. Deming, *Sampling design in business research.* John Wiley, 1960

E. Devons, *Introduction to British economic statistics.* Cambridge University Press, 1956

C. Dice and W. Eiteman, *The stock market.* McGraw-Hill, 1952

S. M. Dornbusch and C. F. Schmid, *A primer of social statistics.* McGraw-Hill, 1955

C. Drakatos, "London share price indexes." *The Bankers' Magazine*, June 1962

E. I. Eaton, "A closer look at prices." *Dun's Review*, April 1952

Economic Trends:

  1. Agriculture: February 1962
  2. Hire purchase: September 1961
  3. Industrial production: June 1959, March 1962
  4. Prices: September 1958, September 1959
  5. Retail sales: May 1962
  6. Transport: February 1960

The Economist, 1864, 18th November 1911, 15th December 1928, 19th July 1952, 4th July 1953, January 1961

F. Y. Edgeworth, "Pierson on the scarcity of gold." *Economic Journal*, March 1895

Papers relating to political economy, Vol. 1. Macmillan, 1925

A. G. Ellinger, *The art of investment*. Bowes & Bowes, 1955

H. J. Eysenck, *Uses and abuses of psychology*. Pelican Books, 1953

Federal Reserve Bank of New York, *Selected economic indicators*, 1954

C. H. Feinstein, "The provisional Index of Industrial Production." *London and Cambridge Bulletin* 47, 1963

W. F. Ferger, "Distinctive concepts of price and purchasing power index numbers." *Journal of the American Statistical Association*, June 1936

The Financial Times, Guide to the F.T.–Actuaries' share indices. Regular issues of the newspaper

I. Fisher, *The making of index numbers*. Houghton Mifflin, 1923

P. Sargent Florence, "Size of companies and other factors." *Journal of the Royal Statistical Society* A, 1959, 122

J. E. Freund and F. J. Williams, *Modern business statistics*. Pitman, 1959

R. Frisch, "Some basic principles of price of living measurements." *Econometrica*, Vol. 122, 1954

Gayer, Rostow and Schwartz, *Growth and fluctuation of the British economy 1790–1850*. Oxford University Press, 1953

D. Glass and E. Grebenik, *The trend and pattern of fertility*. H.M.S.O., 1954

G. H. Ross Goobey, "Pension fund investment." *Stock Exchange Journal*, Winter 1961–62

"The use of statistics in the investment of funds." *Applied Statistics*, Vol. 5, 1956

A. Goudeket, "An application of replacement theory." *The Manager*, January 1961

G. von Haberler, *Der Sinn der Indexzahlen*. Germany, 1927

Haycocks and Plymen, "Investment policy index numbers." *Transactions of the Faculty of Actuaries*, Vol. 23

S. Hays, *Outline of statistics*. Longmans, 1953

Z. Hirsch, *Introduction to modern statistics*. Macmillan Co. of New York, 1957

Sir O. Hobson, *How the City works*. Dickens, 1954

R. L. A. Holmes, *Statistics for professional students*. Pitman, 1953

Hughes and Hughes, *Learning and teaching*. Longmans, 1955

G. P. Hyett, *The Daily Mail Index*. Seminar to the London School of Economics, 1959

The Daily Mail Share Price Index. Associated Newspapers Ltd, 1959

A. R. Illersic, *Statistics*. H. F. L. (Publishers) Ltd, 1952

Sir G. Ince, *The Ministry of Labour and National Service*. Allen & Unwin, 1960

Investor's Chronicle, Beginners please. Eyre & Spottiswoode, 1956

Investor's Chronicle, 27th March 1957, 7th May 1961, 5th January 1962

W. S. Jevons, *A serious fall in the value of gold as ascertained* . . . 1863
  Investigations into currency and finance. 1884
D. C. Jones, *Social surveys.* Home University Library, Hutchinson, 1949
P. H. Karmel, *Applied statistics for economists.* Pitman, Melbourne,
  1957
M. G. Kendall, *Sources and nature of the statistics of the United Kingdom.*
  Oliver & Boyd, 1957
Kendall and Buckland, *A dictionary of statistical terms.* Oliver & Boyd,
  1957
Kendall and Stuart, *Measuring share price changes*
J. M. Keynes, "F. Y. Edgeworth." *Economic Journal,* 1926
  A treatise on money, Vol. 1. Macmillan, 1930
  "William Stanley Jevons 1835–82." *Journal of the Royal statistical
  Society,* 1936
  The general theory of employment, interest and money. Harcourt Brace,
  1936
W. I. King, *Index numbers elucidated.* 1930
R. Knight, *Intelligence and intelligence tests.* Methuen, 1943
Layton and Crowther, *The study of prices.* Macmillan, 1935
R. G. Lipsey, "Does money always depreciate?" *Lloyds Bank Review,*
  October 1960
K. S. Lomax, "Production and productivity movements in the United
  Kingdom since 1900." *Journal of the Royal Statistical Society* A,
  1959
P. Loveday, *Statistics: a second course.* Cambridge University Press,
  1961
R. Marris, *Economic arithmetic.* Macmillan, 1958
A. Marshall, "Remedies for fluctuations of general prices." *Contempo-
  rary Review,* 1887
Mason and Sachs, "Sources and nature of the statistics of the United
  Kingdom." *Journal of the Royal Statistical Society* A, Vol. 118
  "Prices in recession and recovery." N.B.E.R., 1936
F. C. Mills, *Statistical method.* Holt Reinhart & Winston, 1955
Ministry of Labour, *Labour statistics: guide to official sources.* H.M.S.O.,
  1958
  "Method of construction and calculation of the Index of Retail
  Prices." *Studies in official statistics,* No. 6, H.M.S.O., 1959

Ministry of Labour Gazette:
  1. Retail prices: January and February 1941, December 1950,
     October and December 1961, March 1962
  2. Wages and hours: February and September 1957; April 1958;
     February 1959; January, April, and September 1960; June 1961;
     March, July, and August 1962; April 1963

L. von Mises, *The theory of money and credit.* Jonathan Cape Ltd
W. C. Mitchell, "Making and using index numbers." Bureau of Labor
  Statistics *Bulletin* 656
  "Index numbers of wholesale prices." Bureau of Labor Statistics
  Bulletin 284

M. J. Moroney, *Facts from figures*. Pelican Books, 1956

C. A. Moser, *Survey methods in social investigation*. Heinemann, 1958

J. Mounsey, *Introduction to statistical calculations*. English Universities Press, 1958

B. D. Mudgett, *Index numbers*. John Wiley, 1951

J. R. Newman (ed.), *The world of mathematics*. Allen & Unwin, 1960

Paden and Lindquist, *Statistics for economics and business*. McGraw-Hill, 1956

Hargreaves Parkinson, *Ordinary shares*. Eyre & Spottiswoode, 1949

W. M. Persons, *The construction of index numbers*

H. S. Phillips, "United Kingdom indexes of wholesale prices 1949–55." *Journal of the Royal Statistical Society* A, 1956

President's Committee on the cost of living, U.S.A., 1945

Purchasing Officers' Association, *Economic indices*

M. H. Quenouille, *Introductory statistics*. Pergamon Press, 1950

Report of the Radcliffe Committee on the working of the monetary system. Cmd 827, H.M.S.O.

T. Raymont, *Modern education*. Longmans, 1953

Research Services Ltd, *Savings and attitudes to share owning*. Wider Share Ownership Committee, 1962

M. S. Rix, *Investment arithmetic*. Pitman

Stock market economics. Pitman, 1954

H. B. Rose, *The economic background to investment*. Institute of Actuaries/Cambridge University Press, 1960

A. Sauerbeck, "Prices of commodities and the precious metals." *Journal of the Royal Statistical Society*, 1889

Article in *Economic Journal*, June 1895

The course of average prices for general commodities in England. King, 1908

J. A. Schumpeter, *History of economic analysis*. Allen & Unwin, 1955

Securities & Exchange Commission (U.S.A.), *Stock price index booklet*. February 1962

I. H. Siegel, letter to the editor of *The American Statistician*, February 1962

P. Slater, "Percentiles for intelligence quotients." *The Lancet*, January 1942

M. J. Slonim, *Sampling in a nutshell*. Simon & Schuster, 1960

R. Snyder, *Measuring business changes*. John Wiley, 1956

Mary E. Spear, *Charting statistics*. McGraw-Hill, 1952

Spurr, Kellogg and Smith, *Business and economic statistics*. Irwin, 1954

J. Stafford, "Indices of wholesale prices." *Journal of the Royal Statistical Society* A, 1951

The Standard Industrial Classification (revised). H.M.S.O., 1958

Statistics on incomes, prices, employment and production. H.M.S.O.

The Statist, annual article on wholesale prices in *Journal of the Royal Statistical Society*

B. R. Stauber, "The 1959 U.S.D.A. index revisions." *Journal of Farm Economics*, December 1959

Stauber, Hale and Peterson, "The 1959 revision of the price indexes." *Agricultural Economics Research*, 1959

"The *Times* share indexes." *The Times*, 1960, 1963, 1964

Articles on the index in *The Times*, 26th April and 26th May 1960

L. Tippett, *Statistics*. Oxford University Press, 1945

H. M. Treasury, *Government statistical services*. H.M.S.O., 1962

Treasury Bulletin for Industry: regular issues; see especially April 1959, January 1960, May 1960, March 1963

A. M. Tuttle, *Elementary business and economic statistics*. McGraw-Hill, 1957

R. Tyssen-Gee, article in the *Investors' Chronicle*, 2nd February 1962

United Nations *Monthly Bulletin of Statistics*

U.S. Department of Agriculture, *Agricultural Prices* monthly *Journal of Farm Economics*, Vol. XLI, No. 5

P. E. Vernon, *Intelligence and attainment tests*. University of London Press, 1960

Wallis and Roberts, *Statistics: a new approach*. Methuen, 1957

C. M. Walsh, "Index numbers." *The encyclopaedia of social sciences*, Vol. 7

Problems of estimation, 1921

The measurement of general exchange value, 1901

H. Westergaard, *Contributions to the history of statistics*. King, 1932

Westminster Bank Review: "Industrial production, a guide to growth." May 1962

P. Wilsher, "Share graphs out of line." *The Sunday Times*, 4th December 1960

World Trade Information Service (U.S.A.), *Overseas business reports*

F. Yates, *Sampling methods for censuses and surveys*. Griffin, 1953

You Poh Seng, "Some theories of index numbers." *Journal of the Royal Statistical Society* A, 1956

Yule and Kendall, *An introduction to the theory of statistics*. Griffin, 1958

INDEX